FRAGMENTS

of Chicago's Past

FRAGMENTS

of Chicago's Past

The Collection of
Architectural Fragments at
The Art Institute of Chicago

edited by

PAULINE SALIGA

with essays by

ROBERT BRUEGMANN,
DONALD HOFFMANN,
EDWARD N. KAUFMAN,
GERALD R. LARSON, *and*
LAUREN S. WEINGARDEN

The Art Institute of Chicago

Edited by Robert V. Sharp, Associate Director of Publications
Production by Katherine Houck Fredrickson, Production Manager
Designed by Susan Johnson Design, Chicago, Illinois
Typeset in Baskerville by Paul Baker Typography, Inc., Evanston, Illinois
Printed by Mossberg & Co., Inc., South Bend, Indiana

Cover: Louis H. Sullivan, Circular medallion from an elevator enclosure grille from the Schlesinger and Mayer Store (cat. no. 72); D. H. Burnham and Co., Blocks from the Railway Exchange Building (cat. no. 24); Alfonso Iannelli, Study model for the head of a sprite for Midway Gardens (cat. no. 84).

Back Cover: Removal of a cast-iron panel from the roofline of the Max M. Rothschild Building, 210 W. Madison Street, 1972 (see cat. no. 39).

Frontispiece: View of a portion of the installation of "Fragments of Chicago's Past" at The Art Institute of Chicago.

Photography Credits: Unless otherwise noted, all photographs are from the collections of The Art Institute of Chicago and by the Department of Imaging and Technical Services.

Timothy Barton: p. 149, fig. 19. Robert Bruegmann: pp. 100-101, figs. 3-5; p. 102, fig. 8; 105, fig. 13. Chicago Architectural Photographing Co.: p. 148, fig. 17. Chicago Historical Society: cat. nos. 32, 33; p. 70, fig. 2. Ron Gordon: p. 91, fig. 7. John Gronkowski: cat. nos. 24-28, 35, 36, 38, 78, 79, 81, 84, 89; p. 111, fig. 3. Tom Moran: cat. no. 91; p. 169, fig. 4. Richard Nickel: pp. 123-24, figs. 9-10; p. 127, fig. 1; pp. 129-30, figs. 2-4; pp. 136-38, figs. 6-9.

Library of Congress
Cataloging-in-Publication Data

Art Institute of Chicago.
    Fragments of Chicago's past : the collection of architectural fragments at the Art Institute of Chicago / edited by Pauline Saliga; with essays by Robert Bruegmann . . . [et al.].
        p.   cm.
    Includes index.
    ISBN 0-86559-088-5
    1. Architecture — Illinois — Chicago — Catalogs. 2. Chicago (Ill.) — Buildings, structures, etc. — Catalogs. 3. Art Institute of Chicago — Catalogs. I. Saliga, Pauline A.   II. Bruegmann, Robert. III. Title.
NA735.C4A77   1990
720'.9773'1107477311 — dc20   90-44994
                                                      CIP

Contents

. . . .

*T*he Art Institute of Chicago's collection of building fragments has been slowly and thoughtfully acquired over the years with the advice and assistance of a great many individuals whose varied areas of expertise have combined to shape the museum's rich and diverse selection of Chicago and Prairie School ornament. The collection was formed by generous gifts from concerned individuals, architects, management companies, demolition crews, developers, and building owners who cared enough to assume the difficult, and often hazardous, task of collecting fragments of buildings. Through their efforts, we have been able to preserve terracotta capitals, leaded-glass windows, cast-iron grilles, and a great variety of other architectural details representing some of the most significant chapters in Chicago, and by extension, American architecture. In addition, the many generous organizations and individuals who donated funds, often at the eleventh hour, to purchase fragments, provided the only means of preserving these objects that speak volumes about the international importance of Chicago architecture. We are most grateful to the many people whose combined efforts have made the Art Institute's collection of building fragments both outstanding and unique.

Over the past eighty years, the fragment collection has been under the stewardship of several different museum departments. We are deeply indebted to the curators and librarians who collected fragments over the years, and we appreciate that they so conscientiously conserved, photographed, and recorded them. Their forward-looking vision formed the solid core of the collection that the Department of Architecture has the privilege of working with and publishing today. For organizing and overseeing the production of this handsome volume, which features a broad cross section of our finest fragments, we are particularly grateful to Pauline Saliga, Associate Curator of Architecture, and to Robert V. Sharp, Associate Director of Publications. This book provides a new context for understanding the ways in which the Art Institute's collection of building fragments continues a tradition that was begun in Europe in the eighteenth and nineteenth centuries. In addition, it sets a direction for the future use of such collections both as tools for understanding the complexities of past and present American culture, and as artworks of great aesthetic merit.

James N. Wood
Director
The Art Institute of Chicago

Acknowledgments

. . . .

*P*roducing this book about the collection of fragments at the Art Institute was a long-range collaborative project that required the talents and expertise of individuals in a great many fields of endeavor. To publish this richly illustrated handbook and to install the permanent exhibition that complements it, substantial funding was necessary. Therefore, we would like to express our sincere gratitude to the agencies, corporations, and individuals who generously provided funds to enable us to research and publish this collection: the National Endowment for the Arts; the National Endowment for the Humanities; the Illinois Humanities Council, a state agency; IC Industries; and the Seymour H. Persky Fund for Architecture at The Art Institute of Chicago.

Since our goal was to publish a handbook to the collection that would include newly researched scholarly essays, new information about the collection, and high-quality photographic illustrations, we had to call upon the advice and talents of a great many people to whom we would like to express our sincere gratitude. John Zukowsky, Curator of Architecture, helped shape the intellectual focus for the book, suggesting that we divide the collection into four thematic sections dealing with the impact of Chicago's cultural, social, commercial, and industrial growth on the city's unique architecture. The essayists whose articles provide a framework for analyzing the Art Institute's building fragment collection — Edward N. Kaufman, Gerald R. Larson, Robert Bruegmann, Lauren S. Weingarden, and Donald Hoffmann — provide valuable new insights into the history of Chicago architecture, using fragments, often the smallest of decorative details, as a starting point to study both the city's history and the development of the architecture museum.

We also owe a great debt to the researchers who tirelessly worked with the collection in the past four years so we could publish new information reflecting the significance of our fine collection. Primary research and an inventory of the collection was creatively and skillfully undertaken by Audrey Hiller, Carole Cosimano, Steve Michaels, and James Pinto. Additional research was done by Betty Blum, Polly Goodwin, Maya Moran, and Luigi Mumford. In addition, since the histories of architecture, building technology, and architectural ornament are so vast, we relied heavily on expert advice that was freely given by a number of architects and historians who were extremely generous in repeatedly filling in the gaps with much-needed information. In this regard we must mention Timothy Samuelson, an inveterate fragment collector and a Landmarks Preservation Specialist at the Commission on Chicago Landmarks, who shared his invaluable and encyclopedic knowledge of the history of Chicago architecture, particularly the work of Louis Sullivan and Frank Lloyd Wright. By freely offering his insights, he has repeatedly reshaped this book to be more complete and factually accurate.

In addition, we wish to thank other generous advisors: Karen Alexander, for kindly sharing her original research on the earliest collections of the Art Institute — the classical antiquities and the plaster casts; Lynn Springer Roberts and Ian Wardropper, respectively the former and current Eloise W. Martin Curator of European Decorative Arts at the Art Institute, for their perspective on the history of the Institute's period rooms, Thorne Rooms, and plaster-cast collections. Additional valuable technical assistance was provided by David Hanks, former Associate Curator of American Arts and currently head of the consulting firm of David Hanks Associates, for his insights about Sullivan and Wright ornament; Timothy Barton, a Landmarks Preservation Specialist at the Commission on Chicago Landmarks; John Smith, Art Institute Archivist; and Wallace Bradway and Mary Solt, respectively the former and current Executive Director of Museum Registration. We received invaluable assistance in locating spectacular historical images for the book from Jack Perry Brown, Executive Director of the Ryerson and Burnham Libraries, and Mary K. Woolever, Architecture Reference Librarian, as well as from Maureen A. Lasko, Reference Librarian, and Senior Library Assistant Susan E. Perry.

A great many other Art Institute staff members were key to realizing this book, and we owe them a debt of gratitude. They include several people in the Publications Department: Robert V. Sharp, Associate Director, for his skillful and intelligent editing of both words and pictures, and for his informed and enthusiastic love of the subject; Katherine Fredrickson, Production Manager, for overseeing production of the book; and Cris Ligenza, Secretary, for processing the manuscripts. They worked hand in hand with Susan Johnson, of Susan Johnson Design, who did a superb job of designing and producing this book. We thank them all for maintaining the high editorial and design standards evident in this book.

Preparing the objects for photography and presentation in the permanent installation that complements this book was a herculean effort that was ably headed by Barbara Hall, Senior Conservator of Objects at the Art Institute. Those who assisted Ms. Hall with great patience and professionalism included Jean Mandel, Barbara Hamann, Sarah O'Keefe, Julie Tiepel, Margot Pritzker, and Robert Cooper of Cooper Art Glass. Photographing the large, heavy, and often fragile fragments also presented challenges that were skillfully met by Robert Hashimoto, Senior Photographer at the Art Institute, who took very fine photographs of many of the objects in the collection, and Thomas Cinoman, Location Photographer, who took atmospheric photographs of fragments installed at the top of the central staircase, as well as the Chicago Stock Exchange Trading Room and Entrance Arch. Additional photography was done over the years by Howard Kraywinkel, Christopher Gallagher, and Carl Basner of the Photographic Services Department, and by two former members of the department, John Mahtesian and Michelle Klarich. We are grateful to Julie Zeftel for coordinating the arrangements for both two- and three-dimensional photography. Several freelance photographers did a fine job of capturing both fragments and buildings, often just prior to their demise. They include Timothy Barton, Ron Gordon, John Gronkowski, Tom Moran, Bob Thall, and of course, the late Richard Nickel. We thank all of them for the fine illustrations that are the backbone of this book.

For his intelligent installation of the fragments at the top of the Art Institute's Central Staircase, and for the careful restoration of the Trading Room and Arch, we extend our thanks to architect John Vinci and his assistant, Ward Miller. We appreciate their tireless efforts to enrich and refine the display of our collection. For managing the often difficult installation of the fragments, we sincerely thank Herman Weiland of Herman Weiland and Associates.

And finally, we wish to thank James N. Wood, Director of the Art Institute, and Katharine C. Lee, Deputy Director, for their continued support in realizing both the installation of our building fragment collection and the production of this book. We are also extremely grateful to the Committee on Architecture, and its chairman, David C. Hilliard. Only with the continued support of both the administration and our committee have we been able to renew our commitment to display the art of architecture and to publish new and innovative research on the history of Chicago's rich architectural heritage.

Pauline Saliga
Associate Curator of Architecture
The Art Institute of Chicago

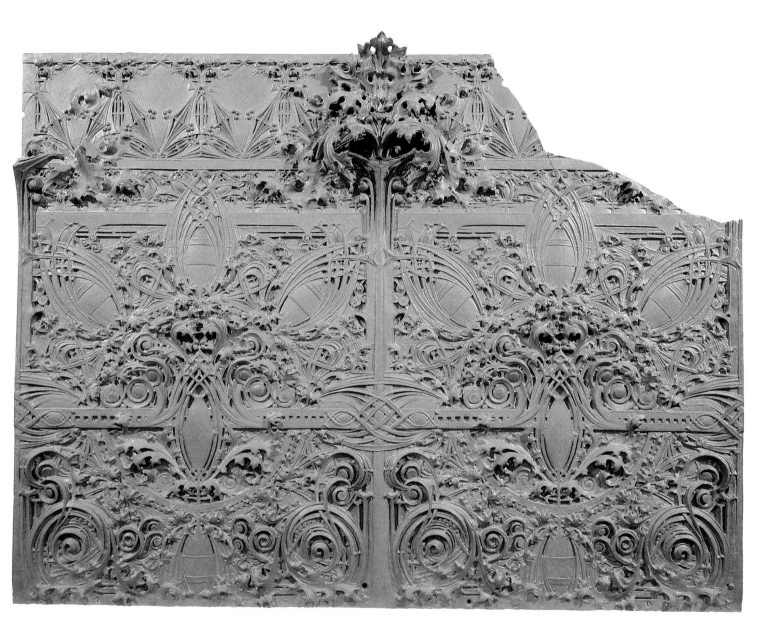

Pl. 1
Louis H. Sullivan,
Spandrel panel from the
first-floor facade of the
Gage Building, 1898-99
(cat. no. 70).

Pl. 2
Burnham and Root,
Engaged capital from the
Church of the Covenant,
1887-88 (cat. no. 11).

Pl. 3
Holabird and Roche,
Fish ornament from
the base of the Oliver
Building, 1907-08
(cat. no. 20).

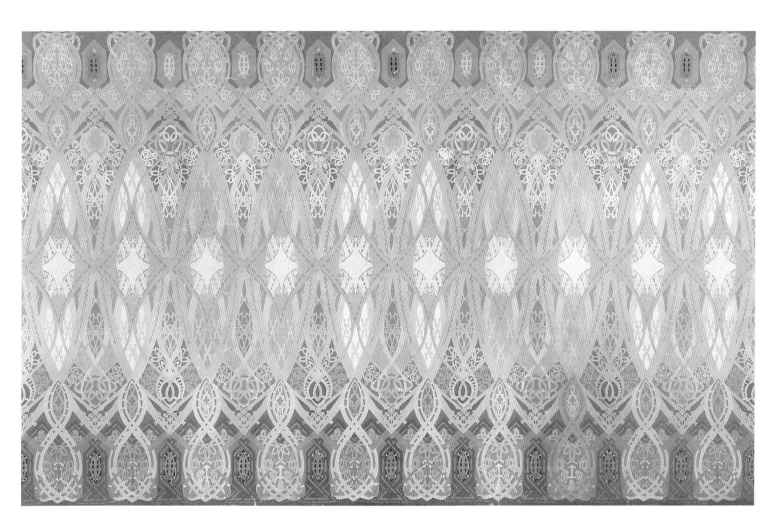

Pl. 4
**Adler and Sullivan,
Section of a stencil from
the Trading Room of the
Chicago Stock Exchange
Building, 1893-94
(cat. no. 68).**

Pl. 5
Louis H. Sullivan,
Circular medallion from
an elevator enclosure
grille from the
Schlesinger and Mayer
Store, 1898-99
(cat. no. 72).

Pl. 6
Louis H. Sullivan,
Teller's wicket from the
National Farmers Bank,
1906-08 (cat. no. 77).

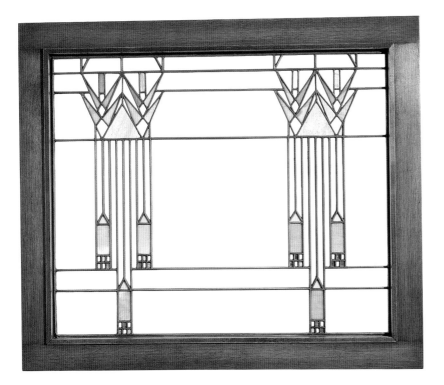

Pl. 7
Marion Mahony Griffin,
Window from the Gerald
Mahony House, 1907
(cat. no. 82).

Pl. 8
Frank Lloyd Wright,
Window from the Emil
Bach House, 1915
(cat. no. 97).

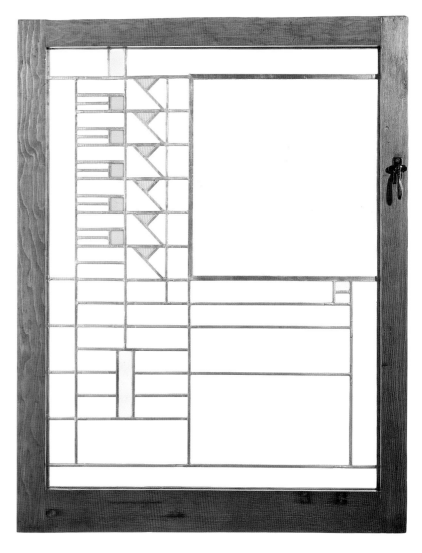

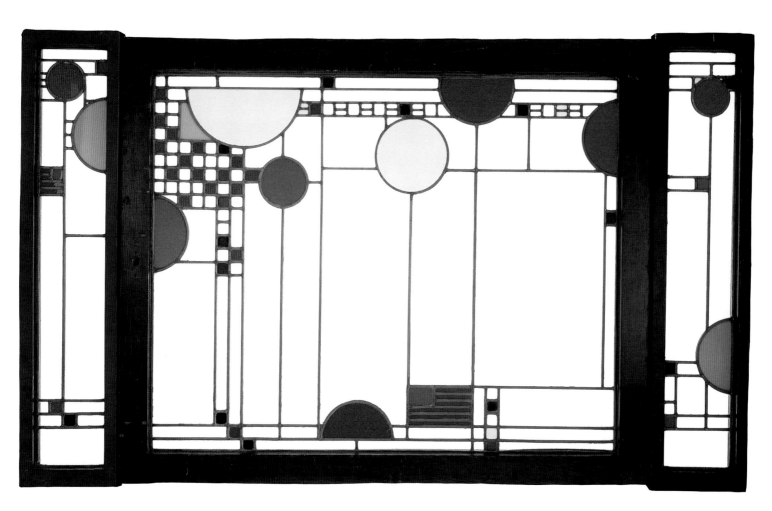

Pl. 9
**Frank Lloyd Wright,
Triptych window from
a niche in the Avery
Coonley Playhouse, 1912
(cat. no. 95).**

Pl. 10
**Alfonso Iannelli, Study
model for the head
of a sprite for Midway
Gardens, 1913-14
(cat. no. 84).**

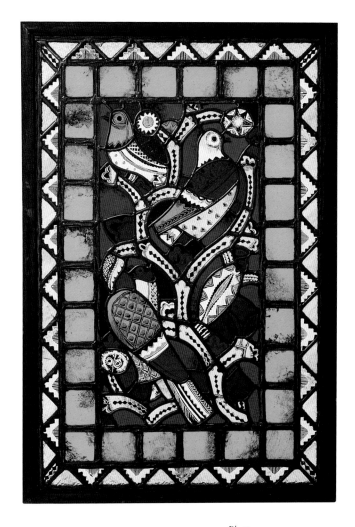

Pl. 11
**Edgar Miller, Window
with bird design, c. 1925
(cat. no. 38).**

*From Napoleon
Through Henry Ford*

by Edward N. Kaufman

Collecting paintings and sculpture is a time-honored pastime. It is also a relatively straightforward one: in principle, one simply chooses the objects of desire, acquires them, and arranges them according to taste. Collecting architecture is both a more recent and a more puzzling phenomenon. Of course, the noble lords of Europe, with their two, three, or even more country houses, can be said to have collected architecture since a very early age; even the landowner with a single estate might be called a collector if, as many did in the eighteenth century, he embellished his garden with miniature temples, pergolas, and grottos. But this is not exactly what we mean by architectural collecting. If what we do mean is the conscious assemblage of works of architecture as specimens of their age or style; if we further stipulate that considerations of domestic comfort or real estate value must be at most secondary; then we must wait until the mid to late eighteenth century — the age of eclecticism and of a growing consciousness of history — for the first collectors and collections of architecture.

What makes the collecting of architecture a puzzling pursuit is that buildings are so much more difficult than paintings or statues to take home. Though surprisingly easy to remove, they are generally very difficult to move. And once moved, they are extraordinarily difficult to arrange and display. To be sure, attempts have been made, but on the whole, collectors of architecture since the late eighteenth century have found it easier to channel their acquisitive urges in the direction of more readily collectable substitutes such as drawings and prints, and this displacement of the collecting urge underlies the entire history of architectural collecting.

Architects have always collected drawings as sources of professional instruction and inspiration: Palladio's, for example, descended through at least six generations of such collections before ending up in public institutions. But drawings also afforded amateurs a means of possessing things and experiences that would otherwise elude their grasp. The Englishman John Tweddell, writing from Tenos in 1798 on his way to Athens, eloquently revealed this displacement of the collector's hunger to drawings:

My collection of Levantine Dresses (I mean drawings of them) *is already considerable, amounting to nearly two hundred* — and will soon be greatly augmented — so that I hope one day to show the richest portfolio perhaps that was ever carried out of Greece, Asia, and Turkey. But Athens especially is my great object. I promise you that those who come after me shall have nothing to glean. Not only every temple, and every archway, but every stone, and every inscription, shall be copied with the most scrupulous fidelity.[1]

As well as providing a surrogate for uncollectable objects, the sheet of paper could constitute the space for an entire museum of surrogate buildings. The most famous examples of this are to be found in the plates of Durand's *Receuil et parallèle des édifices de tout genre, anciens et modernes*, published in 1800, in which typologically similar but geographically dispersed buildings are brought together onto a single sheet. But Werner Szambien has shown that such plates originated in the middle of the eighteenth century.[2] During the nineteenth century, a similar but more pictorial technique was used to suggest landscapes out of widely disparate buildings brought together for the purpose: famous examples exist by the English architects C. R. Cockerell, Sir John Soane, and A. W. N. Pugin.

Mid-eighteenth-century architects like Robert Adam and Sir John Soane also supplemented their drawing collections with plaster casts, whose three-dimensional immediacy recommended them to many architects as vehicles of inspiration. Thus the Greek Revivalist Thomas Harrison wrote to Lord Elgin on the eve of his embassy to Constantinople in 1799, asking him to bring back some Grecian casts to fire the imagination of architects schooled in engravings.[3]

But the hunger for three-dimensional things could lead to more daring exploits. Years later, Lord Elgin claimed that "it was no part of my original plan to bring away any thing but my models"[4]—by which he meant casts. The statement is significant because in 1804 shiploads of marble fragments prized from the temples of the Acropolis— including the famed Elgin Marbles—had begun to make their way back to England (figs. 1, 2). Indeed, as early as 1801, Elgin was writing to his agent in Athens requesting "examples in the actual object, of each thing, and architectural ornament—of each cornice, each frieze, each capital—of the decorated ceilings, of the fluted columns—specimens of the different architectural orders and of the variant forms of the orders,—of metopes and the like, as much as possible."[5]

Elgin intended his importation of architectural drawings, casts, and fragments as part of an ambitious attempt to improve the state of English art. But from the middle of the eighteenth century, architectural fragments had played a quite different role for English collectors. Sir Horace Walpole had scoured the English countryside for bits of old furniture and decorative fragments with which to furnish Strawberry Hill, the villa which he had begun to Gothicize in 1748. His friends did the same on a smaller scale, and a fashion soon developed for "antique" furniture and interiors cobbled together out of architectural fragments. Perhaps the most remarkable expression of this taste for fragments was Plas Newydd, the cottage just outside Llangollen in Wales, where Sarah Ponsonby and Eleanor Butler set up house together after running away from their aristocratic Irish families in 1778.[6] All the world came to visit the famous Ladies of Llangollen—the Duke of Wellington, the Darwins, Wordsworth, Sir

Fig. 1
John Claude Nattes (attributed to), The Elgin Marbles at Burlington House, 1816. *Photo: Courtesy of the Greater London Record Office (Maps and Prints).*

Fig. 2
A. Archer, The Elgin Marbles at the British Museum in 1819. *Photo: Courtesy of the Trustees of the British Museum.*

Fig. 3
**View of the interior
of Richard Greene's
Museum, Lichfield,
England; from
Gentlemen's Magazine
58 (1788), pt. 2, p. 848.**

Fig. 4
**Perspective rendering
of the Monument of
Philopappus; from
James Stuart and
Nicholas Revett, The
Antiquities of Athens,
vol. 3 (London, 1794),
chap. 5, pl. 3.**

Walter Scott—and it became the custom for visitors to bring along a small piece of tribute, a bit of paneling or oak carving, a newel post, or perhaps a piece of stained glass. In due course, these architectural fragments were pieced together and stuck up all over the house, inside and out, until it had been transformed into a sort of lived-in museum of architecture, whose specimens blended together into an enveloping romantic decor, instinct with the histories of travel and tribute, and of personal devotion, which had brought them there.

Somewhat different from casts and fragments are models. Like casts, these have played an important role in the pedagogy of architecture, especially in late-eighteenth-century France. But like fragments, models also had a particular significance for amateur collectors, frequently being found in cabinet collections, those flexible, yet often highly systematic, assemblages of scientific specimens, instruments, freaks of nature, and expensive and marvellous works of art. The famous Parisian cabinet of Joseph Bonnier de la Mosson, assembled during the 1730s, exhibited models of buildings and building machinery amidst an enormous collection of scientific instruments and specimens, faience globes, shells, and other naturalistic specimens.[7] A little later, that of Richard Greene of Lichfield (fig. 3) displayed an enormous clock in the form of a Gothic tower (made about 1748 and one of the incunabula of the Gothic Revival) in the midst of a collection of South Sea curiosities presented by Captain Cook and a wide assortment of what James Boswell, after visiting it with Dr. Johnson, called "truely, a wonderful collection, both of antiquities and natural curiosities, and ingenious works of art."[8]

If a model is inflated to full scale, it becomes a replica, which is quite a different sort of object. The distinction between replicas and originals is indeed ambiguous, especially when the reproduction is not exact. Many late-eighteenth-century garden temples, for example, were close copies after the measured drawings published by James "Athenian" Stuart and Nicholas Revett and others of the Tower of the Winds, the Monument of Lysicrates, and other famous Greek buildings (figs. 4-6): the landscape gardens that contained them might therefore be called informal museums of Greek architecture, and indeed we shall see that such gardens furnished an important prototype for the architectural museums of the late nineteenth and twentieth centuries. But the desire to possess treasured buildings did not stop with their replication in the form of garden temples. Lord Elgin, in the midst of his fragment collecting, considered bribing a local abbot to allow him to carry off the Monument of Lysicrates. He even tried to remove the entire caryatid porch of the Erechtheion, but in the end he had to content himself with a single caryatid. The founders of outdoor museums a century later, collections like Skansen or Greenfield Village, seem to have been more successful: they carried off houses, barns, and shops by the dozen and re-erected them in their museum precincts. Yet in reality, the gap between what they wanted and what they got was just as great, for they wanted not individual houses or shops but whole towns. They wanted village life, tradition, the whole of the national past. Far from attaining the object of their desire, they had merely displaced it into the realm of the immaterial, where it hovered safely out of reach: they could refer to it, could represent it, could collect its material manifestations, but *it* they never could have.

The Poetry of the Architectural Museum

The mechanisms by which architectural museums have represented the unattainable objects of desire are in essence two: synechdoche and metonymy, the representation of things by their parts and by their neighbors. Both had already been heavily exploited in the traditional cabinet collection (and in this regard the influence of the cabinet was particularly important), but the rise of architectural museums in the early nineteenth century was predicated upon a broad cultural recognition of their power. The associational aesthetics of the period, according to which architectural forms were valued for their power to suggest pleasurable thoughts or experiences, were based in part upon metonymy: a chimneystack represented the hearth attached to it, the hearth in turn the family seated around it, so that by a series of linkages, a drift of smoke could signify happy family life. As for the representation of things by their parts, synechdoche stood behind the claim made by admirers of the Elgin Marbles that all the beauty and perfection of the entire frieze could be apprehended within its smallest fragment.

Such claims constituted a powerful endorsement of fragments: in their presence, the early-nineteenth-century artist or scientist did not regret the lack of completeness, for the significance of the whole was somehow fully contained in the part. But there was a poetic dimension, too, for the literary conventions of romanticism used metonymy and synechdoche to pack fragments with rich and soul-satisfying meaning. Thus Mark Twain, confronting an ancient tear-jug in Pisa, heard it speak to him "in a language of its own":

with a pathos more tender than any words might bring, its mute eloquence swept down the long roll of the centuries with its tale of a vacant chair, a familiar footstep missed from the threshold, a pleasant voice gone from the chorus, a vanished form!... No shrewdly-worded history could have brought the myths and shadows of that old dreamy age before us clothed with human flesh and warmed with human sympathies so vividly as did this poor little unsentient vessel of pottery.[9]

Fig. 5
Measured drawing of the Tower of the Winds; from Stuart and Revett, The Antiquities of Athens, *vol. 1 (London, 1762), chap. 3, pl. 3.*

Fig. 6
Perspective rendering of the Arch of the Sergii at Pola; from Stuart and Revett, The Antiquities of Athens, *vol. 4 (London, 1816), chap. 3, pl. 1.*

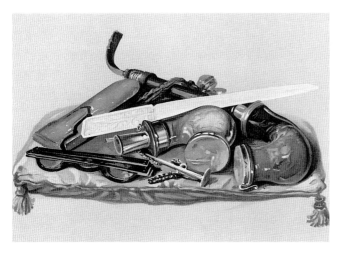

Fig. 7
Mementos of Sir Walter Scott, preserved at his estate, Abbotsford; from Mary Monica Maxwell Scott, Abbotsford: The Personal Relics and Antiquarian Treasures of Sir Walter Scott, *illustrated by* **William Gibb (London, 1893), pl. 6.**

Sir Walter Scott would have understood. Indeed, the impressive antiquarian collection that he assembled at Abbotsford, his Scottish country mansion, included such humble relics as an oat cake found on the body of a dead Highlander at Culloden, or a soldier's diary picked up on the field of Waterloo. Inside his desk was a yet more pathetic collection of objects, whose full impact was reserved for Scott's executors, searching for his testament on the evening after his death.

On lifting up his desk, we found arranged in careful order a series of little objects which had obviously been placed there that his eye might rest on them every morning before he began his tasks. These were the old-fashioned boxes that had garnished his mother's toilette, when he, a sickly child, slept in her dressing-room — the silver taper-stand which the young advocate had bought for her with his first five-guinea fee — a row of small packets inscribed with her hand, and containing the hair of those of her offspring that had died before her — his father's snuff-box and etui case, and more things of the like sort, recalling 'The old familiar faces.'[10]

Scott's mementos of his youth and family became, on his death, mementos of the great author himself, and it is hardly surprising that a whole new category of previously innocuous furnishings, such as pipes, spectacles, and paper cutters, simultaneously made the transition to relic status (figs. 7,8).

What allowed these quite ordinary objects to achieve poetic resonance was not only their associations but also their fragmentary and incomplete quality. An environment dominated by large numbers of such fragments was in effect a breeding ground for anecdotes, reveries, and morals, which were generated almost spontaneously as adjacent fragments coupled in new and often quite unpredictable ways. It was the same with the bits and pieces in the architectural museum. To be sure, odd juxtapositions were unintended, yet fragments possess the capacity to complete one another in unexpected ways that underlie the peculiar poetry of the fragment and, as all the early collectors of architecture understood (Sir John Soane, in particular), of the architectural museum.

It is important to specify the *early* collectors of architecture, for efforts were soon made to stem the illicit minglings of casts and fragments. The architectural museums of the late nineteenth century were far larger and more institutional than the earlier ones, and this naturally tended to work against spontaneity, idiosyncrasy, and self-expression. Yet the poetry of the fragment could never be entirely purged from the architectural museum. For Scott and his descendants, the humble contents of a desk were treasured because they preserved the memory of things lost and regretted. Scott himself collected architecture in the same spirit he collected other fragments, and so, up to a point, did the most important of early architectural collectors, Alexandre Lenoir and Sir John Soane. Much later in the century, the development of the period room and outdoor museum would follow the same pattern, for the intimate odds and ends which composed them—chairs, beds, cooking pots, knitting needles, kerosene lamps, old newspapers—were instinct with the lives of their original possessors, and often of their collectors. They spoke Scott's language of metonymy and synechdoche, and that is what made them worthy of preservation. This is an important point, for architectural preservation has been a recurrent and frequently misunderstood theme in the collecting of architecture. Lord Elgin thought he was saving the Parthenon from the Turks, Lenoir the Sainte Chapelle from his own countrymen; the later history of the architectural museum provides plenty of dramatic rescues, and just as many protestations of preservationist intent. Yet the architectural museum's preservation initiatives have been accompanied by inevitable and often quite deliberate destruction. While architectural collectors have been motivated by a deep-seated and at times intolerably oppressive sense of loss, that sense of loss has generally been focused not on architecture but on the objects of desire represented by it: youth, family, tradition. In short, while gestures of salvage and protection have frequently contributed to the architectural museum's poetry, historic preservation has never been its chief goal.

If the objects in the architectural museum have sung the gentle elegy of the tear-jug, they have also sung sprightlier airs. Sometimes they have been not mementos but souvenirs—essentially the same word but with a very different connotation. Souvenirs are what one brings back from a foreign place to remember it by. Sometimes architectural museums have commemorated travel, as in the fragments embedded in the walls at Plas Newydd; at other times they have simulated it, as in the national pavilions of the late-nineteenth-century world's fairs. Very frequently, too, they have encouraged it, as architectural museums have become tourist sites in their own right, with their own paraphernalia of guidebooks and souvenirs; and then finally, the expansion of travel has spurred the growth of architectural museums, as the Director of the American Association of Museums realized in 1933, when, observing that "it is plainly not just a coincidence that motor cars and historic house museums have multiplied during the same decades and by closely similar stages of progression," he advised the directors of historic houses to exploit the potential of motorized tourism.[11]

The forms of travel are of course many, but one in particular deserves comment: the military expedition, where collecting is pillage, souvenirs booty, and the museum a trophy. The trophy was indeed a popular form of architectural ornamentation during the

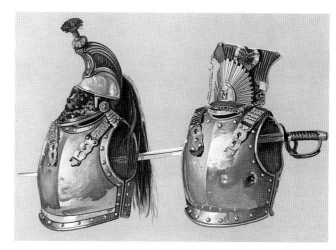

Fig. 8
Pieces of armor and other mementos of the Battle of Waterloo, collected by Sir Walter Scott and kept at his estate, Abbotsford; from Maxwell Scott, Abbotsford, pl. 13.

Fig. 9
Robert Adam, Various designs of trophies for wall and ceiling ornamentation, 1773; from The Works in Architecture of Robert and James Adam. . . (1778; rpt. Paris, 1900), vol. 2, no. 2, pl. 5.

late eighteenth century, attracting the attention of designers like Piranesi, Jacques Dumont, and Robert Adam (fig. 9). Originally an elaborate mound of spolia dragged home from a victorious expedition and displayed for the edification of victors and vanquished alike, the trophy strikingly exemplified the rhetorical power of fragments: its shields, spears, and other precious objects represented the conquered civilization, while their rearrangement made evident the conqueror's superior might. No wonder that the trophy formed one of the most powerful models for the architectural museum.

As John Tweddell contemplated the prospect of Athens, he clearly thought of himself, at least metaphorically, as gathering spoils, and the image of himself triumphantly bringing them home was already adding to their emotional appeal. Robert Adam had surveyed the ruins of Rome in a similarly inquisitive spirit when he arrived there as a student in 1755, proposing not only to have "models made of all the antique ornaments, of friezes, cornices, vases, etc., etc., in plaster," but also to hire "painters, drawers, etc., to do the fountains, the buildings, the statues," and finally, to buy up "all the books of architecture, of altars, chapels, churches, views of Piranesi and of all gates, windows, doors and ornaments that can be of service to us. In short," he concluded, "I intend to send home a collection of drawings. . .which never was seen or heard of either in England or Scotland."[12] Finally, there is James Stuart himself, writing from Athens in 1761:

A Load of Treasure is at Athens. I offer my shoulders to the Shafts, as if I were a Cart-Horse: & regardless of fatigue & danger, resolve to dragg it, where alass tis greatly wanted; even to this fair flourishing Isle. Oh—toilsome task—Ah, tedious way! how slow I move—what obstacles I meet!—from Athens to London, no road has yett been made for such conveyance.[13]

For eighteenth-century enthusiasts of the antique, the spoils were primarily informational: drawings, memoranda, and plaster casts. Soon, travelers like Lord Elgin would begin to send home material spolia of the greatest value and in sufficient quantity to convince anyone of their countries' prowess. What prompted this shift from metaphorical to real spoliation and gave birth to the architectural museum was nothing other than the intervention of real warfare and political turmoil.

The First Museums
When the Revolutionary government of France confiscated clerical and aristocratic goods, a great part of France's artistic heritage lay exposed to the gravest dangers of depredation and destruction. One solution was to establish a depot for works of artistic merit on the site of the old Convent of the Petits Augustins in Paris and to appoint a

young man named Alexandre Lenoir to administer it. Lenoir's initial mandate was in fact quite restricted, but his ambitions soon led him beyond it, and he proposed to form a "special museum, historical and chronological, where one could rediscover the ages of French sculpture."[13] The Musée des Monuments Français opened to the public in 1795 and scored a tremendous popular success.

The main portion of Lenoir's museum was a sequence of galleries, each exemplifying a century from the thirteenth to the seventeenth (fig. 10). These rooms contained not only sculpture but also architectural fragments and decorative objects, and each room was romantically decked out with glowing wall paintings and other contemporary accessories, so as to evoke an enchantingly authentic mood. Outside the museum, these rooms were supplemented by some very large architectural fragments, most notably the frontispiece of the château of Anet and the triumphal arch from that of Gaillon (fig. 11), and by a picturesque garden, called the Jardin Elysée, in which the remains of great Frenchmen were inspiringly entombed.

Lenoir's museological success was based not simply on growing interest in the Middle Ages, nor even on patriotic fervor, but more simply on his insight that centuries could be represented within the space of a museum, with each room having "the character, the exact physiognomy of the century which it represents."[15] To be sure, this equation of time and space was a rudimentary form of abstraction, yet it would prove enormously significant for the collecting of architecture, for it provided a straightforward equation between the most insignificant material fragments and the grandest conceptual schemes. By relying upon it, in conjunction with the rhetorical power of fragments, Lenoir was able to present his comprehensive historical panorama through a collage of fragments picked up as opportunity allowed.

Lenoir actually helped his specimens to combine into new and quite unprecedented configurations. For the centerpiece of his fourteenth-century room (fig. 12), for example, he placed an impressive tabernacle composed of statues of Charles V and Jeanne de Bourbon on top of a cenotaph made up of the "debris" of some ecclesiastical woodwork and ornamented with bas-reliefs from the Ste.-Chapelle; this he crowned with a canopy composed of fragments of "various monuments of this period."[16] Objects like these were not genuine antiquities, however genuine their components, but rather impressive and exotic piles of spolia assembled by Lenoir.

To understand the significance of Lenoir's trophies, we must see them against the background of the international situation around 1800, and in particular, of the vast movement of art works from all over Europe into Paris, and particularly the Louvre. Not that the

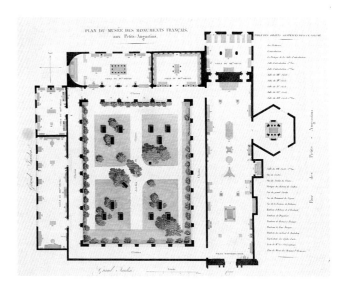

Fig. 10
Plan of the Musée des Monuments Français, established by Alexandre Lenoir, Paris, c. 1791-1816; from B. de Roquefort, Vues Pittoresques et Perspectives des Salles du Musée des Monuments François (Paris, 1816).

Fig. 11
Portion of the facade of the château of Gaillon (called the Arc de Gaillon), installed on the grounds of the Musée des Monuments Français; from Roquefort, Vues Pittoresques.

Fig. 12
Gallery of the fourteenth century, Musée des Monuments Français; from Roquefort, Vues Pittoresques.

traffic in art had only one destination: Lord Elgin's Parthenon marbles began to arrive in London in 1804. But the essential point is not where this or that object went, but the atmosphere in which they were collected. Elgin's position as British ambassador, charged specifically with countering French power, was in complete harmony with the conduct of his antiquarian collecting. At one point, attempting to obtain a man of war for the purpose of removing the entire caryatid porch of the Erechtheion, he wrote to Lord Keith that "Bonaparte has not got such a thing from all his thefts in Italy."[17] The secret maneuvering that took place between Elgin's archaeological agents and those of his French counterpart were notorious and frequently ludicrous, but they could have been exactly matched in Egypt. After the French defeat, indeed, Elgin's personal secretary advised the English general of the importance of securing the Rosetta Stone, discovered by Napoleon's engineers in 1799 and kept under close guard in the French general's own house: in the event, a detachment of gunners was sent to take it away.[18]

Lenoir's trophies, however, also had a more personal significance. A proud and ambitious man, Lenoir identified with his museum to an extraordinary degree. His descriptions of the collection, in which he narrates his hairbreadth rescues of threatened treasures, leave no doubt about this. One story is particularly revealing. It appears that the "asiatic character" which Lenoir sought to give to the room he called "my thirteenth century" was "so well grasped that First Consul Bonaparte, visiting the museum, said in entering this room: 'Lenoir, you transport me to Syria. I am satisfied with your work. Continue your useful researches, and I will always look with pleasure at the results.'"[19] A small, personal triumph, no doubt, yet Lenoir inscribed it upon his objects, thereby entwining his own history with that of France.

In the end, Lenoir's phenomenal success deserted him. With the reestablishment of the church, the museum was ordered to return its art works to their former owners. The very idea of moving art works from their original locations also came under criticism, and in 1816, the museum was closed, its buildings turned over to the Ecole des Beaux-Arts, and its collections made available to their former owners.

By this time, Napoleon's triumphs had also turned to bitterest defeat, and the trophies had begun to flow out again: it was now the turn of Englishmen to exult. That the Duke of Wellington should display Antonio Canova's nude statue of Napoleon in his stairhall was, under the circumstances, perfectly proper. But other collectors also used objects to stake out a personal relationship with the greatest events of the age. Sir Walter Scott was one: among the many objects that crowded his beloved Abbotsford were Napoleon's pen case and blotting book, pistols taken from Napoleon's carriage after the battle

. . . .

of Waterloo, a captured French flag, and a miscellaneous collection of armor and other memorabilia picked up from the battlefield by Scott (see fig. 8).[20] Then there was Charles Stuart, Lord Stuart de Rothesay, ambassador to Portugal and an invaluable ally to Wellington during the Peninsular campaign. After the wars, Stuart became ambassador to the restored Bourbons and amassed an impressive collection of Napoleonic furnishings and memorabilia. Recalled at long last to England, he acquired his last trophy, the Manoir des Andelys, which was being demolished as he passed by on his way home. He had it shipped to England, where the best morsels—especially a beautiful Flamboyant Gothic oriel window—were incorporated into his new mansion, Highcliffe Castle (fig. 13).[21]

One who had no particular Napoleonic relationship to declare was Sir John Soane, the greatest English architect of the age. But Soane held strongly by the diplomatic value of antiquities and was fiercely alive to Britain's cultural prestige. He once concluded a lecture at the Royal Academy with this doggerel, celebrating the influx of cultural treasures into Britain:

> The time not distant far shall come,
> When England's tasteful youth no more
> Shall wander to Italia's classic shore.—
> No more to foreign climes shall roam
> In search of models, better seen at home.

Soane's acquaintance, the antiquarian John Britton, quoted this verse and even expanded upon it in his published—and authorized—description of Soane's museum. The implication was that the entire museum was a sort of prospective trophy of emerging cultural triumph.[22]

Like Lenoir's trophies, Soane's also had a personal dimension. Yet whereas Lenoir's claims to greatness had been largely political, Soane's were essentially artistic: at Pitzhanger Manor, his country house, he embedded fragments in a facade modeled after a triumphal arch; later, at his town house in Lincoln's Inn Fields, Soane lofted his drafting room onto a balcony overlooking a panorama of casts and fragments, so that his own work would be rooted in the debris of history.

Soane also had trophies of a more enigmatic and personal kind, but as his museum was unquestionably the most complex and significant in England, it deserves a more detailed account.[23] Soane, like Adam, had first collected casts as a student in Rome, but he started to think in terms of a museum when he bought Pitzhanger Manor in 1800. At this point, the pedagogical impulse to collect was probably uppermost in Soane's mind, for the collection was intended to form a sort of private architectural academy for his son John.

Fig. 13
Charles Stuart, Lord Stuart de Rothesay, Highcliffe Castle, Hampshire, England; exterior view showing Gothic oriel window from the Manoir des Andelys; from Country Life 91 (1942), p. 854.

Ultimately, the son disappointed the father, but Soane's pedagogical ideals, far from being crushed, blossomed in the more public light of London. There, in 1809, Soane was appointed professor of architecture at the Royal Academy. Already, in the previous year, he had begun to expand his house in Lincoln's Inn Fields to accommodate his ever-growing collection, which the *European Magazine* referred to as "the *Academy* for the Study of *Architecture*."[24]

Soane's museum thus originated within the tradition of professional collecting and teaching. Yet it was far more than an architectural academy. For one thing, it was an extraordinarily diverse collection, containing not only architectural books, drawings, casts, models, and fragments, but also bronzes, gems and medals, Roman cinerary urns, Greek vases, Mexican pots, Chinese ceramics, Indian miniatures, medieval manuscripts, and modern paintings and sculptures. There were also specimens of natural history, and even a few curiosities of the "Wunderkammer" type, like "the Mummies of two Cats, one found...with the Rat in its mouth."[25] Soane's museum, in short, drew heavily upon the tradition of the cabinet collection, as well as on that of the antiquarian interior. Unlike Lenoir, Soane lived in his museum, and whereas Lenoir had tended to complete his fragments artificially, forcing them into "tombs" or "shrines," Soane treated his more as decor, hanging them on pegs, bracketing them out from walls and parapets, setting them on shelves, cornices, and windowsills, until the walls, and even the very ceilings, were encrusted with them (fig. 14). At the center of this seeming chaos, he erected a very type of the whole museum, and indeed of all the early architectural museums, "a kind of trophy composed of a capital of an Hindoo column and of other architectural fragments."[26]

In thus uniting the principle of the trophy with the procedures of antiquarian decoration, Soane raised disorder to an unprecedentedly high level of aesthetic organization. And out of this organized chaos, a new ambiguity emerged. Viewed casually, his fragments tended to dissolve into an overall texture. Yet seen under the right conditions, they seemed to stir with a queer, incipient life, that quiet and dangerous life of fragments that was to be so poetically explored in paintings of casts and masks by Menzel, Corinth, and Ensor, but of which Soane appears to have been the discoverer. The many watercolors made by Soane's pupils Joseph Michael Gandy (fig. 15), George Bailey (fig. 16), and C. J. Richardson show his eccentric spaces mysteriously illuminated, their flickering shadows inhabited by tribes of disembodied fragments. The effect is always eerie and disquieting, and though these watercolors seem to the modern eye exaggerated and implausible, Soane certainly wanted his museum to be perceived in this way: the early-nineteenth-century architect could call upon imagination to supply what his own hand could not.

If Lenoir's museum excelled Soane's in its dedication to public, political, and historical purposes, Soane's excelled Lenoir's in its exploration of the decorative and expressive possibilities of fragments. This was particularly true on the autobiographical level. As we have seen, both men used their collections to construct a certain kind of self-portrait. But in its eerie romanticism, Soane's was far more subtle and more intimate than Lenoir's. It was even, in places, ironic. John Britton's description avers that "the house of an Architect" is a better index to his character than either "phrenological bumps, or craniological organs."[27] Soane's character had a streak of introversion, of melancholy and frustration, even paranoia, which tinged his enjoyment of professional success with ambivalence.

In Soane's Picture Cabinet, for example, a pair of large folding panels hung with pictures hides a second pair, which in turn hides a third; folding back the last pair reveals a statue of Venus shyly clasping her robe in the golden glow of a stained glass window. Nature, or Greek perfection, stands disclosed behind the veils of art. Yet this undraped young lady hovers provocatively above a little chamber called the Monk's Parlor; while from the inner surface of the last shutter the portrait of a man seems to gaze at her with an interest neither religious nor artistic. The emblem that Soane constructs out of hitherto unrelated elements is richly ambiguous and disturbingly intimate—disturbingly because it seems to draw the viewer into an unwanted intimacy with Soane himself. Elsewhere, indeed, the collector puts himself directly into his emblematic collages, as in the dining room, where a large portrait of Soane gazes wistfully across the table at Sir Joshua Reynolds's voluptuous *Love and Beauty.*

The museums of Lenoir and Soane stand at the fountainhead of organized architectural collecting, and an entire generation of collectors and collections may be said to have followed their examples: Scott at Abbotsford, Lord Stuart de Rothesay at Highcliffe, and Alexandre du Sommerard at the Musée de Cluny. Yet as early as the 1820s, new ideas of architectural collecting were being advanced, and this from the most unlikely quarter, a young architect named George Wightwick, who was briefly Soane's assistant from 1826 to 1827 and who helped prepare the plates for Britton's description of the museum. After leaving Soane's office, Wightwick made his way to Plymouth, where he became the partner and soon the successor of the distinguished local architect John Foulston. He tells us that he began to write his best-known book, *The Palace of Architecture*, in the late 1820s, but it was not published until 1840.[28] It is a guidebook to his ideal museum of architecture.

In a sense, Wightwick's title is misleading. There is a palace, a grandly columnar classical affair, but the museum proper is a

Fig. 15
Joseph Michael Gandy, Perspective rendering of the interior of Sir John Soane's Museum, c. 1809-10. Photo: Courtesy of the Trustees of Sir John Soane's Museum.

Fig. 16
George Bailey, Rendering of the installation of casts and architectural fragments belonging to Sir John Soane as arranged in May 1810. Photo: Courtesy of the Trustees of Sir John Soane's Museum.

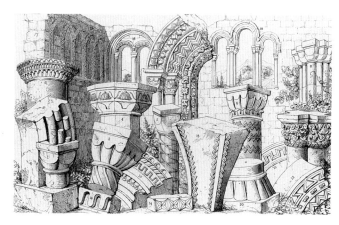

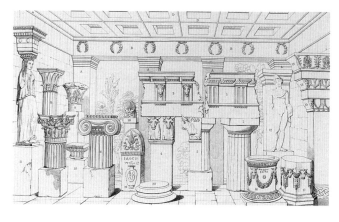

landscape garden, strewn with little buildings and ringed with a wall, through which the public can enter by a domed and spired gateway, weirdly concatenated out of the most discordant elements. The buildings inside the wall are of two kinds. The first are exhibit halls containing jumbles of fragments (figs. 17,18). The second, more novel and more numerous, are exhibits in themselves. There is a little group of Greek temples, some Indian stupas, a miniature segment of the Great Wall of China, and so forth, all disposed in such a way that a stroll through the garden is a voyage through the history of architecture (fig. 19).

Superficially, Wightwick's museum recalls the Jardin Elysée that Lenoir arranged behind his museum, but that is because both drew on the same source, the picturesque English landscape garden. Wightwick had another source of inspiration, too, a remarkable group of public buildings erected by John Foulston in Devonport, just outside Plymouth, in 1823-24. Here were a town hall, commemorative column, chapel, and library, all arranged so as to produce a "picturesque effect, by combining, in one view, the Grecian, Egyptian, and a variety of the Oriental" styles[29] — in short, a veritable museum. Foulston's example must have helped Wightwick to go beyond the conventions of landscape gardening as adopted by Lenoir; in any case, his museum offered perhaps the first demonstration that a landscape garden need not rely for organization upon character and association but could tell a chronological, historical, or even ethnographical story. This would prove an extraordinarily fertile insight.

Wightwick's outdoor museum advanced another significant concept, that such abstractions could best be represented through entire buildings. These little structures offered a greater degree of closure, and a lesser capacity for allusiveness, than Soane's or Lenoir's splintered fragments, and in this they reveal a new and impersonal objectivity, that becomes even clearer within the villa that forms the culmination of Wightwick's museum. From the tower attached to this villa, Wightwick tells us that one can survey the entire museum, "as the poet...can comprehensively estimate the heart of man."[30] The architectural museum is thus an intimate portrait, and one might expect Soanean revelations to follow. But the villa's program is a conventional allegory of life, leading from youth in the breakfast room to death in the chapel. Midway through this progression comes a significant juxtaposition: inside the library, a sculpture of "a boy rising from his completed studies, unconsciously to experience those pure emotions of the heart, which form the Episode betwixt youth and manhood," confronts the *Venus de' Medici*, standing just beyond the doorway to the tower room.[31] The pairing recalls those tense moments in Soane's museum where fragments call out to one

another and men confront feminine beauty, but in the Palace of
Architecture we understand no intimate revelation. The incident is
quite without mystery or complications, smooth, blandly idealistic,
and totally impersonal. It is public in just the way that those grand
pictorial allegories of life made so popular at this time by John
Martin, Francis Danby, or Thomas Cole are public. It is institutional
in just the way that the great public collections of architecture in
England and France were becoming institutional.

The Institutions

In 1820, the new buildings of the Ecole des Beaux-Arts, designed
by François Debret (and later completed to designs by Felix Duban),
began to rise on the site of the old convent of the Petits Augustins,
latterly the Musée des Monuments Français. Legally, the museum's
collections had reverted to their original owners. But many pieces
were never claimed and survived instead in inspiring disorder
around the rooms and courtyards of the old museum. Duban
featured the largest of them, the facades from Anet and Gaillon, in
his design; others were incorporated in trophy-like arrangements
in niches and archways. In many ways, the Ecole des Beaux-Arts was
the natural successor to Lenoir's museum; it even formed its own
cast and fragment collection. Yet it conveyed a quite different mood
from that of its predecessors. The bland lighting of its central
court, roofed over with a magnificent skylight in 1863, was the very
opposite of Lenoir's stained-glass effulgence, or of Soane's disquieting shadows; ranks of graceful statues seemed by their very
orderliness to rebuke the passionate confusion of those earlier
collections. In short, the Ecole des Beaux-Arts had institutionalized
the collecting and display of architectural fragments.

The process of institutionalization that led from Lenoir to the
Ecole can be traced even more clearly in one of England's most
important cast collections, that of the architect Lewis Nockalls
Cottingham. Cottingham, a leading scholar and restorer of medieval
churches, had begun to collect casts and fragments of medieval and
Elizabethan architecture by 1815, and in 1825, he installed them in
a house specially designed for the purpose. To some extent, this
was certainly done in emulation of Soane. Yet his collection differed
significantly from Soane's in that it concentrated on medieval and
Elizabethan architecture. In any case, the house and its collection
soon became famous among architects, and when Cottingham died in
1847, much concern was felt among architects over their future.

One reason for the widespread concern over the fate of
Cottingham's collection is that it had become tied up with a larger
issue, the rise of medievalism. The classicizing slant of most public
institutions was becoming irksome to architects, and Cottingham's

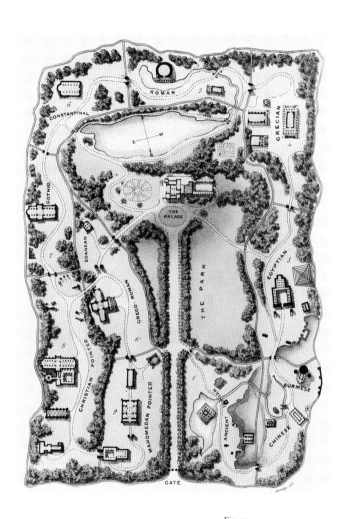

Fig. 19
**Plan of the grounds
surrounding the Palace
of Architecture; from
Wightwick, The Palace
of Architecture, *map
between pp. 4-5.*

collection was seen as an essential counterweight. Already in 1838, Cottingham's former apprentice, the architect Edward Buckton Lamb, had advanced a proposal to turn underutilized cathedral naves into local museums of medieval architecture.[32] Four years later, he was calling upon the trustees of the British Museum to devote space to a "Classification of Gothic Architecture," a proposal which was met with polite indifference.[33] The museum establishment was not ready to place Gothic on an equal footing with classical. But the architectural profession was.

In 1851 Sir George Gilbert Scott spearheaded a move to establish an educational museum and school of art whose collections would consist of architectural models, plaster casts, and actual fragments of medieval architecture.[34] Scott raised funds for the museum, contributed his own collection of casts, persuaded Ruskin and others to do likewise, and secured the bulk of Cottingham's private museum. The Royal Architectural Museum opened in a loft on Cannon Row, Westminster, and remained there until 1857 when it had to seek new quarters. It accepted an offer from the South Kensington Museum, where the Architectural Museum's collections remained for twelve years, in the upper floor of one of the three iron galleries known as the "Brompton boilers" (fig. 20).[35] The Architectural Museum returned its collections to Westminster and celebrated the opening of its own building, at 18 Tufton Street, in July 1869 (fig. 21), containing "specimens not only of the remains of ancient architecture, and ancient casts, but specimens of modern art generously contributed by many of those who are foremost in the good work of renewing art-workmanship in our day."[36] At first, the Royal Architectural Museum thrived, rapidly building up its cast collection, opening a drawing school, and generally carrying out its mission of educating the architectural and artisanal public (fig. 22). Then it fell upon hard times. In 1903 the trustees of the Architectural Museum made a free gift of the Tufton Street building and its contents to the Architectural Association, which, it seems, never grew accustomed to these quarters and sold its lease in 1916. The remaining collections were transferred to the Victoria and Albert Museum.[37] Some of them, portals, statuary, and segments of wall, can still be seen in the great Cast Court, though the smaller specimens lie hidden in dusty romantic heaps along the balconies high overhead. Today, a few of these specimen boards still survive in the lofts of the V & A.

From an architect's home through a professional teaching institution to a public museum, Cottingham's collection followed a trajectory typical of the nineteenth century. But long before the final transformation, other institutions had arisen to serve a broad public. One was the Victoria and Albert Museum itself. Established in 1852, the V & A inherited a collection of casts of ornamental art assembled

Fig. 20
Installation of casts and fragments belonging to the Royal Architectural Museum, housed from 1857 to 1869 in the Brompton Boilers of the South Kensington Museum (now the Victoria and Albert Museum). Photo: Courtesy of the Board of Trustees of the Victoria and Albert Museum.

Fig. 21
Perspective rendering of the Royal Architectural Museum, London, 1869; from Builder 27 (July 24, 1869), p. 583.

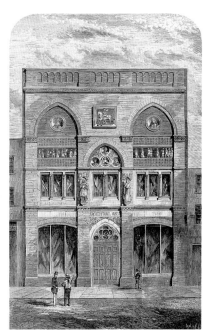

by the Government Schools of Design starting in 1841. After 1857, the V & A hoped that the Royal Architectural Museum's casts would become part of its own collection, and although that did not happen, the V & A became an international leader in the collecting and display of plaster casts. Its director, Henry Cole, even enlisted the aid of the Foreign Office in promoting the international exchange of casts, and in Paris at the Universal Exposition of 1867, he was able to persuade fifteen European princes to sign an "International Convention for promoting Universally Reproductions of Works of Art." After 1873, the V & A's collections of casts were magnificently housed in two enormous glass-roofed halls, either one of which would have been grander than the courtyard of the Ecole, and which together were called the Architectural Courts (fig. 23).

Paris also developed its great cast collections. In addition to that of the Ecole des Beaux-Arts, which seemed to many by the mid-nineteenth century too narrowly classical, there was the Musée de Sculpture Comparée (fig. 24), founded at the instigation of the great Gothicist, Eugène Emmanuel Viollet-le-Duc. Now called the Musée National des Monuments Français, this museum opened in 1882, housed yet more grandly than the V & A in one wing of the Palais du Trocadéro, the vast exhibition palace left over from the International Exposition of 1878. But a great many other cities, all across Europe and North America, developed extensive cast collections of sculpture and architecture during the second half of the nineteenth century and even the first decade or so of the twentieth. In Pittsburgh, for example, the young Carnegie Institute—following the example of museums in Boston, New York, and Chicago—embarked on a massive campaign of cast collecting in 1903; its great glass-roofed Hall of Architecture (fig. 25) opened to the public five years later and is now the finest such collection to survive in this country.

Just as the trophy value of antique fragments during the early nineteenth century is difficult now to conceive, so is the prestige of plaster casts during the later part of the century. In 1887, Louis Courajod wrote a long article claiming François I and Louis XIV as the precursors of the Musée de Sculpture Comparée and providing the making of plaster casts with a distinguished history going back to the Renaissance.[38] Great interest was also shown in the technical refinements of plaster modeling. But most of all, the production and distribution of casts became an immense and well-organized industry. Firms of plaster modelers flourished commercially as they basked in the glow of academic approval: that of Alexandre de Sachy, established within the Ecole des Beaux-Arts in 1848, had a stock of almost 3,000 models by about 1890, casts of which could be ordered from a handsome catalogue. In London, the leading modeler Brucciani ran a shop called the Gallerie delle Belle Arti near the

Fig. 22
Bedford Lemere and Co., Interior view of the Royal Architectural Museum, London, 1869 or later. Photo: Collection Centre Canadien d'Architecture/ Canadian Centre for Architecture, Montreal.

Fig. 23
Perspective rendering of the design for the installation of casts in the western Cast Court of the Victoria and Albert Museum, c. 1871. Photo: Courtesy of the Board of Trustees of the Victoria and Albert Museum.

Fig. 24
Interior view of the Musée de Sculpture Comparée, showing a cast of the portal of Vézelay; from Armand Guerinet, Le Musée de Sculpture Comparée du Palais du Trocadéro (Paris, n.d.), vol. 1, pl. 1.

Fig. 25
Hall of Architecture, Carnegie Institute (now the Carnegie Museum of Art), Pittsburgh. Photo: The Carnegie Museum of Art.

British Museum. His catalogue of Gothic ornaments included 425 items, mostly based on Cottingham's collection; his regular catalogue listed 195 classical architectural ornaments (some retailed from the Ecole des Beaux-Arts), in addition to "Figures for Gas Lights, Lamps, etc.," vases, tazze, anatomical studies, and uncountable busts, torsos, statues, and statuettes, ancient and modern.[39]

Despite the differences in scale and arrangement, the purposes to which the great institutional engines of the late nineteenth century set themselves were not entirely different from those indicated by the smaller museums of the preceding period, although, with the loss of intimacy, those purposes tended to become more fixedly public. Essentially the goals were pedagogical: they focused on the elevation of taste. Sir George Gilbert Scott explained that the Royal Architectural Museum provided objects of study for "art-workmen" who could not afford to travel to the originals.[40] Like Soane, therefore, Scott used his museum as a machine to reverse the flow of tourism, the principal difference lying in the social class that was addressed. On a more broadly public level, the director of the Carnegie Institute's Department of Fine Arts was confident that his new casts were "silently but surely raising the standard of taste in the community."[41] The general intention was loftily vague: "to create by the supreme dignity of the groups an inspiring and uplifting sense of the beauty of art.... The average visitor may forget the historical data, but an enduring impression of beauty will remain."[42] The common premise shared by London and Pittsburgh (and by all institutional cast collections) was that already espoused by collectors like Soane and Elgin, namely that the display of revered models would lead to an improvement in national taste.

The methods by which late-nineteenth-century curators sought to achieve these aims owed a great deal to the methods of Soane and Cottingham. James Van Trump has observed the "bland plaster banality" of the Carnegie Institute's Hall of Architecture.[43] The nineteenth-century cast court had generally little or no decor of its own (the Ecole des Beaux-Arts was a striking exception), because the exhibits were its decor, its furnishings, its architecture. Scott implied as much when he warned the visitor to the Royal Architectural Museum that "he will find within the structure no architectural beauty, but a stark and unambitious interior of naked brick and timber; but he will be startled at finding himself surrounded by innumerable models of architectural art workmanship."[44] These models were deployed with a profusion and disorder reminiscent of earlier private collections: Bedford Lemere's invaluable photographs of the Royal Architectural Museum bring its crowded specimen boards, its encrusted walls and columns hauntingly to life (fig. 26). Even the courtyard of the Ecole des Beaux-Arts must have presented an initial appearance of ungraspable confusion. At the Carnegie Institute, visitors were actually discouraged from too readily picking out the individual specimens: as Dr. Beatty explained, "the great monuments, portals, and columns, and the groups of casts of sculpture have been arranged, not so much as individual examples, but as parts of consistent compositions, the position of each object having relation to the completed group."[45] In fact, the impression of collage was heightened by interspersing models among the casts, thus causing abrupt and sometimes disquieting shifts of scale. If the late-nineteenth-century cast collection could not quite equal the chaotic richness and complexity of earlier collections, it nevertheless made up in sheer extent what it had lost in surface depth and richness. Above all, it offered a sensation of plenitude, and that sensation can still be experienced today, among the looming pillars and portals of the V & A's Cast Courts; in the gently spiraling galleries of the Trocadéro; or in the doorway to Pittsburgh's Hall of Architecture, where 15,000 square feet of fragments rise up to meet one in a single tremendous *coup d'oeil*.

The immensity of the vistas offered by the great cast collections was matched and sustained by the sheer scale of the objects they contained. By the second half of the century, a kind of competition had set in for bigger and more imposing casts. The Trocadéro had its succession of great portals — Moissac, Autun, Vézelay, Chartres, Bourges. The Carnegie Institute had the entire Romanesque porch of St. Gilles du Gard, seventy-five feet long and thirty-eight feet high.[46] The Cast Courts of the V & A are dominated by portals from Bologna and Santiago de Compostella, and by Trajan's column — so tall that it must be broken in half and exhibited in two pieces (fig. 27). Such gigantism was a response to the institutionalization of collecting. But it also reflected the impact of the International Exhibitions, vast exercises in competitive showmanship that had been held regularly in European and American cities since the first one was mounted in London's Crystal Palace in 1851. In fact, the World's Fairs were revolutionizing the collecting and display of architecture in far more significant ways. Before the Victoria and Albert's Cast Courts opened in 1873, indeed, as the very ink was drying on the princely signatures collected by Henry Cole in 1867, the seeds of the cast collection's demise were being sown. They were sprouting all about Cole, in the national pavilions, restaurants, and costume tableaux of the Paris Universal Exposition of 1867.

Fig. 26
Bedford Lemere and Co., Assemblage of architectural plaster casts from Chartres Cathedral, in the Royal Architectural Museum, London, 1872 or later. Photo: Collection Centre Canadien d'Architecture/ Canadian Centre for Architecture, Montreal.

Fig. 27
View of the western Cast Court of the Victoria and Albert Museum, London, following restoration in 1982. Photo: Courtesy of the Board of Trustees of the Victoria and Albert Museum.

Fig. 28
**National pavilions on
"le Quart Anglais,"
outside the exhibition
hall at the Universal
Exposition, Paris, 1867;
from L'Exposition
Universelle de 1867
(Paris, 1867), vol. 2,
pp. 296-97. Photo:
Courtesy of the Special
Collections Department,
Northwestern University
Library.**

From World's Fair to Architectural Museum

We might perhaps, on former occasions, by viewing the products of various nations,...conceive some idea of their manners and customs, but never had we before such an opportunity of studying their every-day life in its most minute details. Without undertaking long and perilous journeys, without running the risk of being frozen in the North, or melted in the South; we have seen the Russian drive his *troika* drawn by Tartar steeds, the Arab smoke the *narghilé* or play the *darbouka* under his gilt cupolas, the fair daughters of the Celestial Empire sip their tea in their quaint painted houses; we have walked in a few minutes from the Temple of the Caçiques to the Bardo of Tunis, from the American log-hut to the Kirghiz tent.[47]

Eugene Rimmel, leading perfume manufacturer and assistant commissioner of the Universal Exposition of 1867 in Paris, alludes above to what he and indeed every commentator regarded as the Exposition's chief novelty, the proliferation of national pavilions. Grandiose displays like the 1867 Exposition fostered intense concentration on national representation through architecture, food, and the display of all manner of agricultural, industrial, and even intellectual productions. They nurtured an insatiable curiosity about the life of foreign peoples; gave a tremendous boost to the study of ethnography; bestowed new meaning and allure on the art of travel; and in the process, established the collecting and exhibition of architecture on a new footing.

Alfred Normand, in his learned monograph on the foreign pavilions of the 1867 Exposition, claimed that this was the first exposition at which architecture had been represented other than by drawings and small models.[48] While this was not strictly true—the various courts built within the Crystal Palace for the Great Exhibition of 1851 had already contained large-scale mock-ups of Greek, medieval, and Islamic architecture—the 1867 fair *was* the first to include a significant number of buildings outside the main exhibition palace. Egypt, Tunis, Morocco, Russia, Austria, Great Britain, Prussia, Holland, Spain, all staked out parcels of the Champs de Mars (fig. 28). There was also a Romanian church, an American school house, an Italian villa, a replica of the temple of Xochicalco, and many other exotic structures (figs. 29,30). In a sense, the 1867 Exposition was the first museum of architecture to present entire buildings, and as such, it laid the groundwork for both the period room and the outdoor architectural museum of the twentieth century.

The magic of the Paris Exposition was not completely novel, however. The principle of arrangement was essentially that of the English landscape garden, as set forth in Wightwick's *Palace of Architecture*. Moreover, as Rimmel's rhapsodic travelogue suggests, the success of the national pavilions was based upon their ability to capture the experience of travel. And, like the early architectural museums, the national pavilions invoked the rhetorical power of fragments to suggest grand but invisible generalities, which were now sought in the abstract but emotionally laden sphere of nationhood and the march of civilization. In what broad terms these little pavilions could speak is suggested by the words of an American commentator who found embodied in the tiny American school house "the great secret of the general intelligence of the American people, the source of their astonishing material progress,"[49] or of the commissioner of the Egyptian exhibition, who remarked that the four buildings under his jurisdiction offered, "in miniature and as if condensed into a very small space, all of Egypt, brilliant, splendid, revealing the grandeurs of its past, the rich promises of its present, leaving to public opinion itself the responsibility of drawing conclusions about the future."[50] One might think that the net of representation could hardly be cast more broadly than that, yet Normand himself claimed that the same four buildings "summarized in a sense all of oriental life."[51]

We can, however, be a little more specific about how and what the national pavilions represented. Most obviously, they stood for national identity, and this function would be strengthened and regularized at later fairs: at those of 1878 and 1900, both in Paris, national pavilions were grouped to form impressive "Rues des Nations." Within these assemblages, the pavilions of rich western countries like Prussia and Great Britain also stood for modernity and progress. But the pavilions that interested Normand most were not those of prosperous modern countries, but rather those from what would now be called the Third World. In his text, he calls attention to two distinct categories among the foreign buildings: first, those of "oriental nations" like Egypt, Tunis, and Morocco, which were "emerging from their isolation for the first time," and second, those of northern countries like Russia, Norway, Sweden, and Austria, "where wood was the principal element of construction." What these two had in common was that both maintained traditional cultures untouched by modern Europe's inexorable march of progress. The architecture of the pavilions articulated this cultural difference quite clearly: they represented foreignness, ethnicity, difference.

In order to see the image of difference, the architects and organizers of fairs had first to construct it. This they quite literally did in 1867, for a great many of the national pavilions were designed by Parisian architects. But more significantly, they had to reach an agreement about what lay within and what without their own civilization. This distinction was articulated in two ways: first, by drawing a spatial line around the perimeter of modern western culture; second, by drawing a temporal line across its threshold. The

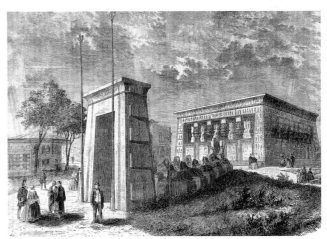

Figs. 29, 30
Chinese pavilion, called "Débit de Thé Chinois," and the Egyptian pavilion at the Universal Exposition, Paris, 1867; from L'Exposition Universelle de 1867, vol. 1, pp. 135, 57. Photo: Courtesy of the Special Collections Department, Northwestern University Library.

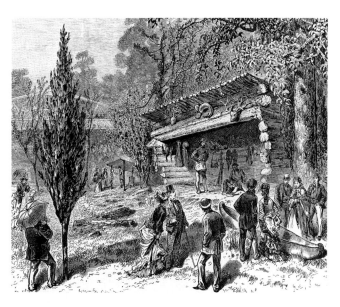

Fig. 31
**Hunter's cabin at the
Centennial Exposition,
Philadelphia, 1876;
from Frank Leslie's
Illustrated Historical
Register of the
Centennial Exposition
1876 (rpt. New York,
1974), p. 86.**

Fig. 32
**C. D. Arnold, View of the
Midway, looking east, at
the World's Columbian
Exposition, Chicago,
1893, showing, at left,
a Polynesian native
village.**

Fig. 33
**C. D. Arnold, View of
the Egyptian exhibition,
at the World's
Columbian Exposition,
Chicago, 1893, with
building at the
University of Chicago
under construction in
the background.**

first defined a realm of foreignness which included Egypt, the Far
East, North Africa, Russia, Scandinavia, and the American West; the
second a realm of pastness which stretched backward from around
1800 into the furthest mists of time. What was left over, the residual
area consisting of Western Europe after about 1800, was the realm
of the fair organizers themselves and their public.

To understand how difference was constructed and displayed, it
must be remembered that the fairgoer of the late nineteenth century
was not primarily interested in buildings but rather in the kind of
experience suggested in Normand's phrase, "all of oriental life."
Burton Benedict has pointed out the rapid proliferation of categories
relating to social life in the organization of the fairs from 1867 on,[52]
and this development had a profound impact on the display of
architecture. On the one hand, the official interest in social welfare
prompted a rapid rise in the popularity of exhibits of workers'
housing, which had already been introduced at the Great Exhibition
of 1851 but which would culminate only much later in independent
exhibitions such as the Weissenhof Seidlung in Stuttgart, begun by
the Deutsche Werkbund in 1925. On the other hand, increasing
attention was paid to the texture of popular life in the past. One of
the great attractions of the Paris Exposition was a History of Labor,
which set forth the development of human skill in a display of well
over 5,000 tools and craft objects dating from the Stone Age to about
1800. Even more entrancing were the exhibits of native costume.
Rimmel particularly enjoyed the Swedish exhibit, which featured
"figures of life-like expression engaged in all sorts of occupations,"
so anecdotally suggestive that he could "build a little story illustrating
Swedish manners and customs" around them.[53]

In exhibits like these, an attempt was made to involve a broad
range of artifacts in a total picture of human life; at the same time,
the artifacts were animated by a human presence. The house itself
was the most complete and expressive of domestic artifacts, the
portrait not only of its owner but of its society—and so the display of
foreign, ethnic, or historic architecture came to be deeply affected
by this preoccupation with social customs. Already at the 1867
Exposition, some of the national pavilions were peopled by characteristic figures: at the Egyptian exhibit Rimmel noted that "*real
natives, varying in shade from light brown to ebony black, work at
several trades*," including turning, jewelry, and barbering.[54] In later
Expositions, the importance of native figures to the display of
architecture increased significantly: at the Philadelphia Centennial
Exposition of 1876, a hunter's cabin (fig. 31) was not only equipped
with "all the paraphernalia that a pushing and ingenious pioneer
would be likely to provide" but also occupied by several real hunters
who, in addition to giving demonstrations of fishing and beaver

hunting, "lounge on the rough log couch, smoke, dress skins, cook and eat, thereby illustrating their manner of living in the West."[55] At the Paris Exposition of 1889, meticulously reproduced pavilions and villages were home to over 400 Indochinese, Senegalese, and Tahitians;[56] and at the World's Columbian Exposition of 1893 in Chicago, such displays of native life proliferated as amusements of the most popular sort (figs. 32-34).

Another spectacular manifestation of the concentration on domestic architecture and domesticity encouraged by the fairs was the "History of Human Habitation" presented at the Exposition of 1889. This was a series of twenty-three full-scale houses designed by Charles Garnier, the famed architect of the Paris Opéra. While few of Garnier's houses pretended to any great accuracy, this hardly mattered: the differences registered by the buildings were not really architectural at all but were rather constructed on the level of popular life and culture, and here Garnier's exhibit worked brilliantly. Like the histories of labor mounted in both 1867 and 1878, it demonstrated the steady rise of civilization, but it also told the story of human lives that were different from those of its viewers.[57]

Other kinds of exhibits encouraged consumption of a much more direct sort. In 1864, the United States Sanitary Commission mounted a series of local fairs featuring restaurants known as New England or Olde Tyme Kitchens.[58] Decorated to suggest the ambience of a colonial kitchen, these were furnished with a bill of fare to match, thereby offering the visitor an evocation of national ethnicity compounded equally of food and ambience. The Universal Exposition of 1867 elaborated the act of eating as a mode of cultural consumption, for alongside the pavilions sprang up a host of national restaurants and bars, which worked hand in hand with the national pavilions to provide an access to foreign modes of life. The Viennese brewer Dreher set up an immense beer hall in the midst of the Austrian village, where the enjoyment of Austrian and Hungarian national dishes, wines, and beer was enhanced by the "blue-eyed *mädchen* in national costume" who served them and who contributed to the "*couleur locale*."[59] Local color was evidently the main attraction: the Russian restaurant caused such a "great sensation" with its booted and pantalooned waiters that "many visitors, in order to have a nearer view of the denizens of the place, venture to dive into the horrors of Russian cooking.... Others less bold, or less wealthy, content themselves with staring in through the windows."[60]

The national compounds of 1887 provided images of foreignness, but as the slightly earlier Colonial Kitchens suggest, the same mixture of sensations could be used to present the native or national past. For this, the chief vehicle came to be the historical theme village. Two exhibitions held in 1886 featured historical recreations based on

Fig. 34

C. D. Arnold, Kwakiutl Indians of the Northwest Pacific Coast at the World's Columbian Exposition, Chicago, 1893.

local topography: Old Edinburgh and Old London. For the Manchester Royal Jubilee Exhibition the following year, Alfred Darbyshire and Frederick Bennett Smith designed another large theme village called Old Manchester and Salford, whose putative site again was not a hundred or a thousand miles away from the fair but was right there, practically on the site of the exhibition itself. The exhibit's most prominent feature, the cathedral tower, even replicated the actual tower of Manchester Cathedral, so that the connection between Manchester within and without the fair could hardly be missed. Yet the Manchester exhibited was Manchester of the past, and the traveler who entered it found himself caught up in a strange sort of chronological collage. "It was a sort of dreamland," wrote the fair's official commentator, "a wonderfully delightful jumble of incongruities" where "nothing happened but the unexpected."

The Roman gateway, guarded by Roman soldiers in full costume, led to Tudor houses. You had stocks and pillory, and hideous ancient crosses, and Chetham College, and the first Exchange, all in a heap; a fine old bridge, spanning a river of cobble stones; a cathedral tower ninety-three feet high, without any cathedral attached. Edward the Third's crossbowmen wandered about the streets; the terribly fierce and warlike bodyguard of the Young Pretender was for ever on parade; and anon you came full tilt upon the ghost of a Georgian watchman, bill-hook and all. There was a post-office where you didn't post; a coach-office from which no coaches started.[61]

From these impressions, three distinct themes can be extracted, and these themes were to remain important in the architectural presentation of the national past, and indeed in the conception of outdoor architectural museums right down to the present. First was the fracturing of time and space which ensured that no coherent picture of Manchester at any given time could ever come into focus, but only the ideal Manchester of all past epochs—Old Manchester. This ideal synthesis was achieved by the same techniques of fracturing and recombining fragmentary specimens that had been perfected by Lenoir. Second was the mixing of heroic and quotidian elements in the tableaux. Third was the populating of this generalized image of Old Manchester with just the sort of ethnic figures and amusements that had become familiar in national pavilions, restaurants, and costume displays. You could watch "Master Caxton and his assistants, all correctly costumed," working an ancient wooden printing press.[62] You could also buy the books whose making you had watched, along with jewelry, umbrellas, and so forth. You could, in short, consume both the process and the product of traditional handicraft along with any number of old-time refreshments, served up in old-time decor.

The main themes and procedures of Old Manchester were soon developed at other fairs, especially at the Paris Exposition of 1900, where a great swath of land along the river was given over to a display of "Le Vieux Paris," whose fruitcake richness of effect exceeded even that of Old Manchester. But the Vienna Fair of 1873 helped to articulate a more explicitly ethnographic or folk-oriented view of national tradition. Part of the fairgrounds along the Danube was reserved for a display of rural houses from various Austro-Hungarian regions. As usual, the emphasis was on the demonstration of differences: traditional timber construction was marveled at, while one illustrated chronicle commented on a peasant house from Hungary: "The contemporary inhabitants of the province of Haudorf take no part in the great progress owing to the immense conquests of modern civilization."[63] Yet an attempt at national self-description was also at work, for these were not the peasants of some foreign country but of the homeland: they and their cottages represented a repository of fast-disappearing native traditions.

Within the same general area of the Vienna Fair was another noteworthy group of buildings. Though individually, the timber houses and church that made up the Transylvanian Village hardly differed in principle from the Haudorf house, or for that matter from the Polish, Alsatian, or Russian farmhouses, their disposition did. For now they were grouped into a rough semblance of a village. This new emphasis on the entire settlement was carried further at the next great Austro-Hungarian fair, the Budapest Millenium Exposition of 1896. Here, the "Ethnographic Group" consisted of two segments, a "Hungarian Street" and a "Nationalities Street," both displaying rustic or peasant houses and both offering craft objects for sale.[64] The "Nationalities Street" represented Romania, Swabia, Bosnia, and other neighboring regions, so that the entire ethnographic group formed an open-air museum of Austro-Hungarian regional folk life and architecture.

A few years before the Budapest Exposition, however, the world's first permanent outdoor architectural museum had opened in a capital city at the other end of Europe's great timber belt, Stockholm. In order to understand its genesis and its relationship to developments at the international expositions, we must go back to 1872. In that year, a Stockholm philologist named Artur Hazelius had taken a holiday trip to the province of Delecarlia. There he became aware of the encroachment of industrialization on the traditional peasant culture and, filled with that sense of impending loss that had motivated architectural collectors from Lenoir onward, he began to accumulate old costumes and implements. He exhibited his new collection in Stockholm, and the following year, 1873, he founded the Skandinavisk-etnografiska Samlingen. In 1876, helped by generous government subsidies, he was able to take his growing collection to the Philadelphia Centennial Exposition. There, his "admirable groups of costumed figures illustrating peasant life" won particular praise. Arranged in anecdotal tableaux like those of the 1867 Paris Exposition, Hazelius's groups were especially noted for their verisimilitude: instead of the usual wax mannequins, he had used plaster figures modeled by a well known Stockholm sculptor, with hands and faces painted in an "exceedingly lifelike" manner. The costumes had all been purchased directly from their peasant wearers, and such great care had been taken to assure "absolute correctness in detail" that when a hand was broken in shipping, it was replaced by another modeled from a Swedish girl.[65]

In 1878, Hazelius again took his collection on tour, this time to the Paris Exposition, where his tableaux again scored a great success. Had Hazelius's story ended here, it would have been merely an incident in the history of the fairs. But Hazelius had greater ambitions. In 1880, his ethnographical collections became the national property of Sweden, and a grand structure, the Nordiska Museet, was built to house them. Still not satisfied, Hazelius, in 1891, opened the world's first permanent outdoor architectural museum, Skansen. This seventy-five-acre park in Stockholm was furnished with a collection of Swedish village buildings, supplemented by traditional crafts, peopled by guides in traditional costume, and animated by demonstrations of folk song, dance, and crafts. It was at once a costume tableau and an ethnographic theme village.[66]

If the outdoor architectural museum grew out of the international expositions of the late nineteenth century, changes in the indoor display of architecture were also bringing traditional art museums in line with the expositions. Throughout the nineteenth century, museums had grouped decorative art objects according to material—silver with silver, glass with glass, and so forth. During the 1890s, this practice began to break down. At the Swiss National Museum in Zurich, for example, the collections were rearranged more naturalistically in sixty-two rooms designed to evoke period settings; the same procedure was followed in Munich, Nuremberg, and elsewhere. In London, Brussels, and Paris, avant-garde galleries of decorative arts adopted a parallel principle of quasi-domestic installations. And though the new methods did not catch on immediately in English or French museums, the period room— the more or less authentic but always evocative architectural setting for the display of domestic furnishings—was well established in museums throughout the German-speaking and Scandinavian lands by the turn of the century.

The other place where both period rooms and outdoor museums caught on and multiplied was in the United States. Until recently, it was generally believed that the first period rooms in America were the three installed by George Francis Dow at the Essex

Institute in Salem, Massachusetts, in 1907. Yet recent research has shown that Charles Presby Wilcomb anticipated him.[67] Born in 1868, Wilcomb grew up in rural New Hampshire, surrounded by just the sort of relics that incited Hazelius's desire. Sometime in the 1880s, he began to collect those relics, but it was his move to California in 1888 that gave him the requisite distance to see his collections in perspective. He was suddenly struck by a perception of cultural difference and, like Hazelius, by a sense that valued traditions were slipping away. Having convinced the commissioners of San Francisco's Midwinter Fair of 1894 to appoint him curator of the museum that would be the fair's permanent memorial, he opened his New England collections to the public in 1896 in two period rooms, a colonial kitchen and a bedroom.

Wilcomb's association with the Golden Gate Park Memorial Museum was unhappy, and in 1905 he resigned. Three years later, he became curator of another California museum, the Oakland Public Museum, where he built up yet another colonial collection and, in 1910, opened yet another pair of period rooms. By this time, however, George Francis Dow had opened his rooms at Salem—the rooms that he himself would later claim to be the first in America.[68] Was Dow unaware of Wilcomb's work? Possibly. He did acknowledge the influence of period rooms in Munich, Zurich, Nuremberg, and Stockholm, and he particularly lauded the outdoor museums of northern Europe. Perhaps, as a cultivated easterner, Dow wished to be seen as an importer of European fashions.

Dow's rooms—a bedroom and parlor and, as always, a kitchen— were constructed in the typical exposition manner out of a mix of original elements, reproductions, and approximations (fig. 35). In the parlor, for example, a genuine mantel by Samuel McIntire consorted with wainscot, cornice, and other woodwork "reproduced from the finish of a house known to have been designed by him."[69] The emphasis was not on the authenticity or historical integrity of the rooms but on the texture of life that was lived in them, and the "illusion of actual human occupancy" achieved by old newspapers, spectacles, and a knitting basket, all disposed with artful casualness.[70]

In 1908, Dow spotted an important late-seventeenth-century house about to be demolished: he had it moved to the back of his Institute, furnished "as though occupied," and peopled with caretakers in period costume. Then he dug a make-believe well, planted an old-fashioned garden, set up a "fully equipped shoe-maker's shop," attached the porch of Nathaniel Hawthorne's famed House of Seven Gables to the rear wall of the Institute, and planted a cupola from the roof of a Salem merchant's house in the garden.[71] The resulting ensemble must have been rather bizarre and was certainly amateurish compared to Skansen. Yet it was almost certainly

Fig. 35
Kitchen from a seventeenth-century house as installed by George Francis Dow at the Essex Institute, Salem, Massachusetts, 1907; from Metropolitan Museum of Art Bulletin 17, 11, pt. 2 (Nov. 1922), p. 18.

Fig. 36
**Room from Hewlett
House, Woodbury,
Long Island, 1745, as
installed in the
American Wing
of The Metropolitan
Museum of Art, New
York, 1924; from R. T.
H. Halsey and Elizabeth
Tower, The Homes
of Our Ancestors
as Shown in the
American Wing of the
Metropolitan Museum
of Art (Garden City,
New York, 1925), pl. 7.**

the first permanent outdoor museum in this country.

The importance of Dow's work cannot be understood in terms of period rooms or outdoor museums alone: at the Essex Institute, both of the new methods of architectural display were introduced together into the mainstream of American museology, and together they would take root and multiply during the 1920s. The period room caught on more quickly, particularly at the Metropolitan Museum of Art, where there was a European connection in the person of W. R. Valentiner, who had been named curator of the new department of decorative arts in 1907. Before coming to this country, Valentiner had assisted Wilhelm Bode, director general of the royal museums of Berlin and a leader in the movement toward period installations, and when he came to arrange the Metropolitan's new collection of French decorative arts in 1908, Valentiner naturally followed the latest European fashion.

Though Valentiner returned to Germany during the First World War, his impact on American museums was just beginning. After the war, he became director of the Detroit Institute of Arts, where period settings were introduced in 1923. In the meantime, his former assistant, Joseph Breck, had become curator of decorative arts and assistant director of the Metropolitan Museum. Valentiner and Breck would wield considerable power at the Metropolitan throughout the formation of what were arguably the most important period-room installations in America, the American Wing and the Cloisters.

The story of the American Wing begins two years after Valentiner's arrival, with a major exhibition of American decorative arts mounted by the museum in connection with the Hudson-Fulton Celebration of 1909. At the same time, the museum purchased a collection of over 400 objects—a daring move, for received opinion held that American craft objects had no place in a serious art museum. The exhibition's success proved otherwise, and demand grew for a permanent display of the museum's new collection. This was to be at once a "complete exemplification" of the "Zurich method" and a vindication of Dow's work at Salem.[72] Accordingly, the museum began to purchase rooms from old houses to serve as period settings, and in 1919, Grosvenor Atterbury was hired to design a new wing to contain them.

The Metropolitan's American Wing opened in 1924, complete with seventeen period rooms (figs. 36,37). It was a great success. Its evocative settings captured public and professional imagination and had immediate repercussions. At the Metropolitan itself, Edward Robinson's Roman Court, a large Pompeian atrium stocked with Greek and Roman sculpture, followed within two years. Far more important, though, were the Cloisters, the celebrated collection of medieval architecture and sculpture amassed by George Gray

Barnard, bought for the museum with a gift of John D. Rockefeller, Jr., in 1925, and magnificently housed a few years later in a romantic compote of genuine and modern medieval settings high above the Hudson River. In 1938, the year of the opening of the Cloisters, the skylit cast court of the old Metropolitan was rebuilt and the entire collection of architectural casts and models swept away: the triumph of the "Zurich method" was complete.

By this time, museums in Detroit, Brooklyn, and elsewhere were also following the Metropolitan's lead. Nor was the triumph of the period room restricted to museums: even shops now sold luxury goods in period room settings (indeed, Neil Harris has shown that museums were strongly influenced by innovations in shop display).[73] More importantly, private collectors had discovered the attraction of period settings for their collections. These were men like George Gray Barnard and George Blumenthal, much of whose collections went to the Metropolitan; William Randolph Hearst, who spent a lifetime and a fortune building San Simeon in California; James Deering and John Ringling, who built splendid mansions in Florida, Villa Vizcaya and Ca d'Zan; Electra Havemeyer Webb, who assembled a splendid collection of decorative arts and transplanted buildings in Shelburne, Vermont; and Henry Francis Du Pont, who, inspired by the examples of Shelburne and the American Wing, began in 1918 to remodel and extend his Delaware mansion, Winterthur, into an enormous collection of American period rooms and furnishings. All of these private house-museums eventually became public institutions, and important ones. Nor must one forget Mrs. James Ward Thorne, who began in the late 1920s to build marvelous miniature period rooms, exhibited them at the Chicago World's Fair of 1933 and the New York and San Francisco fairs of 1939-40, and then donated them to The Art Institute of Chicago, whose curator of decorative arts called the thirty-seven American examples "a fully developed American Wing in miniature."[74]

The re-emergence of the outdoor museum in American museology paralleled the rise of the period room in the 1920s; again wealthy private collectors were in the vanguard. But here, the emphasis was slightly different. The growth of interest in American decorative arts had played a central role in the development of the American period room; in the outdoor museum, the celebration of native tradition was all-important. It has been suggested that the first museum village in the United States was begun in 1925 when a group of log cabins were moved to Decorah, Iowa, and opened to the public.[75] Yet in 1923, Henry Ford had already purchased the famous Wayside Inn in South Sudbury, Massachusetts, complete with over 2,000 acres of land, a church, schools, and houses, which Ford proceeded to restore as a showcase village.[76] More ambitious schemes

Fig. 37
Ballroom from Gadsby's Tavern, Alexandria, Virginia, 1793, as installed in the American Wing of The Metropolitan Museum of Art, New York, 1924; from Halsey and Tower, The Homes of Our Ancestors, *pl. 10.*

· ·

followed rapidly. In 1924, the city of Williamsburg, Virginia, offered itself to Henry Ford as a restoration project on the largest scale; and though he turned the offer down, John D. Rockefeller, Jr., began two years later to rebuild the town, providing it with all the accoutrements of an outdoor museum. In 1927, Ford began to construct his own outdoor museum, originally called the Early American Village (and now known as Greenfield Village), which would open in Dearborn, Michigan, in 1929, in conjunction with a vast indoor museum of American decorative and industrial artifacts. After 1929, the popularity of restoration villages climbed rapidly, so that by 1955, it was estimated that there were more than thirty east of the Mississippi alone; but then, the enthusiasm for American tradition had also increased phenomenally, so that by 1967, those restoration villages could take their place among "more than 630 museums, historical houses turned museum, and townlike enclaves—conserved, restored, or reproduced—that concentrate on the wherewithal of everyday living as our ancestors lived it."[77]

On one level, both period room and outdoor museum represented a reaction against the traditional museum presentation of architecture through casts and fragments. And in both cases, this reaction was expressed by drawing upon the techniques and imagery of the international expositions. Thus many outdoor museums followed the landscape garden model adopted on the Champs de Mars in 1867; or else they grouped their specimens into representative but imaginary streets or villages, as in the Vienna or Budapest fairs. Like these ethnic villages, they presented a varied array of costumed guides, craft demonstrations, and old-fashioned food, all supported by a sophisticated range of tourist services. Like the fairs, finally, they used architecture to focus attention on the details of old-fashioned life.

As for period rooms, these were essentially fairground tableaux: often they were treated explicitly as three-sided stage spaces (a practice exemplified in the miniature peep-show boxes of the Thorne Rooms); and even where all four walls were present, openings were routinely relocated to serve the flow of visitors along the margin. As in fairground displays, scale and proportions were freely altered, and interior ensembles cobbled together out of the most disparate bits and pieces of decoration and furnishing— Hudson Valley portraits, Virginia paneling, London wallpaper— often quite genuine in themselves but historically incompatible. The aim was just the sort of conceptual wholeness or typicality that could be assembled out of fragments—in short, a collage technique that reached back beyond the fairs to the spurious tombs and tabernacles constructed by Alexandre Lenoir.

The debt to the world's fairs shared by period rooms and

outdoor museums was as great on the ideological as on the technical level. In celebrating national traditions, these collections nevertheless created a sense of cultural difference similar to that fostered in the fairs. Their attempt to commemorate or retrieve vanishing traditions was fueled by an acute sense of loss, and this conjunction of loss and retrieval once again brings up the issue of architectural preservation, for both indoor and outdoor museums have repeatedly claimed to be motivated by its spirit. But as with architectural collectors ever since the days of Lenoir and Elgin, destruction was as important to their work as salvation: by 1955, for example, Colonial Williamsburg had restored 82 buildings, reconstructed 375, and destroyed 616.[78] If no one thought to criticize this ledger, that was not only because the destroyed buildings were less esteemed as architecture than those restored, but more importantly because, as with Hazelius and the other organizers of ethnic fairground displays, the preservation urge was rooted in a deeper sense of loss centered less on architecture than on a way of life. A writer in *House Beautiful*, commenting as recently as 1967 on the proliferation of restoration villages and house museums, noted the "delightful preoccupation with domestic archeology" that "now pervades the land."[79] Abbott Lowell Cummings too could put architecture and preservation in the proper perspective: "For those many Americans who have been troubled successively by the vanishing of the Indian, the buffalo, and the familiar locomotive, with its beloved steam whistle there can be added a new cry, 'lo the poor American village!' "[80]

As Cummings suggests, the way of life "preserved" by open-air museums was an idealized, pre-industrial culture revolving around the traditional handicrafts. This was the ideology promoted at the fairs, institutionalized at Skansen, and quite universally followed in open-air museums throughout Europe (and in recent decades in the U.S.S.R.). Sometimes, in the United States, the hostility to industry was palpable, as at Old Deerfield, Massachusetts, whose director praised those who had "had the vision to keep industry off the quaint old Street."[81] But elsewhere, it subsisted in strange harmony with the symbols of industrialism. Thus when Henry Ford opened his Edison Institute, no conflict was perceived between the adulation of traditional handicrafts and village ways of life, which dominated part of the complex, and the adulation of industrial pioneers like Edison, the Wright brothers, and Ford himself, which dominated the rest. So strongly held indeed was the belief in an ideal pre-industrial culture that the geniuses of industrialism were simply ruralized: even Ford's automobile factory, along with other acquired structures (figs. 38,39), was so reduced in scale that it appeared hardly out of context with the surrounding craft shops, the miniature town hall, and the old-fashioned inn.

All the same, this bucolic ideology of the village everyman was complicated by other factors, and not only by the adulation of industrial heroes. There were also political heroes to commemorate. The saintly virtues of relics had always enlivened architectural museums, but in the United States, the concept of the secular relic formed the very foundation of the architectural preservation movement. In 1850, Washington's revolutionary headquarters in Newburgh, New York, had become the first historic house museum in this country. Ten years later, Mount Vernon also became a national shrine.[82] Not all of the ethnographic enthusiasm of the late-nineteenth-century fairs, nor all of Henry Ford's agrarian populism, could eclipse this cult of national fame. On the contrary, Ford went to great lengths to acquire a building dignified by association with Abraham Lincoln. What the prevailing ethnographic populism did was to shape the cult of national heroes in its own image: thus Mount Vernon was equipped with intimate relics of the great man's life, such as a shaving stand presented by the French minister, or a chair that had stood near Washington's death bed, while in the open-air museums, accents of national fame were highlighted against the more subdued background of everyday life.

This pervasive need to bedeck architecture with intimate objects, and to animate the whole with memories, emotions, and anecdotes, points to the same underlying sense of loss that had propelled the European predecessors of the new Americana collections. But in this country, the entire issue of lost or threatened traditions took on a peculiar and paranoid intensity. "Traditions are one of the integral assets of a nation," intoned the official chroniclers of the Metropolitan's American Wing in 1925: "Much of the America of to-day has lost sight of its traditions. . . . Many of our people are not cognizant of our traditions and the principles for which our fathers struggled and died. The tremendous changes in the character of our nation, and the influx of foreign ideas utterly at variance with those held by the men who gave us the Republic, threaten us and, unless checked, may shake its foundations."[83]

The danger so darkly hinted at here was the threat of immigration. The 1920s indeed witnessed strenuous attempts to stem the influx of immigrants, as well as elaborate programs to Americanize those who arrived. Such programs, like Greenwich House or the University Settlement in New York, frequently relied upon colonial architecture and design as environmental influences.[84] Thus, the American Wing, born in 1909 as an artistic adventure, came to maturity in 1924 as an abettor of this rootedly conservative political ideology. Nor was the hostility to non-Anglo-Saxon peoples expressed in mere generalities. The official literature of both the American Wing and Old Deerfield presented an image of the Indians as cruel

and ferocious savages,[85] while anti-Semitism was implicit in Old
Deerfield's campaign against industrial encroachment. As for Henry
Ford, his anti-Semitism was quite explicit and indeed active during
the 1920s; but at Greenfield Village, Ford used patriotic symbols and
public education to promote a more positive program of Americanization, not only in the Early American Village, with its working
schoolhouse and its exemplary New England town hall, but also in
the museum whose vast industrial spaces were prefaced by a full-
scale replica of Independence Hall.

Given their political ambitions and the scale of their funding and
layout, enterprises such as the Early American Village might have
become vast and impersonal ideological machines. Yet just as in the
nineteenth-century fairs, a rigorous ideology of national exaltation
was packaged in a "delightful preoccupation with domestic archeology." The result was a highly contrived atmosphere of intimacy that
served as an enticement to the very nationalistic fervor it masked.
In some ways, the Americana collections went beyond the fairs,
for whereas the fairground exhibits had been mere stage sets for
a simulation of bygone ways, many of the new museums were
conceived as habitats for ongoing life. Hearst and DuPont actually
ensconced themselves within their collections, while Ford, though
not himself living amongst his furniture and farm implements,
tried to establish a community of some 300 people within his Early
American Village. Old Deerfield and Colonial Williamsburg
were rather more successful at this, since they were already living
communities that had only to be redesigned and redefined as
outdoor museums.

The intimate aura of the Americana collections had another
wellspring too. The prototypical architectural collector of the 1920s—
Hearst, Ford, Webb, Du Pont—was neither a museum curator nor a
public servant, but a private collector in the grand manner, passion-
ately acquisitive, opinionated, and above all fiercely identified with
his (or her) collection. Winterthur, Greenfield Village, the Thorne
Rooms, and the Shelburne Museum not only began as private
collections but long preserved that quality of personal vision peculiar
to the private collection. Indeed many architecture and period-room
collections of the time were not only private museums but homes,
shaped as much by domestic predilection and personal taste as
by scholarship and ideology. On one level, then, the architectural
museum of the 1920s, whether indoor or outdoor, represented
a return to the collecting practices of the earliest architectural
collections, of Romantic house-museums like Abbotsford, Highcliffe
Castle, or Sir John Soane's Museum.

Looking back over the hundred or more years that separate
Ford from Soane—or from Lenoir—it is easy to see how nineteenth-

Figs. 38, 39
**Sir John Bennett, Ltd.
Building, London,
demolished and
reconstructed at a
reduced scale at
Greenfield Village,
Dearborn, Michigan,
1930-31; from Geoffrey
C. Upward, A Home
for Our Heritage
(Dearborn, Michigan,
1979), p. 84.**

century museological developments, from the institutional cast collection through the national folk museum, coupled with early twentieth-century ideological influences, shaped Ford's museum complex into something quite different from its Romantic precedents. But one characteristic in particular of the Romantic house-museum remained extremely important for Ford, and this was the notion of self-revelation through objects, of the projection of the collector's most intimate memories and dreams onto his collections — and in Ford's case, onto the inhabitants of his collections, the exemplary citizens, school children, and Americanized immigrants who lived and moved about within the spaces of his village, and who became surrogates for the absent collector.[86] Ford's entire history as a collector was an incremental process of self-reference. Already in 1904, he had purchased one of his own early Quadricycles — his first conscious act as a collector. Ten years later, a casual remark of his wife prompted him to recall some verses learned in childhood, and this set off an intensive search for second-hand copies of the old books: in the end, the collections at Dearborn would include not only more than 450 volumes of McGuffey's *Eclectic Readers*, but also a "McGuffey School" (built out of the timber from an eighteenth-century barn), and even McGuffey's Pennsylvania birthplace.

In 1919, meanwhile, in order to save his family's old farmhouse from the approach of a new road, Ford had it moved and re-erected some two hundred feet from its original site, and he set out to restore it as he remembered it more than forty years earlier. In this, he went to almost fanatical lengths, not only commissioning a Ford Company draughtsman to design a replica of the original windmill but also sifting the dirt around the house for evocative fragments of his childhood, broken plates, hardware, rusty skates, over which he reminisced with his brothers and sisters very much in the manner of Mark Twain over his ancient tear jug, or Sir Walter Scott's descendants over his inkwell. But beyond his own house, Ford's need to discover and expose his own childhood drove him to project his personal hagiography onto the ideological agenda of the entire museum complex at Dearborn. One hero was, of course, McGuffey, but there was also Edison, Ford's boyhood idol and longtime friend, whose miscellaneous relics Ford had begun to collect in 1905 and who was commemorated not only in the name of Ford's complex — the Edison Institute — but also in a rich assortment of relics culminating in a meticulous reconstruction of Edison's Menlo Park research complex, complete with truckloads of New Jersey soil. And then there was Ford himself, represented by the scaled-down replica of his first assembly plant and also by a range of more intimate settings, including not only the family farmhouse but also a mill familiar from childhood, and most interestingly, the chapel. This was dedicated to

Martha and Mary—not those of the Bible but Ford's mother and mother-in-law; and though the design was very loosely based on a colonial church in Massachusetts, the building itself incorporated materials taken from the house in which the Fords had been married. So in this central icon of American values, this distillation of history, country, and religion, the visitor to Greenfield Village was confronted by an ersatz artifact, a collage of Henry Ford's personal mementos.

In its interweaving of private and public narrative, the Martha-Mary Chapel at once epitomizes the spirit of Ford's architectural collecting and reveals its kinship with the greatest early collectors of architecture, Sir John Soane and Alexandre Lenoir. They too had seen architectural collecting as a form of autobiography, and if the intimacies that Ford preferred were essentially banal, he was nonetheless using his collections as Soane had used them, to articulate a self-portrait. More particularly, he used them to mediate a relationship between himself and the public, and to claim a personal stake in the national history. Thus, like Lenoir, Ford treated his objects as trophies, public demonstrations of triumphs both personal and national.

Most of all, however, the buildings in the Early American Village were mementos, material relics of lives lost and regretted, of self and family, friends, heroes, everyman. They had the power to recall these things, and in some wordless way to hold their significance. This power was not magic: it was invested in fragmentary objects through the rhetorical conventions of metonymy and synechdoche, and it operated at McGuffey's birthplace or in the Martha-Mary Chapel just as efficaciously as it had on so many earlier occasions. Orson Welles understood this power of objects perfectly. His film of 1939, *Citizen Kane*—based on the life of another great architectural collector, William Randolph Hearst, and set in a fantasy of San Simeon—turns upon the power of humble domestic objects like a glass globe filled with snowflakes, or an old sled, to evoke the past, to capture and preserve its deepest and most personal significance.

Notes

This essay began as a lecture given at The Art Institute of Chicago in the fall of 1984 and was further developed in the course of lectures given at the Graduate School of Design, Harvard University, in the spring of 1986. I should like to thank both institutions for the opportunities they provided. Thanks also go to Joseph Connors, Mary McLeod, Joel Snyder, Nancy Troy, Clive Wainwright, and Warren Wechsler for many helpful suggestions. My wife, Susan Ball, introduced me to Greenfield Village and provided much incisive criticism of the manuscript. Malcolm Baker and Wim de Wit generously shared with me manuscript and rare printed material in their respective departments at the Victoria and Albert Museum and the Chicago Historical Society; Malcolm Baker also took me up into the balconies of the Cast Courts. The staffs of the Avery Library at Columbia University and the Ryerson and Burnham Libraries at The Art Institute of Chicago were unfailingly helpful, and my research assistant, Chris Kauffmann, provided much needed support. All translations are my own.

1. Quoted in David Watkin, *Thomas Hope, 1769-1831, and the Neo-Classical Idea* (London, 1968), p. 67.

2. Werner Szambien, "Durand and the Continuity of Tradition," in *The Beaux-Arts and Nineteenth-Century French Architecture*, ed. Robin Middleton (Cambridge, Mass., 1982), pp. 251-52 n. 33. Szambien notes that this information came in part from Robin Middleton.

3. William St. Clair, *Lord Elgin and the Marbles*, rev. ed. (Oxford and New York, 1983), p. 7.

4. Ibid., p. 97.

5. Ibid., p. 100.

6. Elizabeth Mavor, *The Ladies of Llangollen: A Study in Romantic Friendship* (London, 1971). See also the illustrations of Plas Newydd in Clive Wainwright, *The Romantic Interior: The British Collector at Home, 1750-1850* (New Haven and London, 1989), pp. 272-73.

7. Marianne Roland Michel, "Le Cabinet de Bonnier de la Mosson, et la Participation de Lajoue a son Décor," *Bulletin de la Société de l'histoire de l'Art Francais* (1975), pp. 211-21. See also Frank Bourdier, "L'extravagant Cabinet de Bonnier," *Connaissance des Arts* 90 (August 1959), pp. 52-60.

8. *Life of Johnson* (London, 1970), p. 709, recording a day spent in Lichfield, March 23, 1776; Clive Wainwright, "The Romantic Interior in England," *National Art-Collections Fund Review* (1985), p. 83. See also J. W. Whiston, "The Lichfield Clock: A Musical Altar-Clock from Richard Greene's Museum, Lichfield," *Transactions, South Staffordshire Archaeological and Historical Society* 18 (1977), pp. 73-82.

9. Mark Twain (Samuel Clemens), *The Innocents Abroad, or The New Pilgrims' Progress* (Hartford, 1869), p. 252.

10. Quoted in Mary Monica Maxwell Scott, *Abbotsford: The Personal Relics and Antiquarian Treasures of Sir Walter Scott* (London, 1893), p. 2.

11. Laurence Vail Coleman, *Historic House Museums* (Washington, D.C., 1933), p. 99.

12. Quoted in John Fleming, *Robert Adam and his Circle in Edinburgh and Rome* (London, 1962), pp. 152-53.

13. Quoted in David Watkin, *Athenian Stuart: Pioneer of the Greek Revival* (London, 1982), p. 47.

14. Quoted in Emmanuelle Hubert, "Alexandre Lenoir et le premier Musée des Monuments français," *Archeologia*, no. 39 (1971), p. 20.

15. Ibid.

16. Alexandre Lenoir, *Musée des Monuments Français, ou Description Historique et Chronologique des Statues en Marbre et en Bronze, Bas-Reliefs et Tombeaux des Hommes et des Femmes Celebres, pour Servir a l'Histoire de France et a celle de l'Art*, vol. 2 (1801), pp. 83ff., 136ff.

17. St. Clair (note 3), p. 101.

18. Ibid., p. 116.

19. Lenoir (note 16), vol. 3 (1802), p. 8.

20. Maxwell Scott (note 10), pp. 31-32, 27.

21. Christopher Hussey, "Highcliffe Castle, Hants.," *Country Life* 91 (1942), pp. 854ff.

22. John Britton, *The Union of Architecture, Sculpture, and Painting; Exemplified by a Series of Illustrations, with Descriptive Accounts of the House and Galleries of John Soane* (London, 1827), p. 47.

23. The most complete study of Soane's collections, both at Pitzhanger Manor and in London, is Susan Feinberg Millenson, *Sir John Soane's Museum* (Ann Arbor, 1987), a revision of her dissertation, *Sir John Soane's "Museum": An Analysis of the Architect's House-Museum in Lincoln's Inn Fields, London* (Ph.D. diss., University of Michigan, 1979).

24. *Sir John Soane's "Museum"* (note 23), p. 76.

25. Ibid., p. 127.

26. Britton (note 22), p. 27.

27. Ibid., p. vii.

28. George Wightwick, *The Palace of Architecture: A Romance of Art and History* (London, 1840).

29. John Foulston, *The Public Buildings Erected in the West of England as Designed by John Foulston* (London, 1838), p. 3. The group is illustrated in plate 80.

30. Wightwick (note 28), p. 206.

31. Ibid., pp. 204-06.

32. Edward Buckton Lamb, "Brief Hints for the Preservation of the Architectural Remains of the Middle Ages," *Architectural Magazine* 5 (April 1838), pp. 159-62.

33. Edward Buckton Lamb, letter of November 7, 1842, in British Museum, Original Letters and Papers, vol. 27, September 1842 - February 1843.

34. The story has been well told in John Summerson, *The Architectural Association, 1847-1947* (London, 1947), pp. 35-41.

35. See photographs of the installation in John Physick, *The Victoria and Albert Museum: The History of its Building* (Oxford, 1982), p. 38.

36. "The Royal Architectural Museum," *Builder* 27 (July 24, 1869), p. 583.

37. Summerson (note 34), pp. 38-41.

38. Louis Courajod, "Le Moulage," *Revue des Arts Decoratifs* 8 (1887-88), pp. 161-68, 250-55, 277-83, 311-15.

39. *Catalogue of Casts from Medieval Art, for Sale by D. Brucciani* . . . (n.p., n.d.); *Catalogue of Reproductions of Antique and Modern Sculpture on Sale at D. Brucciani's Galleria delle Belle Arti* . . . (n.p., n.d.). I am grateful to Malcolm Baker for showing me the Victoria and Albert Museum's copies of these catalogues.

40. Sir George Gilbert Scott, *A Guide to the Royal Architectural Museum* . . . (London, 1876), p. 2.

41. Carnegie Institute, *Annual Report*, nos. 11-12 (1906-07, 1908-09), p. 13.

42. Ibid., p. 17.

43. James D. Van Trump, *An American Palace of Culture: The Carnegie Institute and Carnegie Library of Pittsburgh* (Pittsburgh, 1970), p. 30.

44. Scott (note 40), p. 2.

45. Carnegie Institute (note 41), p. 17.

46. Van Trump (note 43), pp. 31-32.

47. Eugene Rimmel, *Recollections of the Paris Exhibition of 1867* (London, [1868]), pp. 1-2.

48. Alfred Normand, *L'Architecture des Nations Etrangeres. Etude dur les Principales Constructions du Parc a l'Exposition Universelle de Paris (1867)* (Paris, 1870), p. 1.

49. Quoted in Ellen Weiss, "Americans in Paris: Two Buildings," *Journal of the Society of Architectural Historians* 45 (June 1986), p. 166.

50. Normand (note 48), p. 3.

51. Ibid.

52. Burton Benedict, "The Anthropology of World's Fairs," in Burton Benedict et al., *The Anthropology of World's Fairs: San Francisco's Panama Pacific International Exposition of 1915* (Berkeley and London, 1983), pp. 29ff.

53. Rimmel (note 47), p. 205.

54. Ibid., p. 238.

55. Frank Henry Norton, *Illustrated Historical Register of the Centennial Exhibition, Philadelphia, 1876, and of the Exposition Universelle, Paris, 1878* (New York, 1879), pp. 86-87.

56. Benedict (note 52), p. 48.

57. Frantz Jourdain, *Exposition Universelle de 1889*. Constructions Elevées au Champs de Mars par M. Ch. Garnier. Pour Servir a l'Histoire de l'Habitation Humaine (Paris, n.d.), pp. 8-9.

58. See Rodris Roth, "The New England, or 'Olde Tyme,' Kitchen Exhibit at Nineteenth Century Fairs," in *The Colonial Revival in America*, ed. Alan Axelrod (New York, 1985), pp. 159-83.

59. Rimmel (note 47), p. 41.

60. Ibid., p. 42.

61. Walter Tomlinson, *The Pictorial Record of the Royal Jubilee Exhibition, Manchester, 1887* (Manchester, 1888), pp. 127-28.

62. Ibid., pp. 129-31.

63. Edoardo Sonzogno, ed., *L'Esposizione Universale di Vienna del 1873 Illustrata* (Milan, 1873-74), p. 182.

64. Zoltan Balint, *Die Architektur des Millenniums-Ausstellung* (Vienna, [1897]), pp. 22ff.

65. Norton (note 55), p. 87.

66. Outdoor museums caught on rapidly in Scandinavia: Denmark's first, in Copenhagen, opened in 1897; Norway's first, the Norwegian Folk Museum at Oslo, in 1902; its second, the Sandvig Collections near Lillehammer, in 1904; Finland's first, at Folis, in 1908. By 1928, it was estimated that there were about 150 such outdoor museums in Sweden alone.

67. The following discussion is based on Melinda Young Frye, "The Beginnings of the Period Room in American Museums: Charles P. Wilcomb's Colonial Kitchens, 1896, 1906, 1910," in Axelrod (note 58), pp. 217-40.

68. George Francis Dow, "Museums and the Preservation of Early Houses," *Metropolitan Museum of Art Bulletin* 17, 11, pt. 2 (November 1922), pp. 16-20.

69. Ibid., pp. 17-18.

70. Ibid., p. 18.

71. Ibid., pp. 18-19.

72. H[enry] W. K[ent], "The American Wing in its Relation to the History of Museum Development," *Metropolitan Museum of Art Bulletin* 17, 11, pt. 2 (November 1922), pp. 14-16.

73. Neil Harris, "Museums, Merchandising, and Popular Taste: The Struggle for Influence," in Ian Quimby, ed., *Material Culture and the Study of American Life* (New York and Winterthur, Del., 1978), pp. 140-74.

74. Meyric R. Rogers, "Foreword," in Mrs. James Ward Thorne, *American Rooms in Miniature* (Chicago, 1941), n. pag.

75. Abbott Lowell Cummings, "Restoration Villages," *Art in America* 43, 2 (May 1955), p. 12.

76. Geoffrey C. Upward, *A Home for Our Heritage: The Building and Growth of Greenfield Village and Henry Ford Museum, 1929-1979* (Dearborn, Michigan, 1979), pp. 3-4, 15.

77. Marion Gough, "Little Journeys to the Way We Used to Live," *House Beautiful* 109 (1967), p. 148.

78. Singleton P. Moorehead, "Colonial Williamsburg: Problems in Architectural Restoration," *Art in America* 43, 2 (May 1955), p. 64.

79. Gough (note 77), p. 148.

80. Cummings (note 75), p. 12.

81. Henry N. Flynt, "Old Deerfield: A Living Community," *Art in America* 43, 2 (May 1955), pp. 41-42.

82. Paul Wilstack, *Mount Vernon: Washington's Home and the National Shrine* (Garden City, New York, 1916), p. 275.

83. R. T. H. Halsey and Elizabeth Tower, *The Homes of Our Ancestors as Shown in the American Wing of the Metropolitan Museum of Art* (Garden City, New York, 1925), p. xxii.

84. See William B. Rhoads, "The Colonial Revival and the Americanization of Immigrants," in Axelrod (note 58), pp. 341-62.

85. Halsey and Tower (note 83), p. 9.

86. The following discussion is based on facts provided by Upward (note 76) and James S. Wamsley, *American Ingenuity: Henry Ford Museum and Greenfield Village* (New York, 1985).

. . . .

*A Century of
Representing Architecture at
The Art Institute of Chicago*

by Pauline Saliga

From the time it was established in 1879, The Art Institute of Chicago has collected architectonic sculpture, decorative architectural fragments, and a great variety of miniature and full-scale interiors in an effort to present the history of architecture and interior decoration. Among the first architectural artifacts collected were plaster casts of architectural friezes from classical Greek monuments, and of sculpture-laden portals from Europe's medieval cathedrals. Later, with an increasing interest in the display of decorative art objects as part of an architectural setting, the Art Institute began to collect original European and American furniture and interior appointments for display in period rooms. More recently, architecture has been represented in exhibitions through original architectural drawings and models, as well as through building fragments—leaded-glass windows, terracotta friezes, wrought- and cast-iron grilles—primarily from the Chicago region, which are the by-products of thirty years of building demolition, alteration, and restoration. This essay describes the history of the Art Institute's efforts to collect and display three-dimensional architecture-related collections, and it explains the underlying attitudes that have shaped the acquisition and, often, the disposition of these collections.

Plaster Casts
While the first plaster-cast reproductions of artworks were made in Europe in the sixteenth century, large plaster-cast collections were not common until the eighteenth century, and in European and Americans museums only became widespread in the mid to late nineteenth century.[1] Two of the most renowned European collections were those of the South Kensington Museum (now the Victoria and Albert Museum) in London, which opened its Cast Courts in 1873, and the Trocadéro, established in Paris in 1879. As the comprehensive collection of casts of post-classical European sculpture, the Victoria and Albert Museum served as the model for other collections around the world.

The first plaster casts came to the United States shortly after 1800, when art schools such as the Pennsylvania Academy of the Fine Arts purchased antique casts from Paris for use in its drawing classes. The casts, which were provided to the Pennsylvania Academy by permission of Emperor Napoleon, included more than fifty copies of objects and classical sculpture in the collections of the Louvre, and they were shipped in February 1806, before the Academy had even received its official charter of incorporation.[2] Countless other teaching institutions and art museums followed its lead, including the National Academy of Design and The Metropolitan Museum of Art in New York, the Corcoran Art Gallery in Washington, D. C., the Carnegie Institute in Pittsburgh, and The Art Institute of Chicago.

Some institutions like the Carnegie and the Pennsylvania Academy have kept their cast collections on display to this day. Most of the large museum collections, including those of the Art Institute and the Museum of Fine Arts, Boston, were destroyed, sold, or dispersed to other museums and universities where the casts retained their function as tools for teaching.

The Art Institute first acquired plaster casts in 1884, after the Friends of the Art Institute raised $1,800 for the purchase of a collection of casts of antique sculpture.[3] In 1888 the Art Institute acknowledged that the Elbridge G. Hall Collection, formed in his honor by his wife, Mrs. Addie M. Hall Ellis, was "designed to form a comprehensive illustration of the whole history of sculpture."[4] The Hall gift of $17,000 was the largest single donation the Art Institute had received to date. Although the first casts were of Greek and Roman objects, the collection eventually grew to include more than 600 casts that represented a wide cross section of ancient, Renaissance, and modern sculpture. During the summer and fall of 1887, a large portion of the Hall Collection arrived in anticipation of the opening of the Art Institute's newly expanded Burnham and Root building on Michigan Avenue at Van Buren Street, where the collection occupied five of twelve galleries.

The cast collection was significantly enlarged in 1889 when Art Institute President Charles L. Hutchinson and Director William M. R. French took an extensive trip to Rome, Naples, Florence, Venice, Paris, and London. Their purpose was twofold: to study the management and exhibition of displays in the major museums of Europe, and to purchase works of art and reproductions for the Art Institute. In his diary of the trip, French listed the addresses of the agents and major manufacturers of plaster reproductions in Florence, Paris, and London, and the major cast collections they visited, particularly the great Cast Courts at the South Kensington Museum.[5] Although Hutchinson and French primarily purchased books and Greek antiquities on their trip, they also ordered plaster models of ancient buildings, plaster casts of ancient, medieval, and Renaissance sculpture, and architectural friezes for the Hall Collection.

In the late nineteenth century, new museums with limited funds considered the collection of casts and other reproductions as important as the acquisition of original works. Director French expressed this pragmatic attitude in his observations about his European trip: "Collections of certain classes, worthy of any museum, are not very expensive. Such are casts of sculpture, reproductions of metal work and ivory, autotypes, etc. The convenience and appearance of an art museum certainly depend more upon good sense and good taste than upon any more obscure or expensive considerations."[6] Like all

Fig. 1
View of the Michigan Avenue lobby of The Art Institute of Chicago, showing one of the museum's galleries of plaster casts, c. 1901-10.

Fig. 2
Interior view of Blackstone Hall, The Art Institute of Chicago, c. 1905.

Fig. 3
**Partial view of
Blackstone Hall,
showing, in the
foreground, a cast of a
portal from Notre Dame
du Port at Clermont-
Ferrand, and, in the
background, casts of
sculpture by Donatello
and Verrochio, c. 1905.**

the major U. S. art museum directors of the day, French collected reproductions because he wanted to build a comprehensive museum collection that represented the entire history of art. The goal of amassing a comprehensive collection was particularly important for the Art Institute, which had evolved from a school, the Chicago Academy of Fine Arts, and which was first and foremost an educational institution. French built a comprehensive collection of cast sculpture and other types of reproductions at a time when original artworks and the funds to purchase them were in short supply.

The cast collection expanded in 1889 when the directors of the Illinois Inter-State Industrial Exposition of Chicago transferred their collection of casts of antique sculpture to the Art Institute, making its collection one of the largest in the country. Built as a testament to Chicago's spirit in the period of reconstruction following the Great Fire of 1871, the Inter-State Industrial Exposition Building in the 1880s imported a fine collection of casts of antique sculpture. The first considerable collection of its kind in Chicago, it became a part of the regular annual exhibitions at the Exposition.[7]

The first strictly architectural cast collection was acquired by the Art Institute in 1893. It came as part of a larger collection that included casts of sculpture by French artists such as Houdon, Frémiet, and Rodin, as well as architectural elements from France's great monuments, including portals from the Cathedral of Bordeaux and the Abbey Church of St. Gilles, a sixteenth-century tomb from the Cathedral of Rouen, and the choir gallery from the Cathedral of Limoges. The collection was formed under the direction of the French National Committee on Historic Monuments from collections at the Trocadéro, the Louvre, and the Museum of Decorative Arts in Paris.[8] The pieces had been sent by the French government for the 1893 World's Columbian Exposition. The casts were acquired as a partial purchase of the Art Institute and a joint gift of the French Commission of Fine Arts and the World's Columbian Collection.

The large assemblage of French casts from the World's Fair took the museum ten years to install. Much of it had to be stored in a fireproof storehouse at the back of the museum. By 1900 a part of the French cast collection was installed in the Art Institute's great sculpture hall (fig. 1). To facilitate the task of designing the permanent installation, Director William French used a model of the sculpture gallery to arrange clay replicas of the casts. In the 1902-03 *Annual Report*, he recognized the installation of the gallery as one of the museum's greatest achievements of the year. The gallery he described was enormous: 208 feet long, 58 feet wide, and 33 feet high.[9] The exhibition of the entire collection opened on October 20, 1903, under the name of "The Blackstone Collection of Architectural Casts," and the gallery, designed by Shepley, Rutan and Coolidge,

. . . .

became "Blackstone Hall" (fig. 2).[10]

Like the Hall Collection of sculpture casts, the Blackstone Collection grew to be very large, and it eventually contained more than 150 objects ranging from cork models of the Temple of Neptune at Paestum and the Pyramid of Cestius to German, Italian, and French architecture and architectural sculpture from the eleventh to the eighteenth century. Some of the more striking casts in the collection included Donatello's huge equestrian sculpture *Gattamelata* (1443); Verrocchio's Bartolommeo Colleoni (1481-88); the south portal of the Church of Notre Dame du Port at Clermont-Ferrand (late eleventh century; fig. 3); the portal of the Abbey of Charlieu (twelfth century; fig. 4); the lintel of the left portal on the west facade of Notre Dame Cathedral in Paris showing the entombment and coronation of the Virgin (early thirteenth century); and the portal of the north transcept from the Cathedral of Bordeaux depicting the Last Supper and the Ascension (first quarter of the fourteenth century). A slightly separate installation featured column capitals, lintels, and other decorative panels in an orderly arrangement (fig. 5).

In its early years of collecting three-dimensional architectural artifacts, the Art Institute concentrated primarily on reproductions. Only occasionally were actual building artifacts acquired, even though they were readily available. One of the rare early instances when the museum acquired a contemporary architectural artifact was in 1892 when it accepted a plaster model for the door of the Carrie Eliza Getty Tomb, designed in 1890 by renowned Chicago School architect Louis H. Sullivan for Graceland Cemetery. Although there was an *architectural* cast collection at the Art Institute, this piece was accepted into the Hall sculpture collection. This decision indicates that even though the museum began collecting original architectural objects, these items were collected primarily for their decorative qualities and not their historical or functional importance. The only other Sullivan fragment acquired while the architect was still alive was a teller's wicket from his bank in Owatonna donated by the manufacturers, the Winslow Brothers Company, in 1907-08. Apparently it was one of two donated, the other having gone to the Armour Institute, the architecture school then housed in the Art Institute. Unfortunately, except for one Owatonna wicket (cat. no. 77), none of these original fragments remains in the collection.

The same attitude came into play when other original fragments of Chicago buildings were entered into the Blackstone Collection. Among the fragments accepted later were two contemporary capitals and bases from P. B. Wight's Lenox Building carved by James Legge, an English craftsman who was Chicago's leading architectural sculptor of the day, and who also carved the tympana from Wight's

Figs. 4, 5
Partial views of Blackstone Hall, showing casts of a portal from the Abbey of Charlieu and various architectural elements, c. 1905.

55

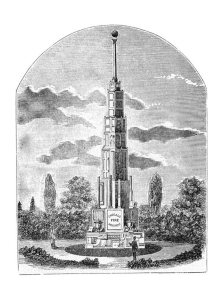

Fig. 6
William Le Baron Jenney, Proposed monument of safes and broken columns to commemorate the Great Chicago Fire of 1871; from Chicago Illustrated: One Year From the Fire (Chicago, 1872).

Fig. 7
Room from 58 Artillery Lane, Spitalfields, London, c. 1750-60, as installed in The Art Institute of Chicago, 1923.

Blatchford House (see cat. no. 3). Also accepted into the Blackstone Collection were eighteen plaster fragments from Henry Ives Cobb's Fisheries Building at the World's Columbian Exposition, presumably because they served as mementos of the fair, one of the single most important events in the city's history. In Chicago the preservation of building fragments as mementos of important events was a time-honored tradition. For example, one year after the Great Fire of 1871 architect William Le Baron Jenney proposed the construction of a park monument composed of broken safes and columns that survived the Fire to symbolize the heroic will of the city that could rebuild itself after such a calamity (fig. 6).

The popularity of the cast collection and its primary importance as a teaching tool, especially for fine-art drawing classes at the School of the Art Institute and architectural classes at the Armour Institute, could do little to avert the change in taste that began to occur in the 1920s and 1930s. No longer satisfied to present art and architecture solely through reproductions of the great monuments of Europe, the Art Institute, like other museums, concentrated on acquiring original works of art and presenting large original architectural details and period rooms. The trend foretold the dispersal and destruction of the architectural cast collection, which in the 1950s steadily fell out of favor with museum professionals and art historians, who viewed the reproductions as a source of embarrassment and who wished to fill their precious gallery space with burgeoning collections of original art.

Period Rooms

In the history of museums, period rooms are a relatively recent phenomenon. They originated in late-nineteenth-century Europe and represented some fundamental changes in the way museums presented interpretive exhibitions of their collections. As Edward Kaufman discusses in his essay in this book, one impulse in this direction was certainly the tableaux of peasant life that Artur Hazelius began to create and exhibit in 1873 in Stockholm and that the Nordiska Museet there was later erected to house. Hazelius's efforts to bring together costumes and artifacts of peasant life with a portrayal of traditional village life and its handicrafts would eventually culminate in the opening of the first permanent outdoor architectural museum, Skansen, in 1891. Meanwhile, within museums proper, another change was becoming apparent. During the 1880s and 1890s museums in Nuremberg, Zurich, and Munich began to organize interpretive exhibitions of decorative arts by style and period rather than medium or material. Other institutions followed suit and installed dozens of such period rooms that brought together domestic furnishings, architectural interiors, and decorative arts.

Inexplicably, English and French museums were slow to embrace the belief that period rooms were the preferred way of integrating architecture and the decorative arts. In America, period rooms did not gain widespread acceptance until the 1920s and 30s.[11]

Scholars have long thought that the Essex Institute in Salem, Massachussetts, in 1907 was the first American museum to install period rooms, but as Kaufman shows in his essay, there were almost certainly earlier precedents. Regardless of who came first, both The Art Institute of Chicago and The Detroit Institute of Arts opened a series of period rooms in 1923 and The Metropolitan Museum of Art organized a large, systematic collection of period rooms in 1924. The Metropolitan Museum's period rooms had a profound impact on the collecting philosophy of American museums, and soon afterwards numerous other institutions installed period rooms, including the Philadelphia Museum of Art and the Museum of Fine Arts, Boston, in 1928, the Brooklyn Museum in 1929, the Baltimore Museum of Art in 1930, and the St. Louis Art Museum in 1930-31.[12]

Although the collecting of period rooms at the Art Institute never reached the scale that it did at other museums, the Art Institute embarked on an active program of collecting that gave it more rooms than it could install. Its first period room was acquired in 1923, when Robert Allerton donated a room from 58 Artillery Lane, Spitalfields, London (fig. 7). This interior, from the period just prior to 1760, was used as a setting for the display of period furniture and more elaborate forms of Chippendale design. The Art Institute also received a French drawing room from the Henry C. Dangler Memorial Collection. This *petit salon* (fig. 8), from the Regence Period (1720-35), came from the house of the Prince de Longueville, rue de Vermeil, Paris. An article in the October 1923 *Bulletin of the Art Institute of Chicago* drew attention to the room's alternating broad and narrow panels of oak, its inlaid floor, and its fireplace set in Languedoc marble. Carvings of flowers, groups of foliage, and musical instruments enriched the top and base of the walls, while the mirrors sported "trophies at arms, ribbons, and fantastic foliage."[13] The Mr. and Mrs. Ebenezer Buckingham Memorial (fig. 9) was a Jacobean interior with oak wainscoting and an ornamental plaster ceiling; the William Gold and Lydia B. Hibbard Memorial brought to the museum an eighteenth-century Dutch interior from Friesland.[14]

The largest and earliest period room in the museum was a vaulted, Gothic style gallery (fig. 10), containing fragments from a collection formed by Kate Buckingham in honor of her sister, Lucy Maud Buckingham.[15] This collection, which concentrated on medieval architectural details, also went on view in 1923. It combined medieval sculpture, tapestries, and decorative arts in a gallery that incorporated original architectural details from that period including

Fig. 8
Drawing room from the house of the Prince de Longueville, rue de Vermeil, Paris, c. 1720, as installed in The Art Institute of Chicago, 1923.

Fig. 9
English room of the Jacobean period installed in The Art Institute of Chicago, 1923.

a late-fifteenth-century portal from a château near Brive in France, and a fifteenth-century fireplace from a château at Laon featuring a coat of arms of Pierre II de Fontette. During the years that the Armour Institute of Technology held its classes at the Art Institute, the medieval fragments were used as teaching tools, like the cast collection, and students drew sketches and watercolors of these architectural details, such as architect Paul McCurry's watercolor of the Laon fireplace (fig. 11). The drawing, done in the characteristic Beaux-Arts style of watercolor rendering in color, light, and shade, reveals the importance placed upon rendering in the Beaux-Arts architectural education system, which was still prominent in architecture schools in the 1920s.

The authentic medieval fragments that were collected in Lucy Maud Buckingham's name, such as the Laon fireplace and the Brive portal, are still in the Art Institute's collection awaiting the reinstallation of a gallery devoted to medieval art. Although it had long since ceased to be a gallery for the display of medieval art, the Buckingham gallery itself was dismantled to make way for the Art Institute's Rice Building, which opened in 1988.

The 1920s continued to be a decade of acquisition of entire rooms and major architectural details. In 1925 Mr. and Mrs. Richard T. Crane, Jr., donated two paneled rooms from the ground floor of an early eighteenth-century house at 75 Dean Street in the Soho district of London. These rooms were furnished with Queen Anne and George I pieces purchased with funds from the Crane family.[16] In 1926, the Art Institute announced the acquisition of a Portuguese interior of the eighteenth century, another gift of Robert Allerton.[17] The only American period room in the collection was an eighteenth-century Tap Room from Stagg Hall, Port Tobacco, Charles County, Maryland. Purchased for the museum in 1929 by Mrs. Potter Palmer II and Robert Allerton, the room was installed sometime after 1947, but it was returned to Charles County in the early 1970s so that it could serve as a history room at the Charles County Community College.

After they had some years to distance themselves from the initial enchantment with period rooms, museum directors and curators began to examine the value of these installations. They recognized that the great weakness of period rooms is their dual function as galleries for furniture and other furnishings and as accurate and stylistic impressions of historical rooms. In actuality, the two functions are often at cross-purposes: good furniture is frequently hidden in poorly lighted galleries, and the period rooms contain too much furniture, of too high a quality, to be historically accurate.[18] Furthermore, the rooms were often altered in their reconstruction within a museum. The paneling in the Art Institute's French room, for

Fig. 10
Gothic style gallery of medieval sculpture, tapestries, and decorative arts installed in The Art Institute of Chicago, 1923.

Fig. 11
Paul McCurry, Rendered elevation and section of a fifteenth-century fireplace from a château at Laon, France, installed in The Art Institute of Chicago; ink and watercolor on paper, 1924; Gift of Paul McCurry.

example, is from two or possibly three places. The current philosophy among museum curators is that only good, accurate period rooms should be installed. The great majority of period rooms, however, are an inaccurate conglomeration of similar architectural elements from more than one building, and their historical inaccuracies keep them from being displayed.

In 1958, Allen Wardwell, formerly Curator of Decorative Arts at the Art Institute, suggested that the Art Institute had collected so few period rooms for a museum of its size because the history of English and American interior design was so well represented by the Art Institute's miniature rooms, conceived by Mrs. James Ward Thorne.[19] Wardwell claimed that the Thorne miniature rooms served as surrogate period rooms for the Art Institute. The Thorne collection, in its present form, includes sixty-eight rooms and depicts highlights from the history of interior design, the decorative arts, and architecture between 1600 and 1940. Originally, the rooms were perceived as architectural models, and they were constructed using detailed working drawings done by a professional architect. Mrs. Thorne, who admittedly had no formal training in the history of architecture or art, strove to depict typical rooms and general impressions rather than literal reproductions of interiors. She saw her miniature creations as "carefully fashioned to recreate a real or imagined room from a bygone era."[20]

Mrs. Thorne began making miniature rooms in the 1920s when she observed the popularity of full-scale period rooms in America's major museums. Clearly, no museum had enough space for full-sized rooms offering a comprehensive overview of English, French, and American interior design. Mrs. Thorne saw the construction of miniature rooms as the ideal solution. Like the plaster-cast reproductions, the Thorne Rooms were to be comprehensive and educational, not authentic. Like the Art Institute's own period rooms, the Thorne Rooms revealed a bias for French and English eighteenth-century interiors (see fig. 12), and they ignored more recent trends in architecture and interior design such as the Arts and Crafts movement and modernism.

Mrs. Thorne presented her rooms to the Art Institute in 1940, after they had been on view at the 1933 Century of Progress Exposition and in museums across the United States. They were installed in 1954 in the Art Institute's American wing, where they remained until 1985, when they too were moved to allow for the construction of the Rice Building in the museum. In 1989 the Thorne miniature rooms were permanently installed in a new gallery, designed by Adrian Smith of Skidmore, Owings and Merrill, at the base of the museum's central staircase.

Fig. 12
English drawing room of the early Georgian period, one of the Thorne Miniature Rooms given to The Art Institute of Chicago in 1940 and installed in 1954; Gift of Mrs. James Ward Thorne.

Fig. 13
**Rapp and Rapp,
Paramount Building,
Broadway at 43rd
Street, New York, 1927
(later altered); view of
an installation of
architectural fragments
in the building's lobby.**

Architectural Fragments in the 1920s and 1930s

At the same time that the Art Institute was beginning to collect period rooms, it also began acquiring original architectural fragments with a new seriousness of purpose. The collecting of architectural fragments, especially from exotic places in Europe and abroad, was very popular in the 1920s, as evidenced in the small installations of building fragments on the base of the Chicago Tribune Tower (1922–25) and in the lobby of the Paramount Building (1927) in New York (fig. 13). At the Art Institute, however, the attitude toward collecting had changed. Unlike the odd fragment from a Chicago building that would have been accepted into the Hall or Blackstone collections, these new objects were seen as components of a more comprehensive collection. One of the Art Institute's first fragment collections was acquired as an architectural memorial after the death in 1926 of Howard Van Doren Shaw, an architect and Art Institute trustee. Among the most active members of the committee named to select objects were Robert Allerton, a museum trustee and a collector of English art, and Shaw's architectural protégé, David Adler, who carried on Shaw's tradition of designing large houses and estates in the Chicago area. Adopting the popular method of presenting architecture through period rooms and details, they set out to acquire a collection of original objects that architecture students could use to study the history of design and that architects could use as a resource for their own work. The committee's approach to acquisitions thus reflected the prevailing notions of the 1920s revival of European architectural styles, and it reflected that the use of fragments as models for students had not changed since the 1800s.[21]

The Shaw collection—acquired over a period of years from the late 1920s to the late 1930s—consisted of European architectural details such as English and American doorways, garden ornaments, and an eighteenth-century English shop front with Greek details from Faversham in Kent. The collection of doorways is a potpourri of architectural styles and details. It includes a relatively simple early Georgian doorway from Lombard Street in London which has two elaborately carved Corinthian columns on either side of the door; a 1756 doorway from Mollington Hall, Cheshire, that features elaborately pierced floral decoration below the architrave and beautifully carved scrolls ending in eagles' heads (fig. 14); a mid-eighteenth-century Chinese Gothic doorway that combines engaged Gothic columns with a pagoda-like pediment (fig. 15); a Rococo style doorway from Norfolk House in St. James Square, London, which was designed (c. 1748/52) by Matthew Brettingham, a student of William Kent; the formal neoclassical entrance to the Adelphi Building at 19 Adam Street in London designed by the Adam brothers,

c. 1770; and an interior doorway designed by Robert Adam from Douglas Castle, Lanarkshire, Scotland, from 1761. The only American doorway in the collection, from an 1819 mansion in Freemansburg, Pennsylvania, has Federal and Pennsylvania Dutch details.

Like the cast collection and the period rooms, the Shaw collection was intended to function as a teaching collection of eighteenth-century building styles. It reveals, however, the prevailing prejudice also evident in the Art Institute's period rooms and Thorne Rooms toward English architecture, and American architecture from the East Coast and Old South. Unlike the cast collection and Thorne Rooms, the Shaw collection was to contain only original architectural details. Unfortunately, because of a shortage of exhibition space in galleries with sufficiently high ceilings, the Shaw collection is currently in storage.

By the late 1930s and certainly after World War II, architects no longer needed a potpourri of architectural details and period rooms as reference points for designing buildings. The dramatic shift in Chicago architecture from eclectic historicism to International Style modernism began in the 1920s with the modernist work of Chicago architects such as Abel Faidy, William and George Fred Keck, Helmuth Bartsch at Holabird and Root, and Bertrand Goldberg. When Ludwig Mies van der Rohe emigrated from Germany to Chicago in 1938, he revolutionized the architectural curriculum at the Armour Institute (later the Illinois Institute of Technology). From Mies, architectural students first learned about structural building components, not about historic styles; no longer did they make watercolor sketches of period rooms and historic details. Instead, they learned to solve seemingly simple, but actually profound, problems such as how to turn the corner of a building or how to design a window in a brick building without interrupting the various coursings. It is interesting to note that before Mies's tenure at Armour, students learned to design buildings with historic references that would become fragments in future years. Mies's design philosophy required students to craft buildings and spaces that, in the end, could not be reduced to exhibitable, component fragments.

At the same time that Mies's teaching was dominating architecture in Chicago, the Art Institute began to dispose of its cast collection. The records in the registrar's office indicate that in 1949 and 1950 a great many of the Hall Collection casts were not relocated, but were simply destroyed. At meetings of the Board of Trustees, the reasons given for disposing of the collection were purely pragmatic: the collection was too expensive to restore and it created a fire hazard. Clearly, the philosophy that had prompted the collecting of casts had changed. The administration did not want any art reproductions. Removing the casts was part of the break that

Fig. 14
English doorway from Mollington Hall, Cheshire, 1756; Howard Van Doren Shaw Collection.

Fig. 15
**English doorway in the
Chinese Gothic style,
c. 1745-70; Howard
Van Doren Shaw
Collection.**

postwar society made with prewar viewpoints. The Art Institute's
1954-55 *Annual Report* acknowledged the popularity of the cast collection but also foretold its destruction: "Blackstone Hall, where the
plaster casts have been a source of interest for students and visitors, is
to be floored over to provide us with two large galleries and a mezzanine. In place of the plaster casts (some of which have deteriorated
beyond repair) we will have spacious galleries for the display of our
world-famous Oriental art, now inadequately housed in a remote
part of the building."[22] Some Blackstone casts were put into off-site
storage until the late 1970s, when they were disposed of. Among the
Blackstone casts that were preserved in institutional collections are
some Egyptian casts that were transferred in the 1950s to the Oriental Institute at the University of Chicago.

With the dispersal of the cast collection, the museum's exhibitions and collections included architecture less and less frequently.
Architectural drawings and sketches, of course, continued to be
acquired under the domain of the Burnham Library, but the
museum's new emphasis was on its traditional fine arts collections of
paintings, sculpture, drawings, etc. With the rise of modernism and
its aversion to decoration and historicism, plaster copies and even
original architectural fragments and details fell further out of favor.

Architectural Fragments, 1960s to 1980s
In the 1960s, the Art Institute again began to collect architectural
fragments. This time around, the collection consisted of Chicago
School and Prairie School fragments that were available as a result of
the demolition of buildings during the city's postwar building boom.
As the great masterpieces of Chicago architecture were being demolished, the museum assumed the responsibility of collecting fragments
from these buildings. To scholars, historians, and curators, the
Chicago School and the Prairie School now represented significant
contributions to American architecture, even if the city of Chicago
was slow to recognize their importance. In order to take advantage of
the large amount of Louis Sullivan and Frank Lloyd Wright material
that was becoming increasingly available, the Antiquarian Society
of the Art Institute, which had been instrumental in enriching the
collections of European and early American decorative arts, began
buying decorative architectural fragments, including balusters from
the Roloson Houses (see cat. no. 86), a circular ventilator grille from
the Francis Apartments (cat. no. 88), and a Tree of Life window from
the Martin House (cat. no. 90), all designed by Frank Lloyd Wright.

Even though the national preservation movement gained
momentum in the 1960s and 1970s as a result of the National Historic
Preservation Act of 1966, important Chicago School buildings were

still being demolished at an alarming rate during this period. The
Art Institute found itself in the unenviable position of setting priori-
ties according to each new demolition crisis, and in some cases it had
to raise special funds to purchase exquisite Sullivan ornament from
demolition sites. One of the major collections of Sullivan ornament
came to the Art Institute in the early 1960s with the demolition of
Adler and Sullivan's Schiller Building, a remarkable highrise that
combined an office tower with a theater for German opera, at
64 W. Randolph Street (see cat. nos. 52-61).

The unfortunate demolition of the Schiller Building occurred
even though the building had been honored by the Commission on
Chicago Architectural Landmarks, which was founded in 1957 as
a blue ribbon committee, sadly lacking any legal authority to stall
or prevent demolitions. The razing of the Schiller Building in 1961
generated public outcry, but it was seven years later that the City
Council finally enacted a landmarks protection ordinance and
created the Commission on Chicago Historical and Architectural
Landmarks. Known today as the Commission on Chicago Landmarks, this organization has the power to designate landmark status
to individual buildings and districts, with the approval of the City
Council. As architecture critic Paul Gapp has written, however, "The
most serious and persistent misconception about landmark designa-
tion is that it makes demolition impossible. Actually, it only sets up a
structured delaying system so that means of saving a structure may
be explored after an owner applies for a wrecking permit."[23]

Despite the Commission's laudable efforts, fragments from
other Adler and Sullivan buildings continued to come into the Art
Institute's collection, as the buildings were demolished to make way
for taller skyscrapers. The most controversial demolition was that
of the Chicago Stock Exchange in 1971. The battle to preserve the
Stock Exchange was the most heated in the history of Chicago, with
demonstrators picketing in front of the building daily, and scorching
newspaper editorials and political cartoons, such as one depicting a
crane from the "Chicago Heritage Destruction Co." poised with open
jaws above the Stock Exchange building.[24] A small but determined
group of architects, students, and preservationists tried valiantly to
preserve the building. Chicago attorney Richard A. Miller founded
the Landmarks Preservation Council to help stem the tide of
destruction by enlisting the support of the public and of elected
officials to back a creative preservation plan in which the city would
have purchased the building and transferred ownership of it to a
not-for-profit organization for renovation and rental as office space.
Unfortunately, the preservation battle over the Stock Exchange was
lost. Rather than taking many small fragments of the building, the
Art Institute decided to make a major statement about the genius of

Fig. 16
Adler and Sullivan, Trading Room from the Chicago Stock Exchange Building, 1893-94 (demolished 1972); reconstructed in The Art Institute of Chicago, 1976-77, supervised by Vinci-Kenny Architects. The reconstruction and reinstallation of the Trading Room were made possible through a grant from the Walter E. Heller Foundation and its president, Mrs. Edwin J. DeCosta, with additional gifts from the City of Chicago, Mrs. Eugene A. Davidson, The Graham Foundation for Advanced Studies in the Fine Arts, and Three Oaks Wrecking, 1971.922.

Adler and Sullivan by reerecting the two most prominent features of the Stock Exchange—its exquisite stenciled Trading Room and its grand terracotta entrance arch (figs. 16 and 17). The installation of these two major building components was realized as part of the construction of the Institute's East Wing (now the Arthur Rubloff Building), which was designed by Walter Netsch of Skidmore, Owings and Merrill, and completed in 1977. The exquisite Trading Room was accurately restored by Vinci-Kenny, Architects, and was stenciled in sixty-five shades of green, red, blue, and gold. The Trading Room is now the Art Institute's only "period room" on view.

Buildings by the premiere Chicago School architects continued to be demolished in the 1970s, falling prey to the "higher and better use" development philosophy that provides a financial rationale for razing entire blocks of small, individual buildings to make way for single, large commercial towers and complexes. As a result, the Art Institute had much to choose from in forming its collection, including pieces from Adler and Sullivan's Rothschild Store, St. Nicholas Hotel, Rosenfeld Building, Lindauer House, and Selz House; Frank Lloyd Wright's Francis Apartments; Burnham and Root's Church of the Covenant and Commerce Building; and Holabird and Root's Diana Court. In 1984, the Art Institute also received fragments from another important, but little-known, Sullivan building that was demolished—the Felsenthal Store (1905). This small commercial project on Chicago's South Side was the design precedent for many of Sullivan's small midwestern banks, particularly the National Farmers Bank in Owatonna, with its cubic central banking hall and office wing.

In the 1980s, older low- and mid-rise buildings continued to be deemed uneconomical and were replaced by larger buildings or complexes. Fragments that came into the collection as a result include a Renaissance style mantel and a Romanesque column and capital from Jarvis Hunt's apartment building at 900 N. Michigan Avenue (see cat. no. 37), demolished for a huge multiuse complex designed by Kohn, Pedersen, Fox; terracotta blocks from William Le Baron Jenney's Fair store (see cat. no. 16), originally demolished to make way for a speculative office building designed by Skidmore, Owings and Merrill, but not yet constructed; and a cast-iron column and a keystone from loft buildings on West Lake Street (see cat. nos. 1, 2), demolished for the construction of the 203 N. LaSalle Building, designed by Skidmore, Owings and Merrill.

Not all fragments came to the collection as a result of demolition, however. Many Prairie School windows and decorative elements have been donated by individuals or purchased through galleries. Other significant additions to the fragment collection were made in the early 1980s as a result of a change in the federal tax laws. The

Economic Recovery Tax Act of 1981 provided an income tax credit of twenty-five percent to an owner who rehabilitated a building listed on the National Register of Historic Places. The provisions of this act were a tremendous boon to historic preservation. Although the law has been amended, since 1981 the Illinois Department of Conservation has certified 141 rehabilitation projects, involving a total expenditure of $323.4 million on the rehabilitation of landmark buildings in Illinois alone.[25] By extension, the large number of renovations of important Illinois buildings boosted the Art Institute's building fragment collection. As buildings were renovated and restored, original fragments that could not be used in the restoration were, in many cases, donated to the Art Institute. Among the fragments that were acquired by the Art Institute as a result of the 1981 Tax Act are a bracket and panel from the balcony of Adler and Sullivan's Charnley House (see cat. no. 51), a capital and decorative panels from Wright's 1896 Heller House (see cat. no. 89), an elevator grille from Jenney's Manhattan Building (cat. no. 15), white terracotta finials from the roofline of Graham, Anderson, Probst and White's Wrigley Building (see cat. no. 34), and white terracotta blocks from the lobbies of D. H. Burnham and Company's 1903-04 Railway Exchange Building and the 1912-14 Conway Building (see cat. nos. 24-27).

Ironically, in the past five years, fragments have become increasingly valuable in the marketplace and at auction, even though the continued stripping and demolition of buildings have provided a ready supply of the valued leaded-glass windows, copper elevator grilles, marble columns, and decorative plaster and terracotta panels. In the past ten years, the auction sales prices of Frank Lloyd Wright and Arts and Crafts style windows and furnishings have increased at least tenfold. That phenomenon has encouraged the unscrupulous to dismember existing buildings in order to sell their valuable component parts.

In 1985, for example, a wealthy Texas collector bought an Arts and Crafts gem, Greene and Greene's Blacker House (1907) in Pasadena, California, and removed the house's custom-designed brass-filigree lamps, chandeliers, and wood-and-silver-inlaid sconces, knowing that these pieces would be worth millions of dollars at auction. Meanwhile, in the Chicago Loop and on the Near North Side, buildings continue to be demolished at an alarming rate. As a result, virtually all types of buildings are endangered today, especially small structures that were typical of Chicago architecture during a particular period, such as the stripped-down three- and four-story brick commercial structures of the 1870s and 1880s (see cat. nos. 1, 2, 5, and 6) that once populated virtually every block in the Loop. Also endangered are small, unique buildings, such as Tree Studios (Parfitt Brothers with Hill and Woltersdorf, 1894), whose specialized design

Fig. 17
Adler and Sullivan, Entrance arch from the Chicago Stock Exchange Building, 1893-94 (demolished 1972); reconstructed in the East Garden of The Art Institute of Chicago, 1976-77. Gift of the City of Chicago. The reconstruction of the arch was made possible through a grant from the Walter E. Heller Foundation and its president, Mrs. Edwin J. DeCosta.

and small scale make them targets for "higher and better use." Regrettably, even the fifteen-story brick and terracotta Chicago Building (Holabird and Roche, 1905), which is one of the best surviving examples of a Chicago School highrise, has an uncertain future. Equally outrageous is the treatment of the Reliance Building (designed by Charles B. Atwood for D. H. Burnham and Co., 1894-95), which has been allowed to deteriorate to the point that it may well be prohibitively expensive to restore, despite its unquestioned importance in the history of world architecture. Chicago has torn down more important buildings than most cities have ever had. How many more landmarks must go before the city takes action, changes its zoning laws, and provides financial incentives to preserve its unique built environment?

Although it has been a fact of life in Chicago for more than a century that small structures are sacrificed for larger ones, it would be unfair to offer a blanket criticism of such developments, because without them some of Chicago's greatest buildings, such as Burnham and Root's Rookery (1886-87), Holabird and Root's Chicago Board of Trade (1929-30), and Mies van der Rohe's Federal Center (1959-73), would never have been constructed. Reyner Banham rightly observed in a 1965 *Chicago Magazine* article that "the misery of Chicago architecture is that the same commercial dynamic that forces the buildings up then destroys or defaces them."[26] Looking at the fragment collection, we are mindful that the development of Chicago architecture is a double-edged sword. Since so many important structures have already been lost, however, the city must strike a balance between preservation of its late-nineteenth- and early-twentieth-century structures that identify Chicago as a mecca of American architecture, and its new large-scale structures that will move the city forward into the twenty-first century. To ignore either preservation or development would be a mistake, but it is not naive to believe that solutions can be found that would allow the two to coexist. Unless the city is able to strike a balance between development and preservation, the Loop will be gutted of its important historic structures, and the Art Institute will have far too many opportunities in the future to add fragments from significant Chicago buildings to its collection.

Although the Art Institute's current fragment installation at the top of the museum's central staircase (see frontispiece and fig. 18) is, admittedly, only the last in a long history of museum ventures designed to present the history of architecture, it is our hope that this publication of the highlights of our collection and the exhibition it records will serve to inform the public about the unique character of Chicago architecture and to foster its preservation.

Fig. 18
View of a portion of the installation of "Fragments of Chicago's Past" at The Art Institute of Chicago.

Notes

1. Malcolm Baker, *The Cast Courts* (London, 1982), p. 1.

2. Helen W. Henderson, *The Pennsylvania Academy of the Fine Arts and Other Collections of Philadelphia* (Boston, 1911), pp. 11-12.

3. The Art Institute of Chicago, *Annual Report of the Trustees for the Year Ending June 5, 1888* (Chicago, 1888), p. 9.

4. Ibid., p. 12.

5. William Merchant Richardson French, *Notes [on a] Journey to Europe with Mr. and Mrs. C. L. Hutchinson Starting from New York Sat'y Mch 9, 1899*, unpublished manuscript in the Special Collections of the Ryerson and Burnham Libraries, The Art Institute of Chicago.

6. The Art Institute of Chicago, *Annual Report of the Trustees for the Year Ending June 4, 1889* (Chicago, 1889), pp. 22-23.

7. David Lowe, *Lost Chicago* (Boston, 1975), p. 107.

8. The Art Institute of Chicago, *Twenty-fifth Annual Report of the Trustees for the Year Ending June 1, 1904* (Chicago, 1904), p. 66.

9. The Art Institute of Chicago, *Twenty-fourth Annual Report of the Trustees for the Year Ending June 1, 1903* (Chicago, 1903), p. 20.

10. *Twenty-fifth Annual Report* (note 8), p. 17. For a list of all the objects in the Hall and Blackstone collections, see The Art Institute of Chicago, *General Catalogue of Objects in the Museum* (Chicago, 1904).

11. Dianne H. Pilgrim, "Inherited from the Past: The American Period Room," *The American Art Journal* 10, 1 (May, 1978), pp. 4-23.

12. Ibid.

13. B[essie] B[ennett], "Period Rooms," *Bulletin of The Art Institute of Chicago* 17, 7 (Oct. 1923), p. 68.

14. Ibid., p. 69.

15. "The Lucy Maud Buckingham Memorial Room," *Bulletin of The Art Institute of Chicago* 18, 5 (May 1924), pp. 54-56.

16. Meyric R. Rogers, "Notes on Some Recent Acquisitions for the Richard T. Crane Memorial," *Bulletin of The Art Institute of Chicago* 44, 2 (April-May 1950), pp. 27-34; see also Bessie Bennett, "A New Setting for Decorative Arts," *Bulletin of The Art Institute of Chicago* 30, 1 (Jan. 1936), pp. 5-6.

17. B[essie] B[ennett], "A Room from Portugal," *Bulletin of The Art Institute of Chicago* 20, 4 (April 1926), pp. 54-55.

18. Pilgrim (note 11), p. 18.

19. Allen Wardwell, "English Decorative Arts at The Art Institute of Chicago," *Antiques Magazine* 89, 1 (Jan. 1966), p. 79.

20. Bruce Hatton Boyer, "Creating the Thorne Rooms," in *Miniature Rooms: The Thorne Rooms at The Art Institute of Chicago* (Chicago and New York, 1983), p. 12.

21. Barbara Wriston, "The Howard Van Doren Shaw Memorial Collection," *Museum Studies* 4 (1969), p. 88; see also Bessie Bennett, "The Howard Van Doren Shaw Gallery of Architecture," *Bulletin of The Art Institute of Chicago* 28, 1 (Jan. 1934), pp. 2-5.

22. The Art Institute of Chicago, *Annual Report, 1954-55* (Chicago, 1955), p. 5.

23. Paul Gapp, "Preservation or Porkopolis? A new focus on protecting our built heritage," *Chicago Tribune* (Dec. 2, 1984), sec. 13, p. 8.

24. John Vinci, *The Trading Room: Louis Sullivan and The Chicago Stock Exchange* (Chicago, 1989), p. 54.

25. Theodore W. Hild, "When is $322 Million Like $1 Billion?" *Historic Illinois* 7, 2 (Aug. 1984), p. 12.

26. Reyner Banham, "A Walk in the Loop," *Chicago Magazine* 2, 2 (Spring 1965), p. 25.

Chicago's Loop, 1830-1890: A Tale of Two Grids

by Gerald R. Larson
University of Cincinnati

*R*eal estate speculation in the United States during the nineteenth century was fueled by two inventions —the railroad and the elevator— that facilitated the quick movement of a large number of people. Both innovations opened up investment opportunities in new areas that were previously thought to be out of reach by even the greediest of speculators. As Chicago was settled just prior to the invention of both these technologies, the development of its urban pattern offers an excellent study of the combined effects that these two forces had on American cities. Therefore, Chicago's urban fabric can be analyzed in relation to these two movement systems: the impact that the railroad had on the horizontal grid of the city's streets, and the rise of the vertical grid of its skyscrapers which was fostered by the elevator.

The reason for Chicago's initial settlement was not the railroad, but the potential for a canal between the Chicago and Illinois rivers to achieve a through-water connection between the Northeast's primary water route, the Great Lakes, and the Mississippi River network, the life-line of the antebellum South and Middle West.[1] Following the completion in 1825 of the Erie Canal, which linked the Hudson River at Albany to Lake Erie at Buffalo and, thereby, opened the Great Lakes to commercial traffic, Congress approved in 1827 a land grant to the young state of Illinois of the alternate five sections along each side of the canal's proposed route.[2] The sale of this land was intended to help finance the construction of the Chicago canal. In the fall of 1829, the State's canal commissioners ordered the survey and platting of a town in Section 9, Township 39, on the south bank of the mouth of the Chicago River, adjacent to Fort Dearborn. To respect the original north-south orientation of the section's boundaries and to simplify the sale of the land, surveyor James Thompson subdivided it into a strict rectilinear grid of square blocks. The block bounded by LaSalle, Washington, Clark, and Randolph streets was subsequently reserved by the commissioners as a public square, for the eventual erection of a courthouse.

Three days before Chicago's town charter was approved on August 5, 1833, two real estate speculators from New York, Arthur Bronson from New York City and Charles Butler from Geneva, arrived in town to inspect the potential of the area, eventually buying 7,000 acres of land adjoining the starting point of the canal that would later be known as Bridgeport.[3] With the first sale of canal lots by the State scheduled for June 1835, Butler sent his brother-in-law, William B. Ogden, to supervise the sale of land on the north bank of the river's mouth, opposite Fort Dearborn, which the two had also managed to acquire. Ogden returned to New York after a very profitable sale, only to travel back to Chicago the following spring in order to procure one of the canal's construction contracts. Within a year, he was elected Chicago's first mayor of the new city's 4,170 residents.

Seemingly anticipating his success the previous fall, Ogden had hired an architect in New York City, John M. Van Osdel, to design and supervise the construction of a house in Chicago.[4] Chicago's first architect was greeted upon his arrival in June by the financial panic of 1837, which had reached Chicago on May 24, only twenty-two days after Ogden's election. Real estate speculation immediately halted and inflated land prices bottomed out, mercilessly stopping Chicago's meteoric growth. The only enterprise that continued to pump needed cash into the city's economy was the construction of the canal, which fitfully continued until it too ended in bankruptcy in March 1843.[5] Construction of a cheaper, "shallow cut" canal finally resumed in the fall of 1845, and by April 1848 the Great Lakes were finally connected with the Mississippi River.

Just prior to the resumption of work on the canal, the nation's economy had started to rebound, and with it interest in real estate investment returned to Chicago after an eight-year hiatus. By 1850, the city's population had exploded to 29,963, a sevenfold increase from where it had stopped with the 1837 Panic. The city was developing in a pattern typical for a river city of its size. The new canal brought wheat from the surrounding farms to Chicago to be shipped to eastern and European

markets. To store the grain until it
could be transferred to ships, large,
multistoried grain elevators (the
city's first skyscrapers) sprouted up
along the river. Wedged between
these were wharves, with their warehouses fronting onto South Water
Street (now Wacker Drive). Down a
block from the river and its warehouses, Lake Street quickly became
Chicago's commercial strip, the high-
light being the block between State
and Wabash, which contained a
series of cast-iron-fronted stores
designed by Van Osdel in 1856.[6] Two
blocks from the river, Randolph
Street, anchored by the Cook County
Courthouse and City Hall, designed
by Van Osdel and erected in 1853 on
the public square, became the location of offices for the city's lawyers
and other professionals.

Therefore, Chicago's urban pattern, conforming to the grid laid
down in 1830, paralleled the main
branch of the river in running east-
west. This east-west axis of Chicago,
however, was as short-lived as the
importance of the canal. Because
the reason for the completion of
the "shallow cut" canal was not to
improve transportation, but to realize a return from land speculation
and to profit from construction contracts, the canal was quickly abandoned by the very people who had
built it, in favor of an idea whose
profit potential was far greater than
that of the canal: the railroad.[7]

While the Loop's horizontal grid
was established before the coming of
the railroad to Chicago, the railroad
would have a profound influence on
the original layout of the city's business district. The railroad's coming
to Chicago was a bitterly fought con-
test between the rival commercial
interests of New York City and
Boston. In order to get the New York

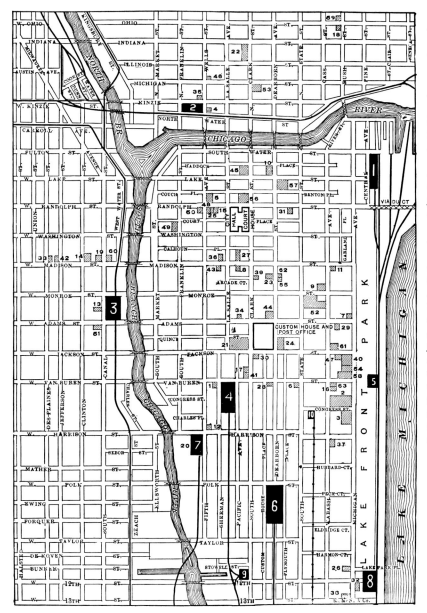

Fig. 1
**Rand McNally and
Co., View of Chicago,
showing the location
of depots and hotels,
1898; from Frank A.
Randall, History of the
Development of
Building Construction
in Chicago (Urbana,
Illinois, 1949), p. 185.
The principal railroad
stations discussed in
this essay include those
for the Illinois Central
and Michigan Central
(nos. 1, 5, and 8); the
Dearborn Street Station
(no. 6) for the Chicago
and Western Indiana,
the Grand Trunk, the
Erie, and the Atchison,
Topeka and Santa Fe
railroads; the LaSalle
Street Station (no. 4)
for the Lake Shore and
Michigan Southern and
the Chicago, Rock Island
and Pacific railroads;
and the Union Passenger
Station (no. 3) for the
Chicago, Burlington
and Quincy.**

Fig. 2
View looking northeast along Michigan Avenue, 1858, showing the Illinois Central Depot (Otto Matz, 1853; demolished 1892), and the lagoon that lay between Michigan Avenue and the Illinois Central tracks.

state legislature to approve the construction of the Erie Canal, which would benefit only the communities in the northern part of the state between Albany and Buffalo, Governor DeWitt Clinton was forced to promise to build a state road in the southern part of the state from New York City to Lake Erie. Despite New York City's initial complaints about the Erie Canal, however, the canal would eventually lead, via the Hudson River, to the city's harbor, giving it a considerable commercial advantage over its rival Atlantic ports. Especially hard hit by the canal was Boston, which had little choice because of its location but to tap into the Erie Canal. Boston's leaders, however, facing an uphill geography, chose the new technology of the railroad over a canal. The route to the canal's terminus at Albany was completed in 1841, but by this time Boston's railroad men had understood the advantages of the railroad and had already joined the campaign to build a "Central" railroad from Albany to Buffalo.

The "Central" route was a response to the start of construction of the New York and Erie Railroad, which had been chartered in 1832 as a substitute for the state road that had originally been proposed. While poor management and opposition to the Erie route stretched its construction over a twenty-year period, the "Central" route was finished by November 1842, so that it was possible to travel from Boston to Buffalo by railroad in less than two days. From Buffalo, a steamship could be boarded that would make the trip to Chicago in eight days.[8]

Following the resumption of work on the Chicago canal in the fall of 1845, a group of Boston investors, headed by John Murray Forbes, purchased the uncompleted Michigan Central Railroad from the State of Michigan in March 1846. On April 23, 1849, they completed the route across the state to Lake Michigan at New Buffalo, reducing to fifteen hours what used to take three days by steamer from Detroit. From New Buffalo, a lake steamer could then be boarded for the final leg of the trip to Chicago.[9] By this date, however, the monopoly to the west enjoyed by the Boston/Buffalo route was threatened by the potential completion of a revitalized Erie Railroad. In addition, a group of New York investors, who planned to forge a potential connection to the west for the Erie, had purchased the bankrupt Michigan Southern Railroad from the State of Michigan. The race to Chicago between Boston's Michigan Central and New York's Michigan Southern was on.

Not surprisingly, local political supporters of neither company seemed to be able to gain the upper hand, forcing the two railroads to align themselves with Illinois companies already chartered to build tracks in the state. On the eve of the long-awaited completion of the Erie Railroad to Lake Erie, the Michigan Southern made the first move in April 1851 by buying into the Rock Island Railroad. The Michigan Central, therefore, had no choice but to follow suit and join forces with the

newly chartered Illinois Central. In an attempt to ring off the business district from the Illinois Central, the Rock Island laid its tracks west from the Indiana border in a flanking maneuver, choosing to enter the city limits on line with LaSalle Street (fig. 1) and the newly completed City Hall.[10]

Eventually, the Illinois Central and the Common Council of Chicago reached a mutually beneficial arrangement that allowed the railroad to enter the city along a right-of-way in Lake Michigan. While the railroad got the unencumbered and free use of the land that would bring it directly to the mouth of the Chicago River, the heart of the city's commerce, the city, in return, got the railroad to build a breakwater that not only would slow down the erosion of the lakefront along Michigan Avenue, where some of the city's richest people resided, but also would create a lagoon that at times provided quite pleasant recreation (fig. 2).

The Illinois Central's primary concern was the transport and storage of the two main products of the West, meat and wheat. As the Illinois Central tracks made their way into the Loop, they were laid adjacent to the Myrick Yards, Chicago's oldest and largest stockyards, located near the lakefront at Cottage Grove Avenue and 29th Street. On May 21, 1852, this route was completed, and the first Michigan Central/Illinois Central train pulled into a station at 13th Street and Michigan Avenue. From here, tracks would have to be built on a breakwater over Lake Michigan to take the cars to their final destination, which was to be the nation's largest station. This station was designed in 1853 by local architect Otto Matz and erected at the end of the Lake Street commercial district, adjacent to the site where Chicago's two largest grain elevators were also being constructed.[11]

Trains to and from the East had to skirt the bottom of Lake Michigan; hence the railroads came into Chicago from the south, not from the west as did the canal that connected the Chicago River to the Mississippi, nor from the east as did lake traffic. The commercial future of Chicago, the railroad hub, lay to the south. Therefore, how the city would rotate to a north-south orientation to meet the railroads would decide the future pattern of its urban fabric and also would determine who would benefit financially from controlling the inevitable real estate development to the south.

The first person who apparently understood what the railroads were doing to Chicago was Potter Palmer, a dry goods merchant who had moved to Chicago from Lockport, N.Y., in 1853 and opened a store in the Lake Street retail district. Late in 1864, Palmer allowed two young and upcoming merchants, Marshall Field and Levi Zeigler Leiter, to buy into his operation. This capital, and his earnings in cotton speculation during the war, allowed Palmer to buy almost a mile of land along State Street, south of Lake Street, with the expressed intent of rotating Chicago's commercial district to link Lake Street with the railroads to the south. Once again, Van Osdel managed to align himself with an important real estate speculator, for by October 1865, Palmer had four buildings under construction along State Street, all designed by Van Osdel.[12]

Anchoring the new development was Field, Leiter and Company's "Marble Palace," completed in 1868, at the northeast corner of State and Washington. To encourage the southward development of State Street, Palmer built the first of his large, palatial hotels four blocks farther south on the relatively isolated northwest corner of State and Quincy (between Adams and Jackson).[13]

Palmer's choice for the location of the "Marble Palace" at State and Washington was not uncalculated, for the First National Bank of Chicago had chosen the southwest corner of this intersection for its new building that also opened in 1868. The bank's decision acknowledged Washington over Randolph as Chicago's premiere office location. Like Randolph, Washington was adjacent to City Hall, but was a block farther away from the river and had gained in significance with the construction of the Chamber of Commerce (in which the Board of Trade was located) in 1865 on the south side of Washington directly across from City Hall. The Chamber of Commerce was also on LaSalle Street, in line with the new LaSalle Street Station of the Lake Shore and Michigan Southern Railroad. This station was built in 1868 to the design of local architect W. W. Boyington, Van Osdel's major competitor. The new station seemed to assure that LaSalle Street would be the north-south replacement for the office district then along Washington. Indeed, the construction at the northeast corner of LaSalle and Monroe of the Nixon Building, designed in 1871 by Otto Matz to be Chicago's most prestigious office building, heralded the southern movement of the office district and the apparent success of LaSalle Street.

The end of the Civil War unleashed a demand for office space that had been pent up since the Panic of 1837. The war had affected the nature of American business, in that it tended to centralize decision making and production, forcing smaller companies to grow or consolidate. Hence was born the modern corporation, which not only required larger buildings as well as regional offices to house its operations, but also had the capital resources to invest in the erection of these buildings. One of the first companies to

understand the new forces of the postwar building boom was the Equitable Life Assurance Company of New York. In May 1870, Equitable moved into its new building in New York City, initially designed in 1867 by Gilman and Kendall, but completed by George B. Post (fig. 3). One can posit that the Equitable Building was the first American skyscraper, for although it contained only five floors, its height was 130 feet, more than double that of a comparable structure. Its height was the result of a conscious decision by Equitable's shrewd vice-president, Henry B. Hyde, to exploit the potential of a new invention that had its origin in New York: the elevator. Although the safety elevator had been invented by Elisha Graves Otis and publicly displayed at the 1853 New York World's Fair, architects and clients had only begun to incorporate them into buildings prior to the Civil War. Hyde perceived that the elevator would permit the floor-to-floor

Fig. 3

Arthur D. Gilman and Edward H. Kendall, revised by George B. Post, Equitable Building, New York, 1870 (demolished 1912); *from* Journal of the Society of Architectural Historians *12 (1953), p. 16.*

Fig. 4
**John M. Van Osdel,
Proposed design for
the Kendall Building,
40 N. Dearborn Street,
1871; from Land Owner
3 (October 1871),
following p. 316.**

height in the new Equitable Building to be almost double that which traditionally had been the limit in walkup buildings.[14] The skyscraper's vertical grid of land speculation had been unleashed in New York by the elevator.

Chicago was quick to follow New York's lead in exploiting the vertical dimension, for Equitable followed its initial success in New York with a proposal to build an even taller building for its branch office in Chicago. Known as the Kendall Building (fig. 4), Chicago's first skyscraper was planned to have one more floor than the Equitable. The honor of designing Chicago's tallest office building was appropriately assigned to Van Osdel, who started designing the building in early 1871, for a site, however, not on LaSalle Street, but on the southwest corner of Washington and Dearborn streets.

Apparently, the shift of the office district to LaSalle was not going to be as easy as was Palmer's development of State Street. The Kendall's foundations were finished and the lower walls were under construction, when on October 8, 1871, the Chicago Fire ended that city's entry into the race with New York to develop the skyscraper. Contrary to what many historians claim, the fire does not mark the beginning of the development of the Chicago skyscraper, for the fire actually snuffed out Chicago's chance to share with New York in the early history of the skyscraper, as well as Van Osdel's opportunity to be credited with designing Chicago's first skyscraper.[15] It would take Chicago nine years to recover sufficiently from the disaster—which was only compounded by the Panic of 1873—before it would once again attempt to speculate in the vertical real estate accessed by the elevator.[16]

Following the fire, it was decided to complete a shorter (five stories instead of six), but better-constructed, version of the Kendall Building. Across the street, on the southeast corner of Dearborn and Washington, rose the new Portland Block (fig. 5), designed by William Le Baron Jenney in 1872 to replace a building of the same name destroyed in the fire. The Portland was owned by Peter and Shepherd Brooks, two investors in Chicago's real estate and grandsons of Boston's first millionaire, Peter Chardon Brooks.[17] The decision by the Brookses to rebuild marked this intersection as the prime office location in the postfire business district, and it prefigured the upcoming spillover of the railroad battle between Boston and New York into a new arena: would Dearborn or LaSalle Street emerge as the north-south replacement for the Washington Street office district?

The battle had become more complicated after the Civil War, for "Commodore" Cornelius Vanderbilt had entered the scene in 1867 by wresting control from the Bostonians of the New York Central Railroad. It took him less than two

additional years to buy the Lake Shore and Michigan Southern Railroad, the Erie's route to Chicago. As a result, the recently completed LaSalle Street Station changed owners and would quickly become the focus of Vanderbilt's commercial interests in Chicago. Four years later in 1873, through a series of clever stock manipulations, he even succeeded in buying the Michigan Central, thereby not only severing the eastern link of Boston's highly profitable Chicago, Burlington and Quincy Railroad, but also gaining a virtual monopoly of all rail traffic between Chicago and New York.

Vanderbilt died on January 4, 1877, leaving his son William a rail empire that controlled the rail outlets for midwestern wheat and meat to Europe. The only route from Chicago to Europe that escaped Vanderbilt was the Grand Trunk in Canada, yet even it had to pay him increasingly prohibitive user fees for the Michigan Central's tracks into Chicago.[18]

The Vanderbilt rail empire ultimately controlled all rail traffic to the northeast. The situation was intolerable to many powerful financial interests, whose only solution was the construction of a new railroad. Responding to the Vanderbilt's challenge, Sir Henry Tyler, the strong-willed president of the Grand Trunk, announced that he would build a new route from Detroit into Chicago. Ultimately, he would be joined by the Bostonians, who were helping to finance another transcontinental railroad in the form of the Atchison, Topeka and Santa Fe Railroad. On June 5, 1879, the Chicago and Western Indiana Railroad was incorporated, destined to become the Chicago entrance for all of Vanderbilt's embittered rivals: Tyler's Grand Trunk Western; the Bostonians' Santa Fe; and even the New York Central's perennial enemy, the Erie.[19] The paramount issue faced by Tyler and the other C. & W. I. investors was where to locate their new station. Its location would not only directly affect the success of the new railroad, but also generate new investments in the land immediately adjacent to the station.

It was quite natural that the final decision on the station's site would be influenced by Bostonians, for much of the financial support of the parent railroads came from Boston. One of Boston's leading railroad experts, Charles Francis Adams, Jr., who was an investor in both the C. B. & Q. and the Santa Fe, was another grandson of Peter Chardon Brooks, thereby related to Peter and Shepherd Brooks.[20] There can be little doubt about the role of these three powerful cousins in Boston in the decision to build a new C. & W. I. station on Dearborn Street. With the upturn of the national economy in 1880, the Brookses signalled a renewal of speculative office construction in Chicago by leasing the site on Dearborn immediately south of the Portland Block to Amos Grannis to build a new seven-story office block (see fig. 5). This lease was negotiated by their Chicago agent, Owen F. Aldis, who through this deal initially became acquainted with the young architects of the Grannis Block, Daniel H. Burnham and John Wellborn Root.[21]

Although they had designed only a few houses since their partnership began in 1873, Burnham and Root had already managed to establish themselves in Chicago's professional, business, and social circles as one of the city's most powerful architectural firms. Their first major commission proved eventually to be responsible for much of the enormous success of the firm. In 1874 a close friend recommended them to John B. Sherman, the general superintendent of the Union Stockyards, who was looking for an architect to design a new house for his family. During the

design and construction of the house, Burnham fell in love with Sherman's daughter, Margaret, whom he married on January 20, 1876.[22]

Burnham's marriage into the Sherman family not only established connections with the stockyards (for which Burnham and Root designed the buildings erected after 1874, allowing the young firm to stay in business during the Depression), but more importantly secured contacts with many of the power brokers on the Board of Trade. The firm's position was further secured in 1879, when Root married Mary Louise Walker, daughter of James M. Walker, former president of the C. B. & Q. and then a lawyer for John Murray Forbes's flagship line.[23] By 1880 Burnham and Root had, in a sense, consummated their relationships with Chicago's Board of Trade and Boston's railroad interests just at the time that the economy was improving and the Bostonians were planning the construction of the C. & W. I. station and the corresponding development south along Dearborn Street.

The march south along Dearborn continued in 1881 toward the planned depot. The Brookses purchased the western portion of the northwest corner of Dearborn and Monroe, the site of the burned U.S. Post Office and Custom House. It is curious that instead of rebuilding the structure on the old site, which was the standard practice for the majority of postfire construction, the government selected a new location. The site was two blocks farther south, a rather isolated block bounded by Dearborn, Adams, Clark, and Jackson, which consisted of hovels that were not cleared until construction began. The move of the Custom House to this downtrodden area not only encouraged the southward development of Dearborn, but also opened up a prime corner at Dearborn and Monroe for further office construction.

Fig. 5
View looking south from Washington Street along Dearborn Street, showing on the corner the Portland Block (William Le Baron Jenney, 1872; demolished 1933), and farther south the Grannis Block (Burnham and Root, 21-29 N. Dearborn Street, 1880; burned 1885); from Alfred T. Andreas, **History of Chicago** *(Chicago, 1884-86), vol. 3, p. 76.*

The importance of the site was underscored in 1881 by the construction of a new building for the First National Bank of Chicago designed by Burling and Whitehouse.[24] The bank's move from its old building at the southwest corner of Washington and State signalled the opening blow to the preeminence of Washington Street as Chicago's financial district. Adjacent to the west of the new site of Chicago's largest bank, the Brookses wisely decided to build Chicago's first skyscraper, the ten-story Montauk Block (fig. 6). Ten years after the 1871 fire had blunted Chicago's first attempt to exploit the elevator, the city was once again ready to join New York in the vertical extension of the urban grid. The design of this historic structure was entrusted, however, not to Van Osdel, but to Burnham and Root, following their successful design of the Grannis Block.[25] The architectural baton of Chicago had been passed on to the leaders of the next generation of designers.

Fig. 6
**Burnham and Root,
Montauk Block, 64-70
W. Monroe Street, 1881-
82 (demolished 1902);
from Andreas, History
of Chicago, *vol. 3, p. 66.***

Fig. 7
**W. W. Boyington,
Chicago Board of Trade,
141 W. Jackson Street,
1882 (demolished 1928);
from Andreas, History
of Chicago, *vol. 3,
frontispiece.***

The Brookses consolidated their holdings at Dearborn and Monroe early in 1882 by purchasing the southeast corner diagonally across from the new First National Bank.[26] Their plans for Dearborn, however, now encountered not only competition, but also outright opposition. Although the first Grand Trunk train had arrived on the C. & W. I. tracks on February 9, 1880, the final location of the new station was still unresolved two years later. The railroad tried to locate the station on the south side of Harrison Street where the Brookses had obtained the land secretly through Shepherd's wife, Clara G. Brooks.[27] Obviously, it was to the railroad's advantage to be as close to the business district as possible in order to compete with Vanderbilt's LaSalle Street Station. However, the Common Council was evidently under the influence of the LaSalle Street interests, for they continually prevented the C. & W. I. tracks from crossing even Polk Street, four blocks

south of the LaSalle Street Station, using the pretext that the new tracks would only compound the existing traffic congestion.

While the Brookses were arduously pushing to link up with the planned Dearborn Station, a group of the directors of the Board of Trade, led by J. R. Bensley and C. C. Counselman, were secretly buying property adjacent to the LaSalle Street Station. They accomplished the acquisitions prior to announcing in October 1880 their intention to move the Board of Trade from its location in the Chamber of Commerce, across from the site of the almost completed, postfire City Hall on the southeast corner of Washington and LaSalle, four blocks south to its present location, directly north of the LaSalle Street Station and across the street from its accompanying hotel, the Grand Pacific (see fig. 8).[28] The proposed location for the new Board of Trade was a stroke of pure nineteenth-century boodle, for not only was it adjacent to Bensley's and Counselman's newly acquired property, but it was also to be placed in the middle of LaSalle Street, which had just recently been opened through to Vanderbilt's station a few years earlier.[29] Thus, although the city had earlier bought the block immediately north of the station in order to open LaSalle Street to the station, this group was now asking the city to donate the same land to the Board of Trade to enable it to build the new building, which would greatly enhance the value of the surrounding property that they had just acquired.[30]

In January 1881, the directors of the Board of Trade approved the move to LaSalle Street. The debate then moved to Common Council where the LaSalle group had already procured its support, for it unanimously voted in June 1881 to close LaSalle Street once again and cede the land to the Board of Trade.[31] By

December 1881, the LaSalle group had held a competition that produced eight designs for the new building. Burnham and Root appeared to be a shoe-in, for they had submitted three of the eight projects, but dissension among the board of directors eventually led to the choice of W. W. Boyington in April 1882 to design the Board of Trade building (fig. 7).[32] While this act has puzzled historians, if one remembers that Boyington had designed not only the LaSalle Street Station but also the Grand Pacific Hotel, it becomes clear whose friends were really in charge of the project. Although Burnham and Root eventually designed five office buildings in the area adjacent to the Board of Trade—specifically, the Rialto, Counselman, Phoenix Insurance, Traders, and Commerce buildings—in addition to the Rookery and Insurance Exchange buildings a block north, the loss of the chance to design Chicago's tallest structure (the tower of the Board of Trade topped off at 302 feet) stuck in their craw for eight long years.

Development along LaSalle Street was not limited to Jackson Street and the vicinity of the Board of Trade: it quickly spread north to connect with the existing business district, resulting in the Chicago equivalent (fig. 8) of New York's Wall Street. Development plans were prematurely

revealed in March 1884 by a proposed ordinance that for the first time attempted to limit the height of buildings to 100 feet.[33] Within a week, permits for three tall buildings on LaSalle Street were obtained. Two of these, the Insurance Exchange by Burnham and Root and the Home Insurance Building by Jenney, were planned for the intersection of LaSalle and Adams, the location of the temporary City Hall (known as the "Rookery" because of the number of birds that occupied the old structure). On November 22, 1884, the new City Hall was completed, leaving the southeast corner of the intersection open for development. The city decided to lease the site for ninety-nine years with the provision that an office building costing not less than $800,000 be erected.[34]

Meanwhile, the C. & W. I. finally admitted defeat in the four-year war with City Hall and in December 1883 started construction of its new station on the south side of Polk Street. The design by Cyrus Eidlitz (fig. 9) was a direct response to Boyington's Board of Trade, for it also incorporated a tall tower that was intended as the termination of the vista down its commerical territory. The final location's greater distance from the business district was compounded by the fact that Dearborn Street was not completed beyond the Post Office south of Jackson, so the station owners were still at the mercy of the city to clear and pave these four blocks of "Dearborn." The city promised to extend Dearborn Street in the summer of 1884, and with the construction of the C. & W. I. Station finally underway, the Brookses began to reveal publicly their plans for the lower part of Dearborn.[35] A twelve-story office block designed by Burnham and Root was announced in April 1884, to be built across from the Post Office at the southwest

corner of Dearborn and Jackson (the site of the Monadnock Block).[36] Three months later the Brookses were ready to erect office buildings on both corners of the north side of Dearborn and Harrison (the site of the Pontiac Building), which would have been directly across the street from the station's originally planned location.[37] Had the station been built at Harrison, these new buildings would have formed a more coherent development that could have contested the Board of Trade area for dominance in the business district.

The promised construction of Dearborn Street, however, failed to materialize. It was not until September 1885, four months after the opening of the new Board of Trade and, more importantly, five and a half years after the first train had arrived in Chicago on the C. & W. I. tracks, that the extension of Dearborn from Jackson to Polk was completed.[38] Even though the C. & W. I. Station finally opened in September 1885, it was obvious that the LaSalle Street supporters had won and the Brookses shelved their grand plans for Dearborn during the next five years. If they could not beat City Hall, they could at least buy it. On May 12, 1885, the Central Safety Deposit Company was awarded the lease of the old City Hall site on LaSalle to build the city's largest office building. Listed among the stockholders of the company were the names of Peter C. Brooks, Owen F. Aldis, and Daniel H. Burnham.[39] Evidently, Brooks and Aldis had seized the opportunity to gain a prime site in the heart of the emerging financial district by once again acquiring vacated public property (as they had done with the Montauk Block on the old Customs House site). The new, eleven-story building by Burnham and Root, affectionately keeping the name Rookery, would make the intersection of LaSalle and Adams, which already contained the Insurance Exchange and the Home Insurance Building, one of Chicago's most architecturally significant locations.

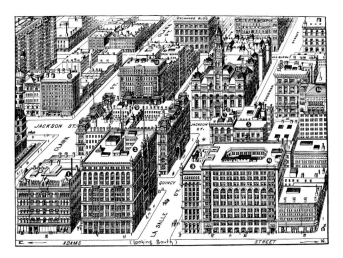

The vast amount of newly constructed office space near the Board of Trade had flooded the market in 1885 to the point that no new tall office buildings were even proposed for the next three years.[40] Meanwhile, the period from early 1886 to the summer of 1888 was marked in Chicago by stagnation in the speculative development market and extreme dissatisfaction within the ranks of organized labor.[41] Undoubtedly, these conditions were, to some degree, brought on by the same railroads that had initially brought Chicago its prosperity. After all, Chicago was no longer at the edge of the

Fig. 8

Rand McNally and Co., Bird's-eye view of Chicago, 1898; from Randall, Building Construction in Chicago, p. 153. Notable buildings include the Rookery, the Insurance Exchange, and the Rand McNally Building (nos. 2, 3, and 4; all by Burnham and Root); the Counselman and Phoenix buildings (nos. 8 and 11; also by Burnham and Root); the Grand Pacific Hotel and the Board of Trade (nos. 9 and 11; W. W. Boyington).

Fig. 9

Cyrus L. W. Eidlitz, Dearborn Street Station, 1883-85; from Andreas, History of Chicago, vol. 3, p. 225.

Fig. 10
**Leroy S. Buffington,
Proposed
"Cloudscraper,"
Minneapolis,
Minnesota, 1888;
from Inland Architect
and News Record 2
(July 1888).**

Fig. 11
**Rand McNally and Co.,
Bird's-eye view of
Chicago, Printer's Row
area, seen from Van
Buren Street, 1898;
from Randall, Building
Construction in
Chicago, p. 179. Notable
buildings shown here
include the Old Colony
(no. 1; Holabird and
Roche), the Manhattan
(no. 3; William Le Baron
Jenney), the Monon (no.
4; John M. Van Osdel),
and the Caxton and
Pontiac buildings (nos.
6 and 7; both by
Holabird and Roche).**

Fig. 12
**Rand McNally and Co.,
Bird's-eye view of
Chicago, looking south
from Adams Street,
1898; from Randall,
Building Construction
in Chicago, p. 157.
Notable buildings shown
here include the Owings
Building (no. 3; Cobb
and Frost), the Post
Office and Custom
House (no. 5; John M.
Van Osdel), and the
Monadnock Building
and Great Northern
Hotel (nos. 7 and 8; both
by Burnham and Root).**

western frontier, and as the railroads continued to open up the West, real estate speculation moved with them. By 1885, two more transcontinental railroads had been completed, creating greater investment potentials in St. Paul and Minneapolis, the terminus of the Northern Pacific, and in Kansas City, the center of the Santa Fe. It now appeared that Chicago was going to suffer a fate similar to that it had just inflicted on its two older rivals, Cincinnati and St. Louis; western expansion, aided by the railroad, was diluting Chicago's geographical and commercial advantage.[42]

In fact, it was not until the Santa Fe completed the construction of its tracks to Chicago in 1888 that speculative office construction returned to Chicago. This was not an act of inconsequential significance, for the railroad had spent $13 million on Chicago real estate and construction.[43] As the Santa Fe was heavily financed by Boston capital, it logically joined forces with the Dearborn Street interests of the Brookses. Its arrival at the C. & W. I. Station marked the beginning of the resurrection of the development plans for Dearborn Street. As LaSalle Street had been the center of the earlier boom during 1881-85, Dearborn would be the focus for the coming boom of 1889-92.

The buildings erected during this period would be of unprecedented height, for the elevator's headlong rush into the sky had just been unleashed by the development of the iron-skeleton frame. In March 1888, the building industry was shocked by a proposal for a twenty-eight-story office building (fig. 10) designed by architect Leroy S. Buffington of Minneapolis.[44] He was able to design a building more than double the height of existing buildings in Chicago because he had developed a revolutionary system of iron framing that enabled the erection of struc-

tures to almost unlimited heights, for which he was granted a patent two months after the publication of his proposal.[45] Buffington's proposal for a "Cloudscraper" produced an intense rivalry that challenged Chicago to regain its momentum with the skyscraper.

The first of the new generation of buildings on Dearborn, the Owings Building (see fig. 12), was a good example of the competition with the Twin Cities. Designed by Cobb and Frost and located across from the Post Office at the southeast corner of Dearborn and Adams, the Owings Building was originally announced on March 10, 1887 to be twelve stories.[46] The next week it was increased to thirteen stories, an apparent response to the announcement that St. Paul was going to build the twelve-story Pioneer Press Building, designed by Chicago architect S. S. Beman.[47] Minneapolis entered the race in May by announcing the thirteen-story Northwest Guarantee Loan (Metropolitan) Building, designed by Milwaukee architect E. Townsend Mix.[48] The Owings Building was then increased to fourteen floors,[49] which ended the argument once and for all. Although Buffington was granted his patent the same week, the Owings Building set off a series of even taller structures in Chicago designed by local architects who ignored the patent and incorporated their own versions of the iron-skeleton frame.

The increasing number and height of the buildings proposed for Dearborn Street in 1889 produced a variety of reactions. While some concern over their safety and environmental impact was to be expected, owners of existing buildings, especially on LaSalle Street, stood to lose a substantial portion of their clients to the newer buildings. Predictably, the summer of 1889 brought Chicago's second half-serious attempt to limit the height of new buildings, this time to the width of the street upon which they fronted.[50] While this restriction was never enacted, the flurry of building permits secured during this threat revealed plans for five buildings over ten stories high to be erected along Dearborn. Three of the buildings were to be located in the printing-house district (fig. 11) between Van Buren and Harrison: Brooks's eleven-story Pontiac at the northwest corner of Dearborn and Harrison, designed by Holabird and Roche; the twelve-story Monon Building designed by Van Osdel; and the sixteen-story Manhattan Building designed by Jenney.[51] Brooks also resurrected the plans to build Burnham and Root's sixteen-story Monadnock Block across from the Post Office on the southwest corner of Dearborn and Jackson.

The Post Office square (see fig. 12), already bounded by the Owings Building, the Grand Pacific Hotel, and Burnham and Root's Phoenix and Monadnock buildings, continued to be the focus as building activity increased after March 1890, when it was officially announced that Chicago would host the 1892 World's Fair. Two months later, the country's largest department store, designed by Jenney and appropriately named "The Fair," was announced to be erected opposite the Post Office at the northeast corner of Dearborn and Adams. Hotels would also be

needed for the large number of visitors anticipated during the World's Fair, and a group of investors approached Burnham for his aid in selecting a site for a large hotel. He suggested the Post Office square, specifically the northeast corner of Dearborn and Jackson, which was diagonally opposite the Monadnock site.[52] The Chicago Hotel (later, the Great Northern Hotel; fig. 13) gave Root the opportunity to begin to avenge the loss in 1886 of the design of the Auditorium to Adler and Sullivan.

Although Root's hotel rose four floors higher than the Auditorium Hotel, Sullivan's tower was still the second highest structure in the city, overshadowed only by the Board of Trade. It was not a coincidence, then, that on the same day that the permit to build the Chicago Hotel was approved, June 21, 1890, the permit to build the country's tallest building, the Masonic Temple, was

also secured.[53] Root, who had already designed Chicago's first and largest skyscrapers, had finally been able to avenge the loss of Chicago's two tallest commissions and set the height of the Masonic Temple at 303 feet, one foot taller than the Board of Trade's tower.[54] Surprisingly, however, Chicago's tallest building (fig. 14) would be built not on Dearborn or LaSalle, but on the northeast corner of State and Randolph, opposite Marshall Field's store, where Potter Palmer had started the rotation of Chicago's grid. Appropriately, Chicago's tallest vertical grid marked the point where Chicago, the river city, had first turned to meet the railroad.

Fig. 13
Burnham and Root, Great Northern Hotel, 237 S. Dearborn Street, 1890-91 (demolished 1940).

Fig. 14
Burnham and Root, Masonic Temple, northeast corner of State and Randolph streets, 1891-92 (demolished 1939).

I would like to acknowledge the financial support of the Graham Foundation for Advanced Studies in the Fine Arts in the research necessary for this essay.

Notes

1.   Although the ability to forge a link between the two water routes was recognized as early as 1673 by Louis Jolliet and Jacques Marquette, it wasn't until both waterways were under the control of the same government that there was any significant interest in settling Chicago. This occurred in 1803, with the signing of the Louisiana Purchase.

2.   The Federal Ordinance of 1785 had divided the Northwest into a rectangular grid oriented north-south and established the section (a square mile of land) as the unit of measurement in the survey. In 1807, Secretary of the Treasury Albert Gallatin first urged the construction of the canal. Herman Kogan and Lloyd Wendt, *Chicago: A Pictorial History* (New York, 1958), p. 65. In 1810, Rep. Peter Porter from New York proposed the use of federal funds to build the canal. James William Putnam, *The Illinois and Michigan Canal* (Chicago, 1918), p. 4. At this time, however, the British still maintained a threatening presence on the Great Lakes, so there was hardly sufficient traffic to justify the canal.

3.   Alfred T. Andreas, *History of Chicago* (Chicago, 1884-86), vol. 1, p. 425.

4.   Van Osdel had all of the millwork and windows manufactured in New York and then shipped to Chicago during the spring of 1837. John M. Van Osdel, "History of Chicago Architecture — Part I," *Inland Architect and Builder* (March 1883), p. 17.

5.   While the apparent failure of the canal would have seemed to threaten the real estate investments of the Bronson/Ogden group, in fact, it allowed them to gain tighter control over the project. In order for its backers to realize a return on their investments, the canal had to be completed, even if it meant that only the shallowest of boats could use it. The bankrupt state, with $5 million already invested in the stalled project, had little choice but to turn control of the canal over to its financers. These included Bronson, who represented the interests of many New York investors, and the London financial house of Baring Brothers. Barings was represented in the construction of the canal by three prominent Bostonians: Thomas W. Ward, Abbott Lawrence, and William Sturgis. Andreas (note 3), pp. 169-71, 434, 436; Ralph

W. Hidy, *The House of Baring in American Trade and Finance* (Cambridge, 1949), p. 316. Barings had also been involved with the building of Boston's railroads since 1839. Arthur M. Johnson and Barry E. Supple, *Boston Capitalists and Western Railroads: A Study in the Nineteenth-Century Railroad Investment Process* (Cambridge, Mass., 1967), pp. 37, 41, 44-48.

6.   These were fabricated by Daniel Badger's Architectural Iron Works of New York, and were, most likely, his first large, multistory commission. Thomas Eddy Tallmadge, *Architecture in Old Chicago* (Chicago, 1941), p. 109. Confronted by the scope and complexity of this project, Badger was forced to send his chief designer, George H. Johnson, to Chicago to supervise the construction. Turpin C. Bannister, "Bogardus Revisited — Part I: The Iron Fronts," *Journal of the Society of Architectural Historians* 15 (Dec. 1956), p. 18n.110. For more information on Chicago's cast-iron buildings, see Gerald R. Larson, "Fire, Earth, and Wind — Part I," *Inland Architect* (Sept. 1981), pp. 20-29; and idem, "Fire, Earth, and Wind — Part II," ibid. (Jan. 1983), pp. 31-37.

7.   Ogden's role in Chicago's first railroad, the Galena and Chicago Union, is a good example. Construction on the canal resumed in the fall of 1845, with Ogden as one of the contractors. On Feb. 17, 1846, Ogden became president of the newly resurrected scheme to build a railroad to Galena, an obvious competitor to the canal. The first construction contract for the railroad was signed on March 1, 1848, only a month prior to the completion of the canal. The canal was in operation for only six months before the first run of the railroad on Oct. 24, 1848. Andreas (note 3), pp. 247-50; George H. Douglas, *Rail City: Chicago U.S.A.* (La Jolla, 1981), pp. 12-16.

8.   Andreas (note 3), p. 241. Prior to the use of steam, the trip took twenty-two days. Bessie Louise Pierce, *A History of Chicago* (Chicago, 1937), p. 76. The completion of the direct rail route from Boston to Buffalo proved to be very timely, for the men from Boston who had helped to finance this project were the same men who had just taken interest in the stalled Chicago canal project; they would be pivotal in securing the financing needed to complete the project.

9.   One of the steamboat lines, the Chicago and Michigan City Steamboat Company, was owned by Ogden. Pierce (note 8), p. 69.

10.   The Illinois Central initially planned to enter the city on a route that would have connected with the Galena and Chicago Union Railroad's station at Kinzie and Canal streets. This would have allowed the Michigan Central to make a direct connection with the Aurora Branch of the Galena, which was already under construction by the Bostonians as the next link in their western route and would eventually become the Chicago, Burlington and Quincy Railroad. The Rock Island got wind of this plan, however, and purchased the right-of-way along this path, forcing the Illinois Central to alter its plans and adopt an initially more expensive route along the lakefront. Douglas (note 7), p. 32.

11.   By the time the station opened on June 12, 1856, the last link in the route from Boston, the Great Western Railroad, had been completed in Canada along the northern shore of Lake Erie between Buffalo and Detroit. Andreas (note 3), pp. 255, 577.

12.   Wayne Andrews, *Battle for Chicago* (New York, 1946), p. 24; Henry Ericsson, *Sixty Years a Builder* (Chicago, 1942), pp. 168-70; Harold M. Mayer and Richard C. Wade, *Chicago: Growth of a Metropolis* (Chicago, 1969), pp. 54-61.

13.   Van Osdel designed the hotel to be an eight-story building with 225 rooms; it opened on September 26, 1870. Andreas (note 3), vol. 2, p. 509.

14.   Winston Weisman, "New York and the Problem of the First Skyscraper," *Journal of the Society of Architectural Historians* 12 (March 1953), pp. 13-21.

15.   While Chicago struggled to rebuild, New York continued to construct taller buildings like the Western Union Telegraph Building (230 feet) designed in 1872 by Post, and the New York Tribune Building (260 feet) designed in 1873 by Richard Morris Hunt.

16.   In reality, it took another fire to finally convince Chicago's builders to address the problem of fireproofed construction. The dangerous conditions that had contributed to the rapid spread of the 1871 fire still existed on the South Side, which had been left untouched by the fire and awaited a similar fate. On July 14, 1874, forty-seven acres bounded by Clark, Polk, Michigan, and Van Buren burned with an intensity reminiscent of the recent holocaust. The National Board of Underwriters demanded that Chicago's

Common Council immediately enact reforms pertaining both to construction and the fire department, or else face the cancellation of all existing fire insurance policies. Chad Wallin, *The Builder's Story* (Chicago, 1966), p. 3.

17. "The Portland Block," *Land Owner* (June 1873), p. 99; Peter B. Wight, "Reminiscences of Chicago in 1859, Architectural and Otherwise — Part 1," *Inland Architect and News Record* (Aug. 1892), p. 3.

18. George R. Stevens, *The Canadian National Railway* (Toronto, 1960), pp. 107-14.

19. Douglas (note 7), pp. 53-54, 61-66.

20. Russell B. Adams, *The Boston Money Tree* (New York, 1977), pp. 189-91.

21. "An Important Improvement," *Real Estate and Building Journal* (Sept. 11, 1880), p. 137.

22. Thomas S. Hines, *Burnham of Chicago: Architect and Planner* (New York, 1974), pp. 19-21. For a detailed account of the importance of the stockyards connection, see Louise Carroll Wade, "Burnham and Root's Stockyards Connection," *Chicago History* 4 (Fall 1975), pp. 139-47.

23. Harriet Monroe, *John Wellborn Root: A Study of His Life and Work* (Park Forest, Ill., 1966), pp. 47-49.

24. For a description of the First National Bank, see *Real Estate and Building Journal* (June 18, 1881), p. 268.

25. For a detailed account of Peter Brooks's role in the design of the Montauk Block, see Carl W. Condit, *The Chicago School of Architecture: A History of Commercial and Public Building in the Chicago Area, 1875-1925* (Chicago, 1964), pp. 51-56.

26. *Real Estate and Building Journal* (Feb. 18, 1882), p. 65.

27. The purchases were made under the name of "D." Ibid. (Jan. 1, 1881), p. 2; (Jan. 31, 1885), p. 54. Brooks bought the northwest corner of Dearborn and Harrison (the site of the Pontiac Building) in July 1884. Ibid. (Aug. 2, 1884), p. 364.

28. Ibid. (Oct. 23, 1880), p. 203. The decision to build a new Board of Trade may also have been a response to Milwaukee's new Chamber of Commerce Building, which opened in late 1880. Ibid. (Nov. 27, 1880), p. 253.

29. Ibid. (Oct. 23, 1880), p. 202; (Jan. 8, 1881), p. 12.

30. This was simply a brazen power play, for the facts were not hidden, first, that Bensley was one of the owners of the site immediately in back of the proposed Board of Trade and directly across the street from the LaSalle Street Station, where the Rialto Building would be built, and second, that Counselman owned the northwest corner of LaSalle and Jackson, directly across from the Board of Trade, where a building bearing his name would be constructed. *Real Estate and Building Journal* (Oct. 14, 1882), p. 399; (Nov. 24, 1883), p. 601. Both buildings would be designed by Burnham and Root, who had somehow managed to avoid being identified with favoring either the Dearborn or LaSalle interests.

31. Immediately, the Washington Street interests secured an injunction from a local judge, but to little avail, for the La Salle group also had political connections with the Illinois Supreme Court, which rescinded the injunction on April 1, 1882. Ibid. (April 1, 1882), p. 123. For a commentary on the battle over the move of the Board of Trade, consult *Real Estate and Building Journal* from October 1880 to December 1882.

32. Ibid. (Dec. 10, 1881), p. 549. The four other submissions were by C. P. Thomas, E. S. Jennison, S. M. Randolph, and Bauer and Hill. In April 1882, five more projects were submitted, bringing the total number of designs to thirteen. Ibid. (April 22, 1882), p. 154.; (April 29, 1882), p. 163. For a description of the Board of Trade, see *Real Estate and Building Journal* (Dec. 16, 1882), p. 500.

33. Ibid. (March 8, 1884), p. 114.

34. In February 1885, a majority of the Common Council voted to accept a bid by H. S. Everhart, even though this was only the third best deal offered. Mayor Harrison vetoed the action, stating that the city could do better. *Real Estate and Building Journal* (Feb. 14, 1885), p. 76; (Feb. 21, 1885), p. 88. It took three months of quiet negotiating before the issue of the Rookery's site was resolved.

35. Ibid. (July 19, 1884), p. 338.

36. Ibid. (April 26, 1884), p. 195.

37. Ibid. (July 19, 1884), p. 338.

38. Ibid. (Aug. 1, 1885), p. 378.

39. Ibid. (May 30, 1885), p. 257; (Dec. 5, 1885), p. 596.

40. The only significant building constructed during this period was the Auditorium.

41. The Knights of Labor and the crusade for the eight-hour working day were central during this period of unrest. The highpoint of the violence was marked by the Haymarket Square riot of May 4, 1886.

42. Minneapolis and St. Paul grew as a short circuit for the midwestern wheat trade to Europe via Lake Superior. *Real Estate and Building Journal* (May 3, 1884), p. 207. Meanwhile, Kansas City quickly challenged Chicago's premiere standing in livestock. Ibid. (May 2, 1885), p. 209.

43. Douglas (note 7), p. 56.

44. *Northwestern Architect* 6 (March 1888), p. 23.

45. For an analysis of Buffington's work on the iron-skeleton frame and the issue of Jenney and the Home Insurance Building, see Gerald R. Larson, "The Iron Skeleton Frame: Interactions Between Europe and the United States," in *Chicago Architecture, 1872-1922: Birth of a Metropolis*, ed. John Zukowsky (Chicago and Munich, 1987), pp. 52-53.

46. *Real Estate and Building Journal* (March 10, 1888), p. 122.

47. Ibid. (March 17, 1888), p. 134; (March 24, 1888), p. 147.

48. Ibid. (May 3, 1888), p. 8.

49. For a description of the Owings building, see *Real Estate and Building Journal* (June 2, 1888), p. 276.

50. Ibid. (June 8, 1889), p. 356.

51. The fifth projected skyscraper for Dearborn was a sixteen-story building on the northeast corner of Dearborn and Jackson for Eugene S. Pike. *Real Estate and Building Journal* (June 15, 1889), p. 373. The project never materialized.

52. Ibid. (Jan. 18, 1890), p. 43. This was the site of Pike's proposed building.

53. Ibid. (June 21, 1890), p. 497.

54. Tragically, Chicago's leading architect did not live to see the completion of the crowning achievement of his career, for on January 15, 1891, John Wellborn Root died of pneumonia.

F. and E. Baumann

Frederick and Edward Baumann were among the large number of German-born architects who practiced in Chicago in the late nineteenth century. Unlike other major American cities, Chicago was unique in that German architects comprised the single largest ethnic group within the profession. Frederick Baumann (1826-1921) received his technical education in Berlin, where he was strongly influenced by the work of that city's leading architect, Karl Friedrich Schinkel, the precursor of modern German architecture. Frederick Baumann arrived in Chicago in 1850 and is considered to be the first German architect to practice in Chicago. He worked in a number of architectural offices in Chicago including John Mills Van Osdel (1851-52 and 1855-56) and Edward Burling (1852-54). From 1858 to 1864, he was a mason and building

contractor, and in 1868 he formed an architectural partnership with his cousin Edward Baumann (1828-1889), a graduate of the polytechnic school at Gradentz who had emigrated from Germany in 1856. Between that date and the establishment of this partnership, Edward Baumann had worked for Edward Burling for approximately ten years. Frederick Baumann contributed a major technical advance to Chicago architecture through his advocacy of the use of isolated-pier foundations for the support of buildings in Chicago's compressible soil. Baumann's concept had an important role in making possible the skyscraper in subsequent decades.

Together the Baumanns actively participated in the massive rebuilding of Chicago following the Great Fire of 1871. Their five-story Winston Block (1872; now demolished; fig. 1) at 124-26 W. Lake Street, for example, was typical of the structures that went up quickly along Lake Street, once Chicago's most important mercantile street. Erected as an

investment by attorney Frederick H. Winston, this commercial loft building was of bearing-wall masonry construction, sharing party walls with the adjoining structures. The Winston Block featured first-floor storefronts with large windows topped by several floors of open loft-spaces for light manufacturing. Its simple facade presented rows of round-arched windows separated by classical columns topped by a decorative overhanging cornice and a flat roof.

The interior of the Winston was divided only by rows of decorative cast-iron columns that constituted the intermediate support of the wood-floor structure between the perimeter masonry walls. These columns were rarely custom designed by the architect, but were instead ordered from catalogues issued by iron foundries in Chicago and the East Coast (see fig. 2). The slender, fluted shaft of the column from the Winston Block (cat. no. 1) was cast in one piece in a large mold; the individual acanthus leaves and other pieces of the Corinthian capital were cast separately and screwed into the top of the shaft. The column was recessed into the wooden floor and attached to a structural beam overhead by the horizontal corbel above the capital. Conservation analysis has indicated that the column was probably painted an off-white color to imitate white marble. Like many other architects, the Baumanns used exposed cast-iron columns in the interior of the Winston, even though it was well documented that such structural members had melted in the intense heat of the fire. Not until the 1880s and 1890s would adequate fireproofing be incorporated into the structure of Chicago buildings (see P. B. Wight entry).

A four-story loft building by an unknown architect next door at 128 W. Lake Street (c. 1872; now demolished), erected by contractor/developer Charles Busby, was similar to the Winston Block with rows of round-arched windows separated by flat, classical pilasters. Each of the nine windows on the facade of the Busby Building was punctuated by a limestone keystone (cat. no. 2), the wedge-shaped block at the crown of an arch that is inserted last and locks the other pieces into place. Its stylized, incised design of an abstracted botanical form is typical of the period. Both the Winston and Busby loft buildings on Lake Street were demolished in 1982 to make way for an atrium office building, 203 N. LaSalle Street (designed by Skidmore, Owings and Merrill), that is part of a large-scale revitalization of Chicago's North Loop.

Fig. 2
View of the interior of a typical late-nineteenth-century commercial building, showing exposed cast-iron columns.

Cat. no. 2
Architect unknown, Window keystone from the Busby Building; limestone, 64 x 36 x 14 cm. Department of Architecture Purchase Fund, 1983.258.

Peter Bonnett Wight

In addition to his notable architectural career in New York in the 1850s and 1860s, Peter Bonnett Wight (1838-1925) is also known as a leading late-nineteenth-century Chicago architect. Wight's first major commission, the National Academy of Design (1865; now demolished) in New York, was one of the first High Victorian Gothic buildings constructed in the United States. Wight settled permanently in Chicago after the Fire of 1871, and he joined in partnership with Asher Carter and William H. Drake. He is credited with bringing John Wellborn Root to Chicago to work as chief draftsman for Carter, Drake and Wight, in which office Root met his future partner, Daniel H. Burnham.

Wight and his firm are credited with designing numerous residential, cultural, and commercial buildings in the 1870s including the Springer Block (1872; now demolished) at the southwest corner of State and Randolph streets, a New Foundlings Home (1872; now demolished) for children orphaned by the fire, and the E. W. Blatchford House (1875-77; now demolished) on North LaSalle Street.

Blatchford's residence, called "Ulmenheim" (German for "home under the elms"), replaced the house that Blatchford lost to the 1871 Fire. The Blatchford House (fig. 3) was an outstanding example of High Victorian Gothic style applied to a residential structure: natural materials such as marble, brick, and stone were combined to enliven the facade with color. Other ornamental motifs were also employed, including four exterior lunettes illustrating the seasons of the year, two of which are

now in the Art Institute's collection (see cat. no. 3). Located over the front windows of the first floor, the lunettes were based on several poems, among them William Allingham's "Ode to Winter": "The branches plumed with snow—Alas! in the Winter dead and dark, Where can poor Robin go?" Wight documented that the lunettes were carved by an English sculptor, James Legge, who did a great deal of work in Chicago in the first few years following the fire. The last work he did for Wight was the Blatchford lunettes in 1873-74. Legge later did sculpture for S. S. Beman's Pullman Building (see p. 85) and Adler and Sullivan's Auditorium Building (see p. 133). It was Legge who introduced Louis Sullivan to Kristian Schneider, the gifted sculptor who carved the complicated molds to produce Sullivan's

foliate ornament for buildings such as the Gage (see p. 143) and the Schlesinger and Mayer Store (now Carson Pirie Scott and Co.; see p. 144). Legge's winter and autumn lunettes were saved by the Blatchford family when the house was demolished in 1929; the other two were presumably destroyed.

Wight planned the interior of the Blatchford house around a three-story central staircase, and he designed all of its furnishings as well. The library, for example, featured built-in bookcases inscribed with inspirational and literary motifs, and a heavy marble mantel with inlaid tiles and carvings formed the centerpiece of the room. It is appropriate that Blatchford would commission Wight to incorporate literary references into the interior and exterior of his house because Blatchford, a wealthy manufacturer, was a prominent member of Chicago's cultural community and a founder of the Newberry Library. Several tiles from

another fireplace designed for the house (see cat. no. 4) feature an ochre terracotta background, each with a different, gunmetal-grey heraldic figure. Given the pristine condition of the tiles, and the fact that no photographs of the tiles in situ have been found, there is some doubt whether they were ever installed in the house.

Wight's architectural career tapered off around 1881, when he began to concentrate on the development of a fireproofing system for the revolutionary new tall office buildings of the 1880s. Wight's patented fireproofing system was used in many of Chicago's tall buildings of the 1880s and 1890s, including Dankmar Adler's 1881-82

Jewelers' Building. Throughout his career, Wight wrote prolifically about fireproofing, the Chicago School, and architectural theory. When he retired in 1918 he donated his collection of more than 250 architectural drawings to the Art Institute, the first collection of such material to come to the museum.

Fig. 3
P. B. Wight, E. W. Blatchford House, 375 N. LaSalle Avenue (now 1111 N. LaSalle Street), c. 1875-77 (demolished 1929).

Cat. no. 4
P. B. Wight, Fireplace tile featuring heraldic figure from the E. W. Blatchford House; glazed terracotta, 12.7 x 12.7 x 4 cm. Gift of Thomas Blatchford, 1983.650c.

Theodore Vigo Wadskier

Born to English parents on the Island of St. Croix in the Danish West Indies, Theodore V. Wadskier (1827-?) studied in Copenhagen, Denmark, and received his architectural education at the Royal Academy of Fine Arts. He began his architectural career in New York in 1850 and later practiced in Philadelphia. After deciding that the West offered more opportunities than Philadelphia, he moved to Chicago in 1857. Wadskier designed many early Chicago churches, commercial blocks, and residences, including the J. W. Doane House on fashionable Prairie Avenue and Unity Church at Dearborn and Chestnut streets. Like practically all Chicago architects, Wadskier lost everything in the 1871 Fire, but he continued to practice architecture, partaking in the massive rebuilding that followed.

One of Wadskier's post-fire buildings was the five-story commercial block for H. B. Ray (1878; now demolished) at 211-21 W. Madison Street, commissioned by an investor in Kentucky. The capital from the exterior of the Ray Building in the Art Institute's collection (cat. no. 5) came from an engaged column separating Gothic arched windows on the top floor of the building. The limestone capital has been three-quarters carved (i.e., on its face and sides) with stylized leaf forms that are compressed from above by a horizontal slab that supported the spring of the arch. The Ray Building was demolished in 1987 to accommodate a highrise, as was the building next door at 223 W. Madison Street (c. 1872; architect unknown; fig. 4). The five-story facade of this latter structure displayed common elements: round-arched windows separated by classical pilasters, a

decorative cornice, and a flat roof. Its ornament—such as the decorative keystone preserved in the museum's collection (cat. no. 6)—is typical of the period in its use of an incised stylized leaf-and-tendril design.

In the late nineteenth century, Solon Spencer Beman (1853-1914) was praised by critics in the United States and abroad for the consistently high quality of his designs for industrial, residential, commercial, and public buildings. Beman is probably most widely recognized for his first major architectural commission—the design in 1879 of the industrial town of Pullman, Illinois, for the railroad sleeping-car magnate George M. Pullman. In the 1880s and 1890s Beman received commissions for important commercial blocks in downtown Chicago including the Pullman Company Office Building (1883-84; now demolished) on the southwest corner of Michigan Avenue and Adams Street and factories such as the Studebaker Building (1885; remodeled by Beman in 1896 as the Fine Arts Building) at 410 S. Michigan Avenue. Much of his early work was influenced by British architectural theory and practice,

although he designed in a great variety of styles, such as his châteauesque W. W. Kimball mansion (1889-90; 1801 S. Prairie Avenue), his Richardsonian Romanesque Grand Central Station (1889-91; now demolished), his classical Market Hall in Pullman (1894; partially demolished), and numerous Christian Science churches in Chicago and elsewhere.

The Pullman-Jennings Building (1882-83; now demolished) was constructed early in Beman's career, only three years after he received the Pullman commission. The building was erected as a manufacturing and salesroom building for two clients—the Pullman Laundry (operated by George Pullman's brother) and E. Jennings and Company, manufacturers of clothing and upholstery goods. This châteauesque style building (pictured in *Inland Architect*, May 1884), was originally six stories, with the uppermost story an elaborate mansard roof. The Pullman-Jennings fragment in the Art Institute's collection (cat. no. 7) was one of four ornamental cast-iron tie-backs that

held two second-story metal window lintels in place. The ornament has been repainted in its original red-orange color, which was intended to blend with the color of the red brick facade. The Beman office used a similar "rolled parchment" ornament on buildings throughout Pullman and on other projects of the 1880s.

The Pullman-Jennings Building was demolished in late 1978 and early 1979 as part of a City of Chicago urban renewal project. During the demolition, the building was gutted by fire on Christmas Day 1978. The ornament was removed from the ruins by a wrecking-crane operator and later donated to the Art Institute.

Cat. no. 7
S. S. Beman,
Ornamental tie-back
from the end of a beam
on the Pullman-Jennings
Building,
1214-22 W. Madison
Street, 1882-83
(demolished 1978);
painted cast iron,
58 x 45 x 11 cm.
Gift of Timothy
Samuelson, 1987.4.1.

Samuel Atwater Treat (1839-1910) was an architect's draftsman on the East Coast until a lack of work during the Civil War prompted him to set up his own architectural firm in Chicago. Frederick Foltz (1843-1916), a German architect who received his education and early training in Darmstadt and Munich, immigrated to New York in 1866. Two years later he also moved to Chicago, where he worked with a fellow German architect, Dankmar Adler, among others. Treat and Foltz established their partnership in 1872, and it became one of Chicago's most prolific firms for the next quarter century. They produced buildings in a wide variety of styles, including High Victorian Gothic and Richardsonian Romanesque apartment buildings, private residences, and large industrial plants. Among

their notable building designs are the Martin A. Ryerson Residence (1886; 4851 S. Drexel Boulevard), the original buildings for St. Luke's Hospital in Chicago; and a bakery in Chicago for the New York Biscuit Company (1890-91).

Treat and Foltz also designed a mixed-use building for E. G. Raymond (1884; now demolished) in an eclectic Queen Anne style. The facade of this narrow, five-story structure, consisted of red brick and unglazed red terracotta with sheet-metal dormers on either side of a roofline pediment. The Raymond Building was demolished in 1985, after having fallen into great disrepair. Fragments from the building in the Art Institute's collection, including a rosette and several variations on a capital (cat. nos. 8, 9), are rather crudely modeled because they date from 1884, early in the development of terracotta as a construction material. In the early 1880s, Chicago companies such as Northwestern Terra

Cotta, which produced the blocks for the Raymond Building, were the first to develop the material to its full potential as a substitute for stone or brick. Within five years, Chicago companies perfected the production of terracotta to such a degree that uniform blocks could be produced with one-eighth inch tolerances, and later, in the hands of artists such as Louis Sullivan, the plasticity of the material was fully realized (see entry on the Schlesinger and Mayer Store, p. 144).

The partnership of Daniel H. Burnham and John Wellborn Root, which lasted from 1873 until Root's premature death in 1891, was one of the most prodigious and successful architectural associations in Chicago's history. Daniel Hudson Burnham (1846-1912) and John Wellborn Root (1850-1891) met in the office of architect P. B. Wight (see Wight entry), where they played small roles in the vigorous activity of rebuilding Chicago in 1872. They decided to establish their own firm in 1873, an unfortunate moment as it turned out, because the nation experienced a severe economic depression that made it difficult for the young firm to get started. In the beginning, the architects received commissions almost exclusively for single-family homes, including one for John B. Sherman, one of the owners of the Union Stockyards and

Transit Company and Burnham's future father-in-law.

In the 1880s Burnham and Root distinguished themselves as designers of tall commercial blocks in downtown Chicago, and they are widely recognized today for their contributions to the Chicago School of architecture — the group of extraordinarily creative architects who rethought the practice of architecture in view of new engineering technologies and design philosophies of the late nineteenth century. Among Burnham and Root's greatest achievements in skyscraper design were the ten-story Montauk Block (1881-82; now demolished), an unprecedentedly tall elevator building that made extensive use of lightweight, fireproofing terracotta tile; the well-known Rookery (1885-88; 209 S. LaSalle Street) in which the aesthetic possibilities of a large interior light court were fully realized; and the sixteen-story Monadnock Block (1890-91; southern addition 1892-93; 53 W. Jackson Boulevard), which is renowned for the clean,

sweeping lines of its unornamented exterior of load-bearing masonry and brick. In all, Burnham and Root designed well over 300 office buildings, private residences, apartment buildings and hotels, railroad stations, stores and warehouses, schools, hospitals, and churches.

The Burnham and Root fragments in the Art Institute's collection all date from the three-year period 1885-88, when the Rookery was under construction and the Monadnock was in the planning stages. The earliest of the fragments is a wrought-iron lunette from the Commerce Building (1885-86; now demolished; fig. 5), a very narrow, eight-story speculative office building for the Commerce Vault Company on LaSalle Street, which was just developing into the city's financial district in the 1880s. The building was designed in the popular Richardsonian Romanesque style (see H. H. Richardson entry, p. 89) with rusticated brownstone piers

Fig. 5
Burnham and Root, Commerce Building, 319 S. LaSalle Street, 1885-86 (demolished 1971).

Cat. no. 10
Burnham and Root, Lunette from the main entrance of the Commerce Building; painted wrought iron, 205 x 232 x 4 cm. Gift of Cleveland Wrecking Company, 1972.812.

Cat. no. 11

**Burnham and Root,
Engaged capital
from the Church of
the Covenant,
Halsted Street at Belden
Avenue, 1887-88
(demolished 1971);
terracotta,
60.3 x 55 x 43.2 cm.
Gift of Cleveland
Wrecking Company,
1971.744.**

Cat. nos. 12, 13

**Burnham and Root,
Capital and block with
curved corner from the
James C. Lombard
House, 1805 Jefferson
Street, Kansas City,
Missouri, 1887-88
(now demolished);
terracotta,
40 x 58 x 28 cm.
and 22 x 42 x 23 cm.
By exchange from
Carson Pirie Scott and
Company, 1987.342.1-2.**

that dissolved at the sixth floor into engaged colonnettes rising to a heavy cornice. The Commerce, like the Rookery and Monadnock, still used the load-bearing wall system of construction, rather than the innovative iron-and-steel-skeleton construction that was being developed at that time.

The wrought-iron lunette (cat. no. 10) was located in a transom above the main doors of the Commerce Building. In order to signify the prominence of the entryway, it was framed by a two-story arch that occupied half the width of the facade. The delicate linear tracery of the lunette is typical of Root's ornament. In the 1930s the Commerce Building was converted into the Board of Trade Hotel, and was later annexed

to another building directly behind it, the Atlantic Hotel, which fronted on Clark Street. Both buildings were demolished in 1971.

The Church of the Covenant (1887-88; now demolished), designed for a Presbyterian congregation on Chicago's North Side, was one of several churches undertaken by Root during this time. A better-known and still-surviving example of Root's work is St. Gabriel's Church (1886-87; 4501 S. Lowe Avenue), which Harriet Monroe described as among the most characteristic designs that Root ever created. The designs of the two churches are not dissimilar, although St. Gabriel's is often identified as Romanesque, while the Church of the Covenant has been called a free translation to modern purposes of Byzantine design. The central focus of the Church of the Covenant was a 1,500-seat auditorium, encircled by a balcony and lit by two levels of arcaded windows.

The Art Institute's engaged terracotta capital from the Church of the Covenant (cat. no. 11; pl. 2) was part of a three-quarter-round column separating the windows of the church auditorium. On two sides of the column are the faces of men, which have been molded in such specific detail that they resemble recognizable, yet unidentified, individuals. The Art Institute also owns two simple dentiform fragments from the building which were part of a belt course on the lower floors of the facade. The church was demolished in 1971. The terracotta fragments from the church and from Burnham and Root's James C. Lombard House (1887-88; cat. nos. 12, 13) reveal the plasticity of a material that begins as pliable clay and can be shaped into portraits or intricate foliate arrangements before it is baked to a brick-like hardness.

Boston architect Henry Hobson Richardson (1838-1886) was the most important and influential American architect of his generation. Richardson was responsible for an interpretation of Romanesque architecture that received such national acclaim that the revival of the style has now come to bear his name. The Richardsonian Romanesque is characterized by red brick and rusticated masonry exteriors with large round-arched windows and entrances. The style is best represented by his massive Marshall Field Wholesale Store (1885-87; now demolished; fig. 6), one of the most influential buildings ever constructed in Chicago. Although it was technically conservative in that it utilized load-bearing masonry walls, and its simple rusticated facade offered no significant design innovations, the impact of the building on Chicago architecture was considerable, particularly on Adler and Sullivan's design of the Auditorium

Building (see p. 132). One reason for its impact is the mammoth scale of the massive seven-story Wholesale Store, which occupied fifty-one downtown building lots, an unprecedented accomplishment in Chicago. With its unified facade and battered granite base of huge stones, the Wholesale Store commanded an entire city block.

The Wholesale Store was one of Richardson's four commissions in Chicago. An early commercial structure for the American Express Company (1872-73) and the Franklin MacVeagh House (1885-87) have also been demolished. The remaining example of his work is the renowned John J. Glessner House (1885-87) on Prairie Avenue. Among Richardson's other important surviving works are Trinity Church (1872-77) in Boston and the Allegheny County Courthouse (1883-88) in Pittsburgh.

In the 1880s the Boston-born merchant Marshall Field had two distinct commercial operations in Chicago—a retail store for the general public on State Street, and a

wholesale store that primarily served midwestern merchants. The Wholesale Store that Richardson designed for Field had a U-shaped plan, and its granite and sandstone facade featured long arcades of broad, rounded arches. In the Art Institute's collection is an example of the type of red sandstone pilaster capitals (cat. no. 14) that separated pairs of windows on the third and fourth floors. Its design consists of two rows of acanthus leaves topped by a pair of volutes, and its relative simplicity is consistent with Richardson's design aesthetic for the entire building. Although the Wholesale Store functioned superbly, by the 1920s Marshall Field's retail business overshadowed his wholesale operations. In 1930 Field transferred his wholesale interests to the newly completed Merchandise Mart on the Chicago River, and in May and June of the same year, the Wholesale Store was demolished to make way for a parking lot.

Fig. 6
H. H. Richardson, Marshall Field Wholesale Store, bounded by Adams, Franklin, Quincy and Fifth (now Wells) streets, 1885-87 (demolished 1930).

Cat. no. 14
H. H. Richardson, Pilaster capital from the Marshall Field Wholesale Store; red sandstone, 61 x 51 x 16.5 cm. Gift of the Lake Zurich Golf Club in memory of Horace Oakley, 1987.44.

Jenney and Mundie

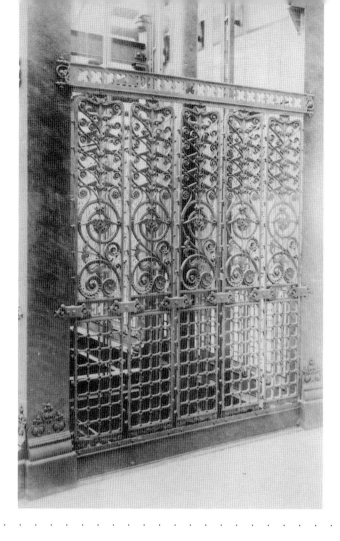

Cat. no. 15
Jenney and Mundie,
Elevator enclosure
grille from the
Manhattan Building;
fabricated by the
Winslow Brothers
Company; cast iron and
copper-plated cast iron,
226 x 229 x 4 cm.
Gift of the Manhattan
Associates, 1981.942-46.

William Le Baron Jenney (1832-1907) made important contributions to the development of the commercial skyscraper in Chicago through the creative use of existing technology. Jenney adapted metal-frame building technology to the construction of tall elevator buildings. Before the end of the nineteenth century, all masonry buildings were supported by a heavy, stone or brick foundation and load-bearing masonry walls. In the 1880s and 1890s architects and engineers, such as Jenney, began to develop a different structural system that transferred the weight of exterior masonry walls to an internal iron- or steel-skeleton frame. That single development revolutionized building design, enabling architects to design taller buildings with more floor space and larger windows. Many Chicago architects who also contributed to the development of the tall commercial block in Chicago, such as Louis Sullivan, William

Holabird, Martin Roche, Daniel H. Burnham, and John Wellborn Root, began their careers in Jenney's office. For that reason, Jenney is considered the father of the Chicago School of architecture, the group of nineteenth-century architects who grappled with the engineering and design problems of constructing tall commercial buildings.

Jenney is also known for his urban design work. In 1869, for example, he worked with Frederick Law Olmsted and Calvert Vaux to plan the town of Riverside, Illinois, the first suburb connected to Chicago by railroad. In the 1870s Jenney executed a series of urban parks in Chicago. By encouraging the integration of park land with commercial, industrial, and residential areas, Jenney had enormous impact on future city planning in America. Jenney, who was educated at Harvard's Lawrence Scientific School and the Ecole Centrale des Arts et Manufactures in Paris, served as an engineer in the Civil War. He came to Chicago in 1867. Jenney was asso-

ciated with numerous partnerships throughout his career, including ones with Sanford E. Loring, William Augustus Otis, and William B. Mundie. A native of Canada, Mundie (1863-1939) came to Chicago in 1884 and worked in Jenney's office as a draftsman and designer until 1891, when he became a full partner in the firm. He was Jenney's partner when the firm perfected skeleton construction in buildings such as the Second Leiter Building (1889-91), the Manhattan Building (1889-91), and The Fair store (1890-91, 1896-97; now demolished).

The sixteen-story Manhattan Building (fig. 7) is a significant product of the early Chicago School because it was one of the first in which Jenney perfected skeleton-frame construction so that the walls of the building have no load-bearing function. Above the grey granite base of three stories rises a complex facade of pressed brick and terracotta. The elevator-enclosure grille

from the Manhattan Building in the Art Institute's collection (cat. no. 15) consists of five copper-plated cast-iron panels joined by copper buckles and at the top and bottom by a copper-plated header and kickplate. This stationary grille consists of a simple grid on the bottom portion and above that, spiraling and stacked plant forms. Both sides of the grille are ornamented because early cage elevator grilles could be viewed from the inside as well as the outside of the cab. The Manhattan Building grilles were fabricated by the Winslow Brothers Company of Chicago, which manufactured the elevator grilles, balusters, and metal decorations for most of Chicago's great buildings of the period, including Adler and Sullivan's Chicago Stock Exchange and Schiller buildings (see pp. 136-41). These same elevator grilles were also used in another Jenney building, The Fair store. The grilles were removed from the Man-

hattan Building in 1982 when the building was converted from offices to residential units as part of the conversion of Chicago's South Loop from an industrial area of printing plants to an area of residential lofts.

A second Jenney fragment in the Art Institute's collection was part of an important Chicago department store known as The Fair (fig. 8). The Fair store was commissioned by the German-born retail baron Ernest J. Lehmann, who had founded his original store on the same site in 1875. Lehmann introduced two merchandising ideas that distinguished The Fair from other State Street operations: first, he initiated the practice of discounting prices and, second, he used promotional campaigns and amusements to create a carnival-like atmosphere so people would enjoy shopping at The Fair. The building that Jenney originally designed was to have been sixteen stories and would have contained more than 1.1 million square feet of space. By comparison, the

world's largest department store until that time had been the Bon Marché in Paris, measuring 430,000 square feet. In the end, the eleven-story, 500,000-square-foot Fair store became a prototype for future retail establishments built on a large scale.

Although the size of The Fair attests to Jenney and Mundie's command of the skeleton construction system, their handling of the exterior of the building was rather clumsy, producing a structure that was unnecessarily massive and weighty, especially when compared to their elegant treatment of the Second Leiter Store (1889-91; later Sears, Roebuck and Co.). The Art Institute's Fair store fragment, an exterior pilaster of brown terracotta (cat. no. 16), consists of four blocks featuring simple designs based on plant forms and a classical torch intertwined in a flat ribbon. The Fair store terracotta is a good example of an architect's experimentation with the plasticity of the material. The technique of cladding a building in terracotta was first fully developed in

Cat. no. 16
**Jenney and Mundie,
Pilaster from the facade
of The Fair store;
unglazed brown
terracotta,
182.5 x 31 x 20 cm.
Gift of the Dearborn
Land Company,
1984.804d-g.**

Chicago, and cladding an entire
building in terracotta was a local
innovation that made late-nineteenth-century commercial architecture in Chicago unique.

In 1963 The Fair store was purchased by Montgomery Ward, and
the ornament on the State, Dearborn, and Adams street facades was
removed in 1964-65 and replaced by
flat blocks of Indiana limestone. The
entire building was demolished in
1985 when Mobil Oil announced
plans to build a 72-story office and
shopping tower on the site. At that
time, the Art Institute's fragment
was removed from the north side of
the building which faced an alley
and therefore had not been stripped
in the 1960s. Over time, this enormous store had fallen victim to
postwar changes in retail shopping
patterns, as retail concerns left the
business centers and downtown areas
began to be redeveloped with even
taller office towers.

The architects Willoughby J. Edbrooke (1843-1896) and Franklin P. Burnham (1853-1909) are better known for their work throughout the U.S. than for what they produced in Chicago. An English immigrant, Edbrooke began practicing in Chicago in 1867. In preparation for the design of the Georgia State Capitol in Atlanta, he formed a partnership with Chicago architect Franklin P. Burnham in 1889. The firm was responsible for the design of a number of homes in the Chicago area including ones for William Hill, H. G. Chase, and F. R. Grimes in Chicago, and for J. B. Kirk in Evanston. Their churches and other public buildings include the Englewood Methodist Episcopal Church and Oakland Methodist Church in Chicago; the Henry County Courthouse in Clinton, Missouri (1886); and an 1887 school in Jefferson, Illinois. Edbrooke was appointed Supervising

Architect of the U. S. Treasury by President Benjamin Harrison in 1891. Edbrooke and Burnham supervised the construction of a number of courthouses in Illinois. After their partnership dissolved, Burnham moved to the Los Angeles area where he designed various buildings including a Christian Science Church in Pasadena.

Perhaps the firm's best-known work in Chicago was the Mecca Apartments (1891-92; now demolished), completed just prior to the 1893 World's Columbian Exposition, at a time when South Side neighborhoods were favored by Chicago's rising affluent families. The building's Roman-brick exterior was particularly attractive, and the interior was distinguished by two light courts roofed with glass and surrounded by continuous balconies. The four-story atrium courts featured such luxurious amenities as fountains and fishponds. Each of the balconies was enclosed by cast-iron railings (cat. no. 17) composed of spiraling and curvilinear forms, covered with curling

leaves, and similar to later Art Nouveau designs. The railing in the Art Institute's collection has been painted a copper color because it is thought that the railings were originally copper-plated cast iron.

With the opening of the Michigan Avenue Bridge in 1920 and the subsequent development of the area known as Streeterville, affluent families flocked to the new luxury apartment buildings on East Lake Shore Drive and in other North Side neighborhoods. Meanwhile the South Side of Chicago was undergoing changes as well: middle-class and poorer tenants began to inhabit the Mecca and other once-fashionable apartment buildings. In 1941 the Illinois Institute of Technology purchased the building to make room for its expanding campus; the building was demolished in 1952.

Cat. no. 17
Edbrooke and Burnham, Section of a balcony railing from the Mecca Apartments, northwest corner of State and 34th streets, 1891-92 (demolished 1952); painted cast iron, 74.5 x 106 x 1.5 cm. Gift of Mr. and Mrs. Vernon P. Reynolds, 1972.306.

93

Eames and Young

· · · · · · · · · ·

that lasted three decades, until
Eames's death in 1915.

The firm became nationally
prominent for their designs of the
Cupples Station in St. Louis; the federal prisons in Atlanta, Georgia, and
Leavenworth, Kansas (1907); and the
U. S. Custom's House in San Francisco (1906-11). In the Midwest they
designed prominent exposition
buildings at the Trans-Mississippi
Exposition in Omaha (1897) and the
Louisiana Purchase Exposition in St.
Louis (1904). They designed many
distinguished homes for St. Louis's
affluent businessmen and numerous
commercial office buildings in the
downtown area.

The Title Guarantee Building
(originally the Lincoln Trust Building), completed in 1898, was probably the most accomplished of Eames
and Young's buildings in St. Louis.
The Title Guarantee was constructed
directly across the street from Adler
and Sullivan's Wainwright Building,
which had gone up seven years earlier on the northwest corner of 7th
and Chestnut. The Renaissance
Revival style Title Guarantee was
sheathed in classical ornamental terracotta panels, and the cornice featured winged female figures (see cat.
no. 18). Each of the dozens of figures
was distinctively finished and shows
the handiwork of individual terracotta craftsmen. All of the terracotta
angels on the building were slip-
glazed with a lilac finish that was loc-
ally produced by the Winkle Terra
Cotta Company of St. Louis which
also produced the terracotta for
Sullivan's St. Louis buildings—the
Union Trust, the Wainwright, and
the St. Nicholas Hotel (see p. 134).

Despite its prominence in the
history of St. Louis architecture, the
Title Guarantee Building was demolished in 1983 along with several
other buildings in the area to make
way for a complex of new office
buildings and parkland.

Cat. no. 18
Eames and Young,
Angel from the cornice
of the Title Guarantee
Building, southwest
corner of 7th and
Chestnut streets, St.
Louis, Missouri, 1898
(demolished 1983);
fabricated by Winkle
Terra Cotta Company
of St. Louis;
slip-glazed terracotta,
213 x 81 x 45 cm.
Gift of the University
Museums, Southern
Illinois University at
Edwardsville, 1985.826.

Eames and Young was among the
most accomplished and important
firms practicing in St. Louis, Missouri, in the late nineteenth century.
William Sylvester Eames (1859-1915)
was born in Clinton, Michigan, and
received his architectural education
at Washington University in St.
Louis. He worked as a draftsman in
various St. Louis offices and later
studied architecture at the Ecole des
Beaux-Arts in Paris. Upon his return
to the U.S., Eames was appointed
Deputy Commissioner of Buildings
for St. Louis. Thomas Crane Young
(1858-1934), a native of Sheboygan,
Wisconsin, also studied architecture
in St. Louis, at the School of Fine
Arts. He was a draftsman in the
offices of William Ware and Henry
Van Brunt and E. M. Wheelwright in
Boston, before studying at the Ecole
des Beaux-Arts and the University
of Heidelberg in Germany. Upon his
return to St. Louis in 1885, Young
and Eames formed a partnership

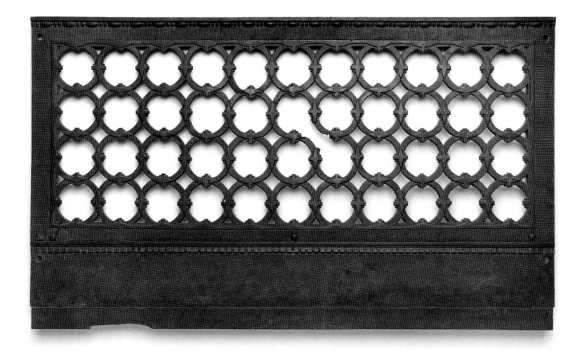

Along with the renowned nineteenth-century firms of Jenney and Mundie, Adler and Sullivan, and Burnham and Root, the Holabird and Roche partnership made tremendous contributions to the development of the Chicago School of architecture. Holabird and Roche was one of the most prolific firms in the history of Chicago, having designed more than 7,500 buildings in Chicago and across the United States. Exhibiting a wide range of styles over the years, the firm adapted their work to the prevailing taste. Their Chicago School buildings stressed function and structure and are considered the archetypal products of that style. The founding partners of the firm, William Holabird (1854-1923) and Martin Roche (1853-1927), met in the office of their architectural mentor, William Le Baron Jenney. William Holabird, born in New York, received two years

of training at West Point, before coming to Chicago in 1875. Martin Roche was born in Cleveland, but he grew up in Chicago and attended the Armour Institute of Technology. Roche entered Jenney's office in 1872.

Holabird and Roche began their practice in 1881, although their first big commission—the design of buildings at Fort Sheridan—was not received until 1884. The commission that catapulted the firm into international prominence, however, was the twelve-story Tacoma Building (1886-89; now demolished). The Tacoma attracted worldwide attention because it employed the most extensive use of skeleton construction to that date, with exterior walls that were opened to an unprecedented degree by means of large, closely placed windows. The Tacoma, in turn, led to dozens of other commissions including the Pontiac Building (1891), the southern addition to the Monadnock Block (1892-93), and the Marquette Building (fig. 9). These works are typical of Holabird

and Roche's Chicago School buildings, as evidenced by their use of what has come to be known as the "Chicago window"—a large fixed pane of glass flanked on either side by narrow, moveable sash windows—and by their handling of a facade that clearly expresses a building's underlying skeletal structure.

Cat no. 19
Holabird and Roche, Base of an elevator grille from the Marquette Building; cast iron, Bower-Barff finish, 51 x 88 cm. Gift of Timothy Samuelson, 1987.4.3.

Fig. 9
Holabird and Roche, Marquette Building, 140 S. Dearborn Street, 1893-95; addition 1905-06.

The full embodiment of their functional Chicago School designs was realized in the Marquette Building (1893-95; addition 1905-06). Often considered the culmination of a sequence of Chicago School skyscraper designs, the Marquette featured a facade devoid of all but the most simple ornament. What ornament there was combined American Indian motifs with classical details, but it was all subordinated to the architectonic mass and structure of the building. Although its massing is based on a Renaissance palazzo precedent, its exterior is distinguished among Chicago School buildings because it so directly expresses the building's underlying steel structural system. In order to initiate innovative planning in this building, Owen Aldis, the building's manager, developed eight basic principles of design and profitable management necessary for a first-class office structure, among which were provisions that accommodated as much light and air as possible, kept building materials simple and easily cleaned, and enhanced the public space with an elegant lobby, elevator cabs, corridors, and other features that gave a visitor a lasting impression of the building's quality. The lobby of the Marquette, for example, features an ornate mosaic—designed by J. A. Holzer and fabricated by Tiffany Glass and Decorating Co.— at the mezzanine level detailing the early travels of Pere Jacques Marquette and Louis Jolliet through the Illinois region. The elevators were likewise well, but simply, designed, as can be seen in the kickplate (cat. no. 19) from a cage elevator that had been removed in 1979 prior to renovation of the building. The simple interlocking circular motif on the grille is similar to the design executed in brown terracotta on the exterior of the building. Similarly, doorknobs and hinges from the building feature incised meander patterns, appropriately simple for a

building that combines Indian motifs with the design of a classical Renaissance palazzo. As a result of Aldis's overall principles, the Marquette stands as one of the very first tall buildings to utilize efficient planning, and it greatly influenced subsequent commercial architecture.

In the Marquette Building, Holabird and Roche expressed their structural and design ideas in a form that came to characterize their later buildings. The Oliver Building (1907-08; fig. 10), for example, contains all of the elements associated with the Holabird and Roche formula for tall, commercial style buildings. Built for the Oliver Typewriter Company, the building features an interesting variation on the formula in the cast-iron ornament that surrounds windows and doors, because it is based on traditional Renaissance motifs of fish, dolphins, foliage, and candelabra. The cast-iron fragment in the Art Institute's collection (cat. no. 20; pl. 3) was dislodged from the first-floor entrance when a truck crashed into the build-

ing. Discarded at first, the fragment was later retrieved by Tim Samuelson.

While they were pursuing these spare, functionalist structures, the firm also began to receive commissions for opulent hotels, among them the Hotel LaSalle (1908-09), the Sherman House (1911; addition 1920), and an annex to the Auditorium Hotel (1893, 1902, 1907; now the Pick Congress Hotel). Nonetheless, the firm continued to design large, severely styled facades for State Street department stores, including the Mandel Brothers (1900, 1905, 1912), the Rothschild Store (1912), and the Boston Store (1905-07), and for office buildings such as the McCormick (1908-12) and the Monroe (1912), both of which were simple rectangular blocks faced with brick and terra-cotta. The McCormick Building is larger than the firm's Marquette Building, but it follows the planning

precedents established in the earlier building. A doorknob from the McCormick Building (cat. no. 21) features a relief design of initials that form a logo for the building.

Following the death of William Holabird in 1923, Martin Roche continued the firm, but the two most active forces in the firm became Holabird's son John A. Holabird and John W. Root, Jr., the son of one of Chicago's most famous architects. Like architects across the nation during the early 1920s, the young partners designed in a variety of revival modes including the Gothic Chicago Temple Building (1922-23), the grand classical temple of Soldier Field (1923-25), and their largest and most opulent hotel, the Stevens (1925-27; now Chicago Hilton and Towers). With the death of Martin Roche in 1927, the two principals were free to assume control of the firm, rename it Holabird and Root, and embark on several successful decades of design in the modern idiom (see Holabird and Root entry, pp. 112-13).

Cat. no. 20

Holabird and Roche, Fish ornament from the base of the Oliver Building; painted cast iron, 79 x 29 x 13 cm. Gift of Timothy Samuelson, 1987.4.2.

Fig. 10

Holabird and Roche, Oliver Building, 159-69 N. Dearborn Street, 1907-08.

Cat. no. 21

Holabird and Roche, Doorknob and escutcheon plate from the McCormick Building, 332 S. Michigan Avenue, 1908-12; brass and iron, 22.9 x 7.5 x 7 cm. Bequest of Leander McCormick, 1967.495a-b.

. . . .

by Robert Bruegmann
University of Illinois at Chicago

*T*he fragments of terracotta from Daniel H. Burnham's Railway Exchange Building (1903-04) in the collection of The Art Institute of Chicago (see cat. nos. 24, 25) are clearly the product of a specific time and place, the large American city at the turn of the century. It is not the design of their ornamental patterns that betrays their origin. On the contrary, the dominant motifs, the Greek key or fret, in which the lines interlock like a rectilinear wave, and the dentil, with alternating raised squares forming a kind of checkerboard, have been common on classical buildings since antiquity. What is unusual here is the material out of which they were made and the fashion in which they were used.

Instead of the marble out of which ornament might have been laboriously sculpted by hand for a classical temple or a Renaissance church, the ornament in this case has been interpreted in glazed white terracotta, an inexpensive, mass-produced, bricklike material that first came into widespread use in the 1890s. And unlike the use of orna-

ment in classical or Renaissance buildings, where patterns like the key or dentil were usually used to mark a specific band of transition, the reveal of a window, or the frieze of a cornice, on buildings of relatively small size, at the Railway Exchange Building the ornamental terracotta blocks were used hundreds of times, across entire elevations, even when they marked no important transition or when they were so high up that their pattern was lost on the viewer below. Nonetheless, this treatment did give a textural relief and liveliness to a building's facades. In fact, architects imagined—for a few years at least— that the widespread use of inexpensively produced terracotta ornament might be just the material they had been looking for to provide a new sense of order and consistency to a city whose buildings increasingly dwarfed anything that had been produced in the world's great cities.

This example suggests that one of the most interesting things about the study of the Railway Exchange fragment and others of this period in the collection of the Art Institute is the way that, in the most successful examples, even the smallest fragments of ornamental terracotta, iron, or cut stone can mirror many of the architect's most basic assumptions about buildings and their place in the city. In this essay I will examine a few fragments from buildings constructed between the turn of the century and the Great Depression to see what they convey about attitudes toward the making of buildings and the urban landscape as a whole.

The City Beautiful
By 1900 Chicago was no longer a frontier boomtown. After three decades of frantic growth, the city had matured. Although it was not immediately obvious, the era of great population increases and economic growth had ceased. Chicago had become the undisputed artistic center of the American heartland, but as they looked around them, many Chicagoans were increasingly dissatisfied with what they saw. Chicago's Loop was certainly impressive, yet few would argue that it possessed much of the beauty of Paris or London.

One clear indication of the mounting dissatisfaction with the city's appearance was the enactment by the city council of a building height limit in the 1890s. In part this legislation was sparked by businessmen who feared that, unregulated, the new skyscrapers would throw their own buildings into permanent shadow and thereby lower their property value. But this building code also reflected a growing feeling on the part of the population at large that increased governmental intervention might be necessary to create a more orderly city, even if that meant some sacrifice of growth and individual initiative. This popular movement paralleled a strong professional trend in which architects tried to subdue the wilder aspects of late nineteenth-century styles in favor of the simpler massing and more conventional ornamental schemes of the classical styles.

The 1893 World's Columbian Exposition had provided the entire country with a dazzling vision of what a unified, coherent urban ensemble might look like. In the years following the fair, Chicago's architects and business leaders gave serious thought to what could make

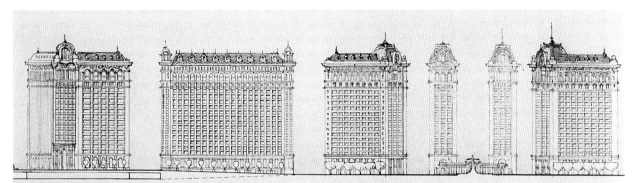

Fig. 1
**Daniel H. Burnham
and Edward H. Bennett,
"Section Looking
North . . . "; from
Plan of Chicago
(Chicago, 1909),
pl. 126 (detail).**

their own city as beautiful as it was useful. In their 1909 *Plan of Chicago*, Daniel H. Burnham and Edward H. Bennett produced the classic document of the City Beautiful movement. Although the majority of the book dealt with specific proposals for roads, harbors, and other practical matters, underlying the document was an assumption that utilitarian and aesthetic concerns were intimately related. The parks proposed in the plan, for example, were considered important both for practical reasons of health and as places of beauty. Likewise, the authors of the plan apparently took for granted that commercial buildings that were solid and handsome would also be profitable. They did not say much about the appearance of these buildings, but they reproduced a series of magnificent plates showing how the center of town would look when it was filled with orderly rows of massive buildings rising in regular fashion with matching cornice lines along the streets (fig. 1).

Probably the best place to get some idea of what they envisioned is along the city's front facade, Michigan Avenue facing Grant Park. Even

with later intrusions of quite different materials and scale, this stretch of streetscape has today a coherence and dignity virtually unequaled in urban America. The tone for this frontage was clearly set between 1900 and 1910 when several monumental buildings by the firm of D. H. Burnham and Co., among them the Railway Exchange (fig. 2), were erected. Since this massive structure fills its entire site between the streets and alleys, the architects ensured light and air to the interior by creating a central light court. On the street side the building rose as high as height limits permitted. When other buildings equally tall and bulky were built in close proximity, the result was a smooth cliff of masonry rising up from the sidewalks to more or less even cornice lines. One might imagine this wall as a set of Renaissance palaces blown up to several times their original height and placed cheek by jowl.

The Railway Exchange was unusual for the period in its use of projecting bay windows, a common feature in the 1880s and 1890s but one that was about to disappear as the city clamped down on the private use of space above the public sidewalks. The building was also novel in its extensive use of glazed white terracotta. Glazed terracotta had been used on Chicago buildings of the mid-1890s such as the Reliance

Fig. 2
**D. H. Burnham and Co.,
Railway Exchange
Building (now Sante Fe
Center), 224 S. Michigan
Avenue, 1903-04.**

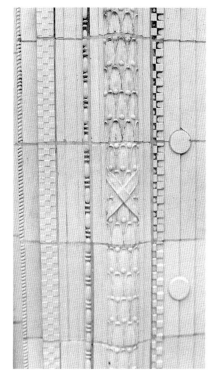

Figs. 3, 4
**Exterior details of
the Railway Exchange
Building.**

Building on State Street (Burnham and Root, 1890; enlarged D. H. Burnham and Co., 1894-95), but the large scale and prominent location of the Railway Exchange made its use especially noteworthy. Terracotta was ideal for architects of this generation because it was comparatively inexpensive and much lighter in weight than stone, allowing considerable savings in the cost of structural steel. It was thought to require little maintenance, was a satisfactory fireproofing material, and could be applied fairly speedily. Terracotta was also extremely versatile: it could be used to imitate almost any kind of stone or could be applied in what were obviously thin sheets to express the presence of the steel frame underneath.

From a distance the terracotta on the Railway Exchange does look like a thin skin stretched taut across the bones of the building, but at close range the low relief gives it the look of finely carved marble. The building also gives evidence of how architects of the day became masters in combining terracotta with traditional materials. Instead of using terracotta for the entire building, for example, which would have been the easiest and least expensive solution, the architects apparently felt that the low relief of the terracotta was not sufficiently robust, so they created a base of gray granite block in which a series of classical convex and concave moldings step back at each side of the upper portion to meet the slightly recessed portions of the terracotta covering the structural pier above. The granite, with its compacted forms, provides a sturdier, more durable base at eye level and allows the viewer almost to feel how the loads are carried to the ground.

A similarly fine adjustment occurs at the juncture of the terracotta wall and the window (fig. 3). A functional necessity in keeping the joint watertight, the narrow band of bronze that joins the bronze window frames to the terracotta wall is composed of a set of moldings that echoes those on the granite base and culminates in a three-quarter molding at the juncture of the planes where the wall and window reveal meet. This entire band is incised with a leaf pattern that spirals around it. Beneath the band on the lower edge of the window, the Greek key pattern appears again in bronze in a band separating the window from the black marble panel under it.

A single arched opening on Michigan Avenue signals the entrance. On each side of the door the reveals are decorated in "grotesque" figures, that is, playful forms recalling the painted decorations visible on Roman ruins or grottos. Highly sensuous, with an ample admixture of robust female anatomy, these pieces give the otherwise massive building an unexpectedly light touch at eye level. They are, in turn, flanked by wide banks of moldings that create a rich frame for the door (fig. 4). It is unlikely that many passers-by have stopped to look carefully at these moldings or bronze leaf patterns, or at the way the marble of the base is fitted to the terracotta above, but these small details give the building a richness of surface and liveliness. They are also what make this building such a good neighbor. The straightforward simplicity of the overall conception, along with the elaboration of its parts in the finest materials, corresponds perfectly to the City Beautiful ideal in which massive buildings of simple form fill up their sites with dignity and with an infinite variety in the details.

The impulse of the City Beautiful led to the creation of some of Chicago's most impressive buildings such as the Peoples Gas Building just up the street (122 S. Michigan Avenue, D. H. Burnham and Co., 1910-11), a structure that is practically a sister to the Railway Exchange, although it uses pink granite instead of terracotta for the body of the building; the stately Northern Trust Bank (northwest corner of LaSalle and Monroe streets, Frost and Granger, 1905); the blockbuster Chicago City Hall and Cook County Courthouse (LaSalle Street between Randolph and Washington streets, Holabird and Roche, 1911); and others. The climax of this development was undoubtedly the great 208 S. LaSalle Street (now Continental National Bank), designed by D. H. Burnham and Co., finished in 1914, and certainly one of the grandest buildings ever erected in Chicago.

Although the major flowering of City Beautiful ideas started to wane after World War I, some of the most impressive monuments of this movement were erected in the postwar era, especially in places where a monumental treatment was called for. One of the most splendid examples of the City Beautiful to be found anywhere is the Michigan Avenue Bridge and its flanking staircases, esplanades, and pylons with their allegorical sculpture and fine Roman lettering (figs. 5, 6).

Figs. 5, 6
Edward H. Bennett with Thomas G. Pihlfeldt and Hugh E. Young, engineers, Michigan Avenue Bridge, 1912-20, and detail of one pylon.

Figs. 7, 8
Graham, Anderson, Probst and White, Wrigley Building, 410 N. Michigan Avenue, 1919-21 (north addition 1924), and detail of exterior rusticated stonework.

The Romantic City

By the time of the completion of the Wrigley Building in 1921, another impulse had entered the world of commercial architecture in Chicago. This change was probably caused in part by a feeling that, while a few buildings like the Peoples Gas were beneficial, a whole city of them would be monotonous. One means of avoiding the blockiness of turn-of-the-century office buildings was to exploit those provisions of the building laws that permitted uninhabited towers and other features above the applicable height limits. These legal allowances permitted churches to erect steeples and factories to have their exhaust stacks and water towers, but the provisions for dormers, domes, and parapet walls signaled an intention to encourage architectural variety and the development of a less utilitarian city. These provisions were exploited only timidly on most Chicago buildings because purely ornamental features could not be justified economically, but in the Wrigley, which was a kind of monument to the man who founded the company, they provided the chance for dramatic expression.

At the Wrigley Building, the desire for something new and different coincided with an extremely dramatic site at the end of the long axial vista up Michigan Avenue. Clearly, the Wrigley Company and other American businesses were becoming increasingly aware of consumer advertising and the publicity value of their own buildings. The Wrigley Building and a cluster of neighboring structures at the Michigan Avenue Bridge all experimented with new ornamental treatments and signaled a new wave of the romantic picturesque in the years right after World War I.

The southern and more dramatic portion of the Wrigley Building (fig. 7), constructed to designs by Graham, Anderson, Probst and White, starts out at the bottom in a fashion similar to the buildings of the first decade of the twentieth century. The first two floors, still under the level of the Michigan Avenue upper deck, are of limestone laid up in the most sober way (fig. 8). The face of each block is lightly scored with parallel lines on the face and bordered by a smooth, rounded margin. The joint on each block is recessed to allow a deep channel between the courses. This technique, known as rustication, gives the wall the appearance of a greater weightiness. At the top of the stone base, and at about the height of a full-grown man along the Michigan Avenue upper deck, the stone yields to glazed white terracotta. Although the relief is higher than at the Railway Exchange and the ornament on the spandrel panels is more exuberant, the central section of the building is surprisingly sober and still adheres closely to the model of the City Beautiful.

It is only at the top that something very different happens. At the first of the upper cornices, the primary piers step outward, creating for the top of the wall a more three-dimensional effect. Each secondary pier, the member that divides the windows between each set of structural piers, on the other hand, rises unexpectedly into the figure of a great eagle with wings outstretched that seems to have been caught and pinned on to the underside of the cornice as it was soaring up the masonry cliff. Following this line of flight upward, the viewer's eye passes another cornice with an intricate floral frieze, before reaching an even more elaborate street wall cornice with its blind arcades, friezes, and heavy parapet, surmounted by a series of urnlike finials punctuating the skyline. These finials are of two types: one, a relatively simple assemblage of classical moldings at the top of the secondary piers; the other, the set above the primary piers, a riot of moldings, high-relief leaf patterns, brackets, and other devices, all conspiring to give it the appearance of some kind of demented funeral pyre.

But one has still not reached the top of the building. Above the street wall cornice rises a slender tower, set back toward the middle of the building mass. Here all remaining reserve is abandoned: the eye passes a square section containing several more floors of windows, then a great, four-sided clock, then another cornice with balusters serving as a transition to what looks like an open loggia surmounted by yet another cornice, surmounted in turn by a circular temple held up on slender columns supporting a final piece of terracotta related in form to the urns below but even less classifiable.

The model for this incredible, ornamental tour de force was the Giralda Tower at Seville, a Moorish monument rebuilt in the sixteenth century with early Renaissance detail. Amazingly, for a commercial building in Chicago, much of the Wrigley tower was not even usable, since it rose above the permissible height of habitable sections of the building. It was strictly there for image and for ornamental effect, and effect it certainly had. With its glazed white terracotta graduated in hue from grayish or creamy colored at the base to pure white at the very pinnacle, it gave the impression of glowing from within, an effect that was heightened by night floodlighting. Generation after generation of visitors, driving north up Michigan Avenue for the first time, have been amazed to come across this fairy castle dedicated to chewing gum.

The romantic, exotic quality of the Wrigley Building was never quite equaled elsewhere in the city, but for a few years a number of exuberant fantasies on the theme of a tower on a base were put up, especially in the immediate vicinity. The most remarkable of these were the Chicago Tribune Tower (435 N. Michigan Avenue, Howells and Hood, 1922-25), with its flying buttresses modeled after those of the Butter Tower at Rouen Cathedral; the London Guarantee Building (360 N. Michigan Avenue, Alfred S. Alschuler, 1923) with its circular temple; the improbably narrow Mather Tower (75 E. Wacker Drive, Herbert Riddle, 1925); and the Jeweler's Building (35 E. Wacker Drive, Giaver and Dinkelberg with Thielbar and Fugard, 1926) with its extravagant display of cream-colored terracotta, its great central dome, and corner candle-snuffer turrets.

The Jazz Age City

If Michigan Avenue is the place to see Burnham's City Beautiful, and the juncture of Michigan Avenue Bridge over the Chicago River the locus of post-World War I romantic architecture, then LaSalle Street is the place to go to see the ideas that guided architects in the last, tumultuous years of the 1920s building boom. LaSalle Street provides the clearest example in Chicago of the effect of the new zoning laws that swept the country after 1916. These laws preserved the street height feature of earlier ordinances, but in large cities like Chicago and New York, they often allowed buildings in the densest business areas to reach higher if they stepped back from the street according to various complex formulas designed to minimize the

Fig. 9
Holabird and Root, Chicago Board of Trade Building, 141 W. Jackson Street, 1929-30.

blockage of light and air to the street below. As architects and builders experimented with the laws, they realized that by paring away all of the projecting cornices and applied ornament, not only could they get the most rentable space for the client's dollar, but they could also create structures that were impressive enough with their dramatic mountainous massing to need little ornament.

Almost without exception, the great office buildings of the late 1920s hug the street line, rising sheer to the limit permitted by the law. Above this, they step back, creating a telescoping effect and the high, narrow V-shape of the street canyon. Impressive as this would be in itself, on LaSalle Street the channeling of this canyon toward the Board of Trade creates another of Chicago's most spectacular vistas (fig. 9). Even

Fig. 10

Detail of the entrance to the Chicago Board of Trade Building.

from the north edge of the Loop, something of the internal ordering of the Board of Trade (141 W. Jackson Street, Holabird and Root, 1929-30) can be read. The huge trading floor is signaled by its great north-facing four-story-high windows. Above the base, the regular rows of windows in the set-back slabs signal the office floors. At the pinnacle, the sculpture of Ceres, goddess of grain and of the harvest, clearly proclaims the function of the building.

Although ornament has been strictly subordinated to the massing, it is by no means absent. Approaching the entranceway, the visitor sees polished pink granite walls incised in low relief. At the entranceways the granite wall is beveled inward toward the door in a series of steps, each bounded by a gleaming strip of stainless steel (fig. 10). These strips

are streamlined versions of the brass pieces that surround the windows of the Railway Exchange Building, but, while harkening back to the classically detailed buildings of Burnham's era, they appear here like machine parts, as sleek as any automobiles of the day. The jagged flaring profile also announces in miniature the shape of the building above with its multiple set-backs. Above the door a kind of abstracted keystone is created in steel, but in place of a classical lintel a rippling sheet of translucent glass — apparently meant to be backlit at night — was placed behind a series of zigzag metal bars forming an abstract but vaguely anthropomorphic pattern. All of this merely hints at the glowing richness just inside, where marble, glass, and metal cascade along the sides of the tall, narrow, central hallway leading to the elevators.

Above the ten-story base a great clock flanked by relief sculptures eases the transition to the next stage in which the central section recedes in a deep well in order to give light and air to the offices. At the twenty-third floor the building reaches the street wall height limit. Although by the end of the 1920s the use of a cornice had fallen out of fashion, its place is taken here by a rich band of carved stone ornament that continues the lines of the street cornices of surrounding structures. From here the tower leaps upward, stepping back at the very top in five or six small steps to terminate in a tile-covered pyramidal roof and the statue of Ceres, by Chicago sculptor John Storrs, presiding at the pinnacle of the city.

In the few years before the deepening of the Great Depression put an end to all major new building in the city center, developers and architects put up sleek towers in a frenzy of building activity, among them, the old Chicago Daily News

(now Riverside Plaza, 400 W. Madison Street, Holabird and Root, 1929), the Civic Opera Building (20 N. Wacker Drive, Graham, Anderson, Probst and White, 1929), 1 N. LaSalle Street (Vitzhum and Burns, 1930), and the Palmolive Building (later Playboy Building, 919 N. Michigan Avenue, Holabird and Root, 1928-29). Perhaps the single most expressive interior was the magnificent atrium of the Michigan Square Building at 540 N. Michigan Avenue (Holabird and Root, 1929-31). With its change in level, sweeping staircases, central sculpture by the Swedish sculptor Carl Milles and glass panels by Edgar Miller (see cat. nos. 32, 33), the Michigan Court interior fulfilled the age old dream of the *Gesamtkunstwerk*, the total work of art incorporating architecture and the other arts in an indissoluble whole.

The furthest extension of the logic of subordinating detail to mass came with the completion of the Field Building (fig. 11; now LaSalle National Bank Building; Graham, Anderson, Probst and White, 1934). Here the decorative aspects of the Board of Trade have been pared away still further to create the most stripped down and undecorated of all the buildings of the era. On the Field Building the surfaces are even flatter and the relief lower than at the Board of Trade. At street level the building is faced with a jet-black granite polished to mirror smoothness (fig. 12). Into this stone are cut letters spelling out the name of the building and the date, but in a relief so shallow that only the rough texture of the background makes them legible. Flanking the high central portal are twin flagpole standards of nickel-plated steel . The cord used to raise and lower the flag hanging across these raking profiles and sharp edges gives these forms a sleek, nautical image.

Fig. 11
Graham, Anderson, Probst and White, Field Building (now the LaSalle National Bank Building), 135 S. LaSalle Street, 1930-34.

Fig. 12
Perspective study of the entrance to the Field Building, drawn by Henry Harringer; charcoal and pencil on tracing paper, 41 x 32.5 cm. Gift of Olaf Harringer, 1982.

End of an Era

At first glance it is surprising how close the finely honed, machinelike facade of the Field Building comes to the polished metal panels of the Inland Steel Building (30 W. Monroe Street, Skidmore, Owings and Merrill, 1957), one of most elegantly detailed of the post-World War II structures (fig. 13). How similar is its use of sleek materials and precise joints; at the same time, however, what a gap separates them. It is hard to imagine the Art Institute acquiring a fragment from the Inland Steel Building, since the very idea of most postwar buildings was to create a seamless whole. At Inland Steel a variety of materials is used but, as is the case in most postwar buildings, these materials are juxtaposed in a very direct manner, usually with a shadow joint between so that each material maintains its integrity. In fact, with its absolutely straight and undeviating lines and cantilevers, the building seems to defy rather than celebrate the forces of gravity. How different from the buildings of the prewar period in which part is juxtaposed to part with an infinite succession of transitions between them, each demonstrating how the loads are channeled to the ground. Likewise, the postwar city with its discrete blocks each set on its own platform, often with plazas and set-backs, is completely different from the logic of the prewar city with its ideal of the street wall defined by shared cornice lines and tightly knit ranks of masonry piers defining endless vistas of regularly spaced windows.

The Art Institute's fragments are clearly relics of another era, one that in some ways seems as remote as that of Renaissance Florence or Louis XIV's Paris. There have been many recent attempts to resume the use of rich materials and ornamental patterns and to recover the exacting craftsmanship needed for their handling. In some cases these efforts have been successful. What is still missing, however, is the consensus among architects and clients that allowed the pieces to participate in a unified vision of what the city might look like. These fragments from an earlier age may offer some suggestive lessons.

Fig. 13
Skidmore, Owings and Merrill, Inland Steel Building, 30 W. Monroe Street, 1957, detail of entrance.

D. H. Burnham and Company

Following the death of John Well-born Root in 1891, Daniel Burnham continued the highly successful Burnham and Root firm (see entry) under the name of D. H. Burnham and Company. Burnham's immediate concern was the planning and construction of the 1893 World's Columbian Exposition. One of the most influential fairs of the nineteenth century, the Columbian Exposition was held on Chicago's South Side in Jackson Park. For the fair, which celebrated the 400th anniversary of Columbus's arrival in the New World, Burnham and a team of architects, including Richard Morris Hunt, George B. Post, McKim, Mead and White, and Charles B. Atwood, created an impressive array of glimmering white classical buildings that surrounded a large, central lagoon, called the Court of Honor. Many

people, and most notably architect Louis Sullivan, felt that Burnham's Beaux-Arts style buildings ignored the considerable efforts of nineteenth-century architects to develop an architecture unique to America. For this reason they felt that the fair set back the cause of American architecture. Despite such criticism, the impact of the fair was tremendous both on Chicago architecture, which for the next twenty years was dominated by a variety of revival styles, and on city planning, in which Burnham became involved, using the planning principles he had learned as Director of Construction and Planning for the fair. He subsequently drew up master plans for the cities of Washington, D.C. (1902), Cleveland (1903), San Francisco (1905), and Manila and Baguio (1905) in the Philippines.

In 1909 Burnham and his assistant Edward H. Bennett published a plan for the city of Chicago that changed the city dramatically in the next twenty years, long after Burnham's death in 1912. Features of the

plan included the development of the Chicago lakefront and Lake Shore Drive for public, rather than industrial, use; the construction of Grant Park and Buckingham Fountain; and the construction of the Michigan Avenue Bridge and the subsequent transformation of North Michigan Avenue from a residential street to the city's premiere commercial boulevard. Burnham's Chicago Plan also called for the creation of tree-lined boulevards to link the city's outlying parks, and for the development of a consolidated railroad center in the West Loop, where Northwestern and Union stations are currently located. Realization of many other aspects of the Burnham Plan were curtailed by the escalating costs of large-scale public works, particularly in the face of the Great Depression.

In addition to Burnham's urban-planning activities, his firm also continued as one of the city's most prolific architectural offices, designing such buildings as the Reliance (1890; enlarged 1895), the Fisher (1895-96), the Railway Exchange (1903-04), and the Marshall Field store (1892-1914), which were design prototypes that he would use in the Flatiron Building (1901-03) in New York, in Wanamaker's Department Store (1909) in Philadelphia, in Self-ridge's Department Store (1906) in London, and in numerous other major cities. Between 1891 and 1896, Burnham's firm grew to be one of the largest in the United States, and as a result of Burnham's careful structuring of his office, the firm became the organizational prototype for today's large corporate architectural offices. Given Burnham's great success both nationally and internationally, some critics of the day dubbed him "the architect of capitalists."

The Fisher Building (fig. 1), one of D. H. Burnham's early premiere buildings, was constructed to accommodate the growing printing industry and commercial trade of the city, which was steadily moving southward as that end of downtown became a railroad terminus with the construction of the Dearborn, Grand Central, and LaSalle Street stations in the 1890s. The Fisher is thought to have been designed by Charles B. Atwood, who joined Burnham's firm as chief designer in April 1891 after Root's death. The eighteen-story building, engineered by Edward C. Shankland, was of skeletal construction, in contrast to the masonry load-bearing construction of Burnham and Root's Monadnock Block diagonally across the street. Like the Reliance Building, which Atwood also designed for Burnham, the Fisher has a high proportion of

window area and makes extensive use of glazed terracotta. The result, as described in the May 1896 issue of *Inland Architect*, was "a building without walls." The Fisher Building is ornamented inside and out with fish and aquatic details, visual puns on the name of the original owner, Lucius G. Fisher. Among the Art Institute's holdings are a portion of an elevator enclosure grille (cat. no. 22) and a doorknob and escutcheon plate (cat. no. 23). The elevator grille, from the upper portion of the elevator doors, features a pair of fish with intertwining tails that originally encircled a floor indicator. A band of open Gothic tracery and trefoils along the bottom of the grille tie this interior cast-iron ornament to its exterior terracotta counterparts. Both elevator grille and doorknob feature a dolphin or fish motif, variations of which appear on the light fixtures and on the neo-Gothic terracotta ornament of the building's facade. Despite its highly creative ornamentation, it is still the high

Cat. no. 24

D. H. Burnham and Co., Blocks featuring a repeated meander pattern from the Railway Exchange Building (now the Santa Fe Building), 224 S. Michigan Avenue, 1903-04 (restored 1983); white glazed terracotta, 27 x 69 x 13.5 cm. Gift of the Santa Fe Southern Pacific Corporation, 1984.805b.

Cat. no. 25

D. H. Burnham and Co., Block featuring a foliate design from the Railway Exchange Building; white glazed terracotta, 43.5 x 45 x 10.5 cm. Gift of the Santa Fe Southern Pacific Corporation, 1984.805a.

D. H. Burnham and Company

Fig. 2
D. H. Burnham and Co.,
Conway Building
(now the Chicago Title
and Trust Building),
111 W. Washington
Street, 1912-14
(remodeled 1983-84).

Cat. no. 26
D. H. Burnham and Co.,
Block featuring a
meander pattern
from the lobby of the
Conway Building; white
glazed terracotta,
17 x 30.5 x 7 cm.
Gift of Jack Train
Associates and Pepper
Construction, 1983.906.

Cat. no. 27
D. H. Burnham and Co.,
Block featuring a
fleur-de-lis pattern
from the lobby of the
Conway Building;
white glazed terracotta,
20 x 87.5 x 7.5 cm.
Gift of Jack Train
Associates and Pepper
Construction, 1983.907.

level of technical proficiency for which the building is noteworthy. An addition to the Fisher was designed by another Burnham protégé, Peter J. Weber (see entry, p. 160), and added in 1907.

As the impact of the 1893 fair was felt far beyond the fairgrounds itself, Burnham was determined to rid the city of the sooty black buildings that ringed the Loop, and to replace them with elegant white structures that would instill a new sense of civility in the city. The seventeen-story Railway Exchange (see Bruegmann, fig. 2) was one of Burnham's early efforts in this direction. It was sheathed, both inside and out, with white terracotta, featuring classical meander patterns (cat. no. 24) and lively sprays of foliage and acanthus leaves (cat. no. 25). For a while Burnham maintained offices on the top floor of the Railway Exchange, where he and Bennett worked on the 1909 *Plan of Chicago*.

The Conway Building (fig. 2), built for the estate of Marshall Field, was similar in plan and details (cat. nos. 26, 27) to the Railway Exchange, and like it, was designed with offices surrounding a central atrium core, a feature that was first perfected in Burnham and Root's Rookery. The Conway was one of the last buildings to come from Burnham's office before his death on June 1, 1912. In fact, the building was completed in 1914 by his successor firm, Graham, Burnham and Company. Although the atrium has been restored in the Railway Exchange, the atrium of the Conway was filled in to accommodate office space for the Chicago Title and Trust Company in 1947. Fragments from both buildings became available when the buildings were renovated in the early 1980s as a result of the 1981 Tax Act, which offered tax incentives for the renovation and restoration of historically significant buildings.

In the years following Burnham's death, his firm split into two successor firms. Graham, Burnham and

Company was headed by Burnham's second-in-command, Ernest R. Graham. Other architects who went with Graham were Peirce Anderson, Edward Probst, and Howard J. White, all of whom eventually combined efforts to form their own firm, Graham, Anderson, Probst and White (see entry, p. 114) and produced such Chicago landmarks as the Wrigley Building (1919-21, 1924) and the Merchandise Mart (1930). The second splinter firm, which carried on the name of D. H. Burnham and Company for a short time, was established by Burnham's two sons, Daniel, Jr., and Hubert. Eventually they renamed their firm the Burnham Brothers and produced such notable buildings as the Carbon and Carbide Building (1929; 230 N. Michigan Avenue).

A native Chicagoan, Alfred S. Alschuler (1876-1940), attended Armour Institute of Technology and The School of The Art Institute of Chicago. From 1900 to 1905 he worked as a draftsman for Dankmar Adler and for Samuel Atwater Treat. In 1907, at the age of thirty-one, Alschuler established his own firm, which at the start specialized in residential architecture; the firm designed a number of houses in Chicago's Hyde Park area. But Alschuler was soon to become known for his commercial office buildings and industrial lofts, buildings like the Rogers and Hall Building (1911, 1914); the Westminster (1912; now demolished), the first business block Alschuler designed in the Loop; the Thompson Commissary (1912); and the Cunard Building (1915), which was demolished to make way for Daley Plaza.

Among Alschuler's industrial buildings was the Thompson Commissary, built for restauranteur John R. Thompson. Thompson had begun his innovative chain of cafeterias in the 1890s, and by the end of the First World War, his was the largest chain of restaurants in the U.S. with more than 100 establishments in 43 cities. Thompson attributed his success to attention in two areas: innovations and standardization, both in the daily menus and in the appearance of his restaurants, all of which featured interiors covered in glossy white ceramic tile.

As the Thompson Commissary exemplifies, Alschuler's industrial buildings were never purely utilitarian. Instead, he tailored his designs to suit the function of a building and, often, the importance of the building in the larger scheme of Chicago architecture. As a result, buildings such as the Rogers and Hall loft were designed as simple masses without elaborate ornament. On the other hand, the Thompson

Building, which housed offices, a kitchen, testing laboratories, a laundry, storage, and a huge bakery, was sheathed in white terracotta on the exterior and in the interior to announce the importance of this corporate headquarters, and to symbolize the cleanliness of its kitchens. This use of architectural imagery preceded similar applications by fast food chains such as White Tower and White Castle. Alschuler's white terracotta was also a reaction against the dark, undistinguished brick industrial buildings that then surrounded much of the Loop. His elegant building contributed to Burnham's vision of Chicago as a refined city that could rival the finest cities of the Old World. A polychromed terracotta block from a frieze in the lobby of the Thompson Commissary (cat. no. 28) depicts ears of corn and other types of grain; the image underscores the building's role in food preparation. This fragment, now in the Art Institute's collection, was removed when the Commissary was renovated into an

office building in 1982.

Alschuler is best known for his design of the London Guarantee Building (1922-23; now the Stone Container Building), one of the four major skyscrapers at the Michigan Avenue and Wacker Drive gateway leading from the Loop to North Michigan Avenue. The classical London Guarantee Building prominently features a concave main facade and an elaborate cupola on top, the latter a variation on a Greco-Roman lantern. The success of the building was immediate; with the two other buildings constructed at that junction — the Wrigley Building (1919-21, 1924) and the Chicago Tribune Tower (1922-25) — it presented a new cosmopolitan image for the city. Afterward, Alschuler's career flourished, as he received commissions for numerous other highrises, including the Mercantile Exchange (1927) at 110 N. Franklin Street, and buildings at 180 N. Michigan Avenue (1926-28) and 1209 N. Astor Street (1926).

Cat. no. 28
Alfred S. Alschuler,
Portion of a decorative
frieze from the lobby
of the Thompson
Commissary,
350 N. Clark Street,
1912 (renovated 1982);
glazed terracotta,
46 x 57 x 10.3 cm.
Gift of Lonn Frye and
Jon Construction
Company, 1982.1634.

Newhouse and Bernham

Until its demolition in 1984, McVickers Theater was the oldest theater in Chicago and the third oldest in the nation. In its early years, the theater starred such luminaries as John Wilkes Booth, Sarah Bernhardt, and John Barrymore. Later it housed the nation's first musical comedy, along with vaudeville, grand opera, stage shows, and Chicago's first motion picture. The original brick theater, built in 1857, was designed by Wheelock and Thomas for James McVicker, a prominent Chicago actor. The architecture of the theater, located on the same site at 25 W. Madison Street for 127 years, has changed several times. As architectural historian Robert Twombly has described in his monograph on Louis Sullivan, the McVickers Theater has had an "exceptionally tortured history" due to repeated fires and remodelings. For example, the

1871 Great Fire destroyed the building only five days after the completion of its first remodeling, valued at $90,000. It was rebuilt the following year and again in the early 1880s. Apparently dissatisfied with the result, the owner hired Adler and Sullivan to make further modifications between 1883 and 1885. Adler and Sullivan's renovation was highly regarded. One critic wrote, "In magnificent decoration, and in elegance of appearance and beauty of finish in all its details, it is the model theatre of our times, typical of the position, prestige, progress and promise of the city it represents." In August 1890 the theater was again destroyed by fire. Adler and Sullivan designed a replacement that stood until 1922, when Newhouse and Bernham were commissioned to gut and modernize the theater.

For the 1922 renovation Chicago architect Henry L. Newhouse enlisted the assistance of New York theater designer Thomas White Lamb (1871-1942). Lamb attained

national prominence for his design of large modern theaters, including Madison Square Garden, the Hippodrome, and the Strand, all in New York. Newhouse, who had studied at MIT, was the architect of numerous Chicago-area houses and apartment buildings, among them the Patio Apartments and the Normand Court Apartment Building, both built prior to 1906. After 1910 his work included the Cooper-Carlton Hotel, now the Del Prado in Hyde Park. Newhouse's 1922 remodeling was designed in association with Felix M. Bernham, who shared his office and had worked collaboratively with him since 1913.

Every trace of Adler and Sullivan's work was demolished in the Newhouse and Bernham renovation, which kept only the building's side and back walls. Their renovation gave the McVickers Theater an entirely new interior, geared toward motion pictures, and a new facade of huge Ionic columns topped by a pediment. The pediment was adorned with shell-shaped acroteria with acanthus leaves (cat. no. 29). The lower floors featured glass-fronted shops flanking the entrances. By modeling this building after a classical Greek temple, the architects reflected the considerable influence of the classicism of the 1893 World's Columbian Exposition. Removed in 1984 when the building was demolished, the acroteria were donated by National Wrecking Company at the request of the Art Institute.

The Triangle Restaurant on West
Madison Street was one of a chain of
restaurants established by Dario L.
Toffenetti in the 1920s. The chain
received its name from the first of
Toffenetti's restaurants, which was ·
located at the triangle created by the
intersection of Broadway, Sheridan
Road, and Montrose Avenue. The
restaurant on West Madison Street
was the only one to feature an elaborate Art Deco facade, which had
been applied to an existing three-
story loft building of the 1870s. The
ornament on the facade consisted of
overlapping chevrons, fan shapes,
stylized sunbursts, and flowers. At
the roofline a central design featured the letter "T" to signify the
name of the chain. The Triangle
Restaurant (fig. 3) was demolished in
the winter of 1986-87 to make way
for a highrise office building.

   The Art Institute's collection
includes a white, green, and yellow
chevron and sunburst block from the
roofline and a block of inverted fan
shapes that was located between the
second- and third-floor windows
(cat. nos. 30, 31). This type of elaborate, multicolored ornament was
typical of Art Deco buildings
in New York and Miami, but was
not generally characteristic of
Chicago buildings.

   It is believed that the building's
impressive terracotta facade was produced by the Northwestern Terra
Cotta Company of Chicago. The
quality of design, modeling, and
glaze colors points to Northwestern,
which was one of the premiere sup-
pliers of high-quality Art Deco terracotta. The company employed a
number of French-born terracotta
modelers who had worked on the
1925 Exposition International des
Arts Decoratifs in Paris. The modelers were brought to Chicago by
Northwestern to produce similar
Art Deco designs for American
buildings.

. . . .

Fig. 3 (cat. nos. 30, 31)
**Joseph G. Ludgin,
Blocks featuring
chevron and sunburst
shapes from the roofline
and blocks featuring
inverted fan shapes
from a spandrel between
the second- and third-
floor windows of the
Triangle Restaurant,
169-71 W. Madison
Street, 1929
(demolished 1986-87);
white, green, and yellow
glazed terracotta,
dimensions unavailable.
Gift of Miglin-Beitler
Developments,
1987.49.1-17.**

Holabird and Root

In the late 1920s the firm of Holabird and Root, the successors to the famous Chicago School firm of Holabird and Roche, was a major force in the development of modernism in the United States. Their renowned setback skyscrapers—333 N. Michigan Avenue (1927-28), the Palmolive Building (1928-29), and the Board of Trade (1929-30)—are the product of liberalized zoning laws in 1923 and the firm's attempt to develop a vocabulary of form appropriate for the new American skyscraper, which soared to unprecedented heights of thirty-five and forty-five stories. Although Holabird and Root's buildings have characteristics typical of Chicago skyscrapers of the 1920s—limestone towers with sheer setbacks and the skillful incorporation of simplified, stylized ornament with few historical references—they still retain the symmetry and logical floor plans of earlier Beaux-Arts buildings.

After the death of its last surviving founding partner Martin Roche in 1927, two designers in the Holabird and Roche office—John A. Holabird (son of the firm's other founder, William Holabird) and John Root, Jr. (son of the renowned Chicago School architect John Wellborn Root)—formed the firm of Holabird and Root. Both Holabird and Root had studied architecture at the Ecole des Beaux-Arts in Paris. In the late 1920s the firm surpassed their chief competitors, Graham, Anderson, Probst and White (see entry), to become the architectural design leaders in Chicago. The Architectural League of New York awarded the firm of Holabird and Root with a Gold Medal for "the great distinction and high architectural quality which they achieved in the solution of the American office building." Their work, from the founding of the firm until the end of the Second World War, reveals a remarkably unified design vision. Historian Robert Irving has written that "the decade of the '30s saw the

dissemination into architecture of artistic concepts proclaimed by painters in the years before World War I, and championed the antihistorical, the 'machined' and the modern." These concepts are reflected stylistically in buildings like 333 N. Michigan and the Chicago Motor Club. As with other architectural firms practicing during the Depression, the number of commissions received by Holabird and Root declined as the economy worsened. Nonetheless, they were key planners in the Century of Progress Exposition held on Chicago's lakefront in 1933 and 1934. The firm designed the streamlined Chrysler Motors Exhibition Building for the fair, taking advantage of the effects of artificial light to delineate the building at night.

One of Holabird and Root's most beloved works in Chicago was the Michigan Square Building (1929-31; now demolished) at 540 N. Michigan Avenue. This eight-story structure was part of the large-scale development of North Michigan Avenue following the opening of the Michigan Avenue Bridge in 1920. In the design of the Michigan Square Building, Holabird and Root were influenced by the 1925 Exposition International des Arts Decoratifs in Paris, from which the term "Art Deco" came, and by ocean-liner designs of the late 1920s which influenced many building designs.

The focus of the building was a central semicircular rotunda called Diana Court (fig. 4), designed by architect Helmuth Bartsch. The building's upper six stories contained offices, while the lower two floors around the rotunda housed sixty-two upscale shops, including design and furniture shops that were the first to offer modern chrome-and-glass furniture to Chicagoans. In the center of Diana Court was a large fountain depicting Diana, goddess of the hunt, by the eminent Swedish sculptor Carl Milles. The clerestory level featured a series of etched glass panels of Diana designed by Edgar Miller (see entry, p. 117), set high into the curved wall of the rotunda and illuminated from behind. The Diana Court panels in the Art Institute's collection (cat. nos. 32, 33) depict Diana with a bow and a quiver of arrows, and with a stag and a pair of falcons; both images are symbols of the hunt. The Art Institute's holdings also include a nickel-silver directory frame from the building and two elaborate cylindrical chandeliers, which present on a smaller scale the streamlined modernism of the building's overall design.

Diana Court was the last grand space constructed on North Michigan Avenue between the onset of the Depression and 1976, when Water Tower Place was built. Chicagoans mourned the loss of Diana Court when it was demolished in 1973 to make way for the present Marriott Hotel. The demolition of Diana Court, along with the recent demolition of nearby buildings at 900 and 920 N. Michigan Avenue (see entry on Jarvis Hunt, p. 116), demonstrates that as real estate values continue to escalate, five- to ten-story buildings of the 1920s and 1930s give way to multiuse megastructures such as the John Hancock Tower, One Magnificent Mile, and the new 900 N. Michigan Avenue.

Cat. nos. 32, 33
Edgar Miller for Holabird and Root, Glass panels depicting the goddess Diana, with bow and arrows and with stag and falcons, from the clerestory of Diana Court, Michigan Square Building; fabricated by Alfred Muenzenthaler; sandblasted and acid-etched glass, 180.5 x 100.4 cm. Gift of Fred A. Goldberg and Harvey A. Goldberg, 1973.346-47.

Graham, Anderson, Probst and White

. . . .

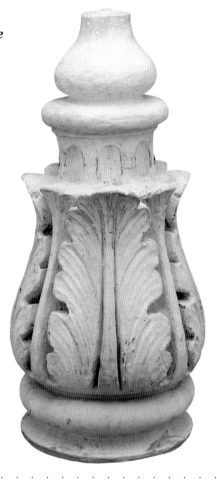

Chicago's two leading architectural firms in the 1920s and early 1930s were Holabird and Root (see entry) and Graham, Anderson, Probst and White. Both firms, conservative in nature and drawn to big corporate clients, were descendants of large and powerful nineteenth-century architectural firms — Holabird and Roche, and D. H. Burnham and Company, respectively. Following Burnham's death in 1912, the firm that bore his name was reorganized into Graham, Burnham and Company. In 1917 the firm branched into two: one headed by Burnham's two sons, Daniel, Jr., and Hubert, and the other led by Ernest R. Graham (1866-1936). Graham had joined Burnham in 1894, and he advanced to second-in-command, controlling the firm's business affairs. Many of Graham's partners in the splinter firm also had long-standing careers in the D. H. Burnham and Company office. Peirce Anderson (1870-1924) joined Burnham in 1900 and was the

chief of design during some of the firm's most prosperous years, from 1912 to 1919. Edward Probst (1870-1942) joined Burnham in 1893, and in 1908 he was charged with supervising the working drawings of buildings. Howard Judson White (1870-1936) came to the parent firm in 1898 as a draftsman, and in 1905 he became Graham's assistant, assigning contracts and supervising construction.

The success of Graham, Anderson, Probst and White was due in large part to the unique blend of talents that the partners possessed. Their eclecticism enabled them to design a great variety of buildings, including public structures, such as the U.S. Post Office (1911-14) and the Columbus Memorial (1912) in Washington; office buildings, like the Equitable Building (1914) in New York and the Strauss Building (1924) in Chicago; railway stations, such as Union Station (1924) in Chicago and Pennsylvania Station (1932) in Philadelphia; and museums, such as the Field Museum of Natural History

(1911-19) and the John G. Shedd Aquarium (1930), both in Chicago.

The firm's most renowned building is, undoubtedly, the Wrigley Building (1919-21, 1924) in Chicago. The Wrigley Building (fig. 5), the glimmering white symbol of the Wrigley chewing gum company, houses the firm's corporate offices. It was constructed on one of the city's most prominent sites, at the northwest corner of Michigan Avenue and the Chicago River. Designed by a newcomer to the firm, Charles G. Beersman (1888-1946), the structure was the first of four buildings that were constructed at that juncture following the completion of the Michigan Avenue Bridge in 1920. As such, it was a key element in the realization of Burnham's 1909 *Plan of Chicago*. The design of the Wrigley, with its central clocktower and skybound lantern, was based on the Moorish and Renaissance Giralda Tower in Seville. But its steel-frame construction and white terracotta sheathing also reflect the tripartite Chicago skyscrapers of the 1890s, and in particular, D. H. Burnham and Company's Reliance Building (1890; enlarged 1895). Floodlights illuminate the building at night and the effect on Chicago's night skyline is dramatic. The roofline of the building is punctuated by decorative finials ranging in size from thirty inches to ten feet in height. In 1984, the weather-worn terracotta finials were removed and replaced by exact fiberglass duplicates. The Art Institute has two such finials, one original (cat. no. 34) and one replacement. These finials, a composite of acanthus leaves and fluted shafts, are among the smaller ones on the building. One of the best-loved buildings in Chicago, the Wrigley stands today as a fitting architectural symbol of the civic and corporate pride of the 1920s.

At a time when Lora Marx (born 1900) was receiving recognition as a sculptor (she won an award in the Art Institute's 1936 exhibition of American painting and sculpture), her husband, the architect Samuel Marx, was redecorating the Tavern Club. His new decor continued the original Art Deco motif of designers Winold Reiss of New York and John Hopkins of Holabird and Root. The Tavern Club has been a tenant of the 333 N. Michigan Avenue building (1927-28) since its opening, occupying the 25th and 26th floors as well as the adjoining roof terraces. The building's sleek, towering shape was greatly influenced by Eliel Saarinen's second-place entry to the international Chicago Tribune competition, held in Chicago in 1922.

The two painted plaster heads by Lora Marx in the Art Institute's collection (cat. nos. 35, 36) were appropriate additions to this architecturally important interior. Both the club's original Art Deco design and Marx's alterations to it in the late 1930s were a dramatic break from the look of traditional men's clubs, which, as David Lowe has observed in *Chicago Interiors*, were "noted mainly for leather and dark wood paneling." Some of the qualities of Art Deco can be seen reflected in the flattened planes and stylized simplicity of Lora Marx's two sculptures. It is believed that these busts were removed from the club during a subsequent renovation in the 1950s.

Cat. nos. 35, 36
Lora Marx, Male and female busts designed for the Tavern Club, 333 N. Michigan Avenue, c. 1936; painted plaster, 38 x 20.3 x 20.3 cm. Gift of the Tavern Club, 1986.878-79.

Jarvis Hunt

When the economic depression that followed the First World War lifted in the 1920s, Chicago experienced a boom in apartment-house construction. The boom was at its height in 1926 when Jarvis Hunt (1859-1941) designed one of his last buildings, at 900 N. Michigan Avenue. This nine-story, brick-and-stone apartment cooperative reflected a new trend in apartment buildings, as it combined luxurious residential space with ground-floor commercial shops. Vaguely classical in style, the building was also suitably scaled to the character of the street and to other nearby buildings. It contained apartments and duplexes arranged around a secluded, landscaped court that opened to the south. Originally, the building was designed to support an additional twelve stories and a tower, but these were never constructed because the building was never a financial success, even though it was owned by a corporation of thirty-six prominent Chicago businessmen, all of whom resided in the building. Resident shareholders included the corporation's president, Cyrus McCormick, Jr., as well as Charles K. Knickerbocker, Robert B. Upham, and Jarvis Hunt himself.

The luxury cooperative apartment building was located in Streeterville, an exclusive highrise residential area that developed north of the commercial area around the Wrigley and Tribune buildings. The exclusivity of the area in the 1920s is ironic given its origins. Captain George Wellington Streeter, a gambler and gunrunner, ran his schooner aground on a sandbar just east of the mansions and townhouses on Michigan Avenue in 1886. He settled there and subsequently filled in the lakefront with rubble and trash, a practice that gave birth to the foundations of a shanty town. Captain Streeter was evicted in 1918, in preparation for the development of a landfill that was slated to become East Lake Shore Drive and North Michigan Avenue. The area still bears his name.

The apartments in 900 N. Michigan Avenue were spacious, and many had unique handcrafted and imported architectural features. The fragments in the Art Institute's collection (see fig. 6), including a Romanesque style column (cat. no. 37), a Renaissance style mantel, and a stair railing with an abstract floral motif, reflect the eclectic character of this building. The fragments represent the interest in reviving historical styles, a trend prevalent in the 1920s in both residential and commercial design. The fragments became available when the building was demolished in 1984, falling victim to the "highest and best use" philosophy that has resulted in the demolition of many buildings on North Michigan Avenue to make way for taller and larger structures.

Jarvis Hunt, a nephew of New York architect Richard Morris Hunt, was born in Weathersfield, Vermont. He attended Harvard University and studied architecture at MIT. Hunt came to Chicago in 1893 to supervise construction of the Vermont State Building at the World's Columbian Exposition. He remained to form his own firm, Jarvis Hunt Associates, and he practiced in Chicago for nearly thirty-five years. Some of Hunt's most significant work in Chicago includes the Saddle and Cycle Club (1898), the American Trust and Savings Bank (1906), the Kelley, Maus and Company Warehouse (1914), the Boulevard Building (1914), and 30 N. Michigan Avenue (1914), the site of his offices, as well as the Chicago Tribune Plant (1920) and the Lake Shore Athletic Club (1924). He also designed the original thirty-nine buildings of the Great Lakes Naval Training Center in Great Lakes, Illinois (1906-11).

Edgar Miller (born 1899) was active
in Chicago in almost all areas of
artistic endeavor, particularly those
related to architecture, from the
1920s to the 1960s. Miller came to
Chicago from Idaho in 1917 to study
at The School of The Art Institute of
Chicago. After a short stay at the Art
Institute, he worked as an apprentice
for four years in the studio of Chicago artist-craftsman Alfonso Iannelli (see entry, pp. 162-63). Through
these experiences, Miller became
skilled in a variety of media, primarily sculpture, stained glass, mural
painting, and graphic arts. He regularly exhibited at the Art Institute,
including the Exhibition of Modern
Decorative Arts of 1925 and
the Chicago Architectural League
Exhibition of 1928. In the 1925
exhibition, Miller won the prestigious Logan Prize for his stained-glass
window depicting birds (cat. no. 38;
pl. 11); the work was purchased at
that time by the Art Institute. The
window, which displays sophisticated
design and construction techniques,
features thick pieces of transparent,
colored, and hand-painted glass.
Its antiqued surface and thick lead
cames are reminiscent of folk art and
medieval stained glass. Miller usually
incorporated figures such as birds
and animals into his work because he
felt that figurative art was more
meaningful to the viewer than
abstract art.

In 1927 Miller joined efforts with
portrait painter Sol Kogan to renovate two groups of studio residences
for artists. Known as the Kogan-
Miller Studios, the buildings were
located at 155 Carl Street and 1734
N. Wells Street in Chicago. The renovation of these buildings prompted

the development of an artistic
community in the area known as Old
Town. Local artists were recruited to
live and work in the complexes, and
some were allowed to contribute art
in lieu of rent. Miller furnished all of
the interior designs: ceramic tiles,
mosaics on the walls and sidewalks,
and stained-glass windows; all bear
his unique sense of design. The studios combine aspects of Prairie
School architecture with Art Deco
and southwestern Indian motifs.

Miller was frequently commissioned by Chicago architects Howard
Van Doren Shaw, Thomas Tallmadge, Andrew Rebori, and Earl
Reed to design stained glass, sculpture, murals, mosaics, and other
decorative features for their residential and commercial buildings. In
1929, for example, Holabird and
Root asked Miller to design a series
of etched-glass windows depicting
aspects of the goddess Diana for the
Michigan Square Building (see cat.
nos. 32, 33). He was later commissioned to paint murals for the 1933
Century of Progress Exposition. The

attention these murals attracted
increased the number of architectural commissions he received. His
sculpture for the Technological
Center of Northwestern University,
for the North Dakota State Capitol—
both by Holabird and Root—and for
the lobby of Perkins and Will's U. S.
Gypsum Building in Chicago, as well
as the stained-glass windows for
Holabird and Root's Palmolive
Building and for Barry Byrne's
Christ the King Church in Tulsa,
Oklahoma, all rank among his most
renowned commissions.

Miller practiced in the Chicago
area until the 1960s when he retired
first to Florida, and later to California. Since that time, there has been a
resurgence of interest in Miller and
his work. He returned to Chicago
in the 1980s and has resumed reno-
vating and completing details in
the Old Town apartments that he
began in 1927.

Cat. no. 38
Edgar Miller,
Window with bird
design, c. 1925;
blue, red, yellow,
and orange stained
and painted glass,
69.2 x 20.3 cm.
Mr. and Mrs. Frank G.
Logan Fund, 1925.45.

Louis H. Sullivan's Search for an American Style

. . . .

by Lauren S. Weingarden
Florida State University

*I*n addition to his extremely successful architectural practice, Louis H. Sullivan was also a prolific essayist. In his 1896 essay "The Tall Office Building Artistically Considered," Sullivan presented a fully developed theory of design that he applied to the problem of the skyscraper.[1] In both his built work and his essays, he used a nineteenth-century rationalist discourse as a point of departure for his own efforts to create a new American style, what he elsewhere called "the true, the Poetic Architecture."[2] An examination of Sullivan's essay "The Tall Office Building" and the influences upon it will reveal that the design of the now-demolished Schiller Building (1891-92) in Chicago, one of Sullivan's first mature skyscraper schemes, is directly related to the theoretical tenets he presented in his treatise on the new building type.

It is generally assumed that Sullivan, like his Chicago School colleagues, adapted nineteenth-century rationalist theories from Eugène Emmanuel Viollet-le-Duc, the French theorist whose *Discourses on Architecture* (1863, 1872) Sullivan owned.[3] What has been largely neglected is that Sullivan, unlike his colleagues, combined Viollet-le-Duc's rationalist discourse with Ralph Waldo Emerson's transcendentalist theories of organic expression.[4] Sullivan followed Emerson's model in the essay "The Poet" of transforming the real into the ideal. Clearly, Sullivan wrote "The Tall Office Building" to explain his own achievement in artistically refining the skyscraper. While his accomplishments had won Sullivan contemporary critical acclaim, he also used this essay to mitigate the "pessimism" of the structural and practical conditions that gave rise to the skyscraper. Consequently, "The Tall Office Building" is more a philosophical analogy than a formula for designing a tall building. By using Sullivan's analogy as a lens through which to view the Schiller Building, one can begin to see the exterior composition as a visual metaphor for organic expression. Likewise, the interior structural system and spatial layout of the building can act as a visual synonym for his rationalist design solutions.

Viollet-le-Duc was the preeminent theorist of rationalism in the late nineteenth century. His widespread prestige in both Europe and the United States was primarily due to the anti-academic position he assumed.[5] Instead of accepting only classicist standards of truth and beauty, he studied styles from all periods to discover timeless principles of design that were logically conceived and free of historical influence.

Progressive architects viewed Viollet-le-Duc's treatise as a refutation of and an alternative to revival-style copyism. To restore truth and originality to architecture, Viollet-le-Duc formulated a self-generating, teleological design process:

The generating idea once found, the secondary ideas fall into their proper order and present themselves when they are wanted . . . The conditions of stability and the methods of construction indicate to [the architect] the eternal appearance. . . . This shell indicates the parts which should be enriched and those which should be eliminated. This is how the architect designs.[6]

Sullivan paraphrased passages from Viollet-le-Duc's treatise in the first part of "The Tall Office Building." At first glance, these references seem to suggest that from him Sullivan derived a rational process of design and a corresponding means of representation. Sullivan followed Viollet-le-Duc's method of deductive reasoning and adhered to his quest for new forms of expression to comply with the new technological conditions. Sullivan began his essay with a statement concerning the immediate socio-economic causes of the new building type. He initiated the first phase of Viollet-le-Duc's rationalist design process when he posed "the tall office building . . . as a problem to be solved — a vital problem, pressing for a true solution." Sullivan then turned to the more specific practical, technological, and material forces that shaped the new form:

The invention and perfection of the high-speed elevators make vertical travel, that was once tedious and painful, now easy and comfortable; development of steel manufacture has shown the way to safe, rigid, economical constructions rising to a great height; continued growth of population in the great cities, consequent congestion of centers and rise in value of ground, stimulate an increase in number of stories; these successfully piled one upon another, react on ground [i.e., property] values—and so on.[7]

Proceeding to the second stage of Viollet-le-Duc's design process, Sullivan moved from conceptualizing the general problem to articulating his logical solutions. As might be expected, he offered a rationalist analysis of his own skyscraper style beginning with the exigencies of the plan and following with the tectonic and spatial results in the superstructure. According to this scheme, Sullivan first treated the basement as a hidden container for the central electrical, plumbing, heating, and ventilating equipment. He rendered the next two groups, comprised of the ground- and second-story banking and retailing facilities, with large, open layouts enhanced by widely spaced structural piers and by broad glass-plate windows for direct, natural light. Regarding the uniformly treated office cells of the fourth group, Sullivan bluntly stated that these cells "look all alike, because they are all alike."

When Sullivan described the solution for the fifth and sixth elements of the skyscraper—the attic story and the main entrance—he responded to the last, artistic phase of Viollet-le-Duc's design process; that is, he clarified primary masses and their functions, and subordinated the parts to the whole. Sullivan especially drew attention to the attic story where "the circulatory system [emanating from the machinery con-

tained in the basement level] completes itself and makes its grand turn, ascending and descending." He also identified the surface treatment of the attic as an artistic feature since, unlike either the office cells or main floors, "the spacings and [window] openings in the attic are of no importance whatsoever." Finally, by contrasting the broad expanse of the attic wall with the strong horizontal projection of the cornice, Sullivan stated "the fact—namely, that the series of office tiers has come definitely to an end."[8]

Up to this point in the design process, Sullivan repeated the logical sequence of Viollet-le-Duc's methods so as to meet the latter's standards for a completed work of art: "Art in architecture...consists in the distinction of form and the most truthful expression of requirements.... Any form whose *raison d'être* cannot be explained, cannot be beautiful, and in architecture, every form that is not suggested by the structure must therefore be cast aside."[9] In following this edict, Sullivan attained what Viollet-le-Duc defined as "style," an artistic attribute that the French writer also observed analogously in nature. Sullivan would have concurred with Viollet-le-Duc's notion that art in architecture is tantamount to style in nature.[10] They shared a common nineteenth-century goal to renew stylistic origins in nature, origins determined by philosophical inquiry. But whereas Viollet-le-Duc, following earlier French rationalist philosophers, viewed nature as an analogue of the human mind and sought to discern the laws of nature through the faculty of human logic, Sullivan regarded this logical view of nature as "almost exclusively intellectual" and "static."[11] Likewise, he considered the end-product of a logical

Fig. 1
Adler and Sullivan, Schiller Building (later the Garrick Theater), 64 W. Randolph Street, 1891-92 (demolished 1961).

Fig. 2
Adler and Sullivan,
Perspective rendering
of the Schiller Building;
from Architectural
Record 1 (January-
March 1892), p. 227.

design process simply a mechanical solution to practical demands. He reviewed the skyscrapers designed by his Chicago School colleagues as examples of the logical design process, and he endorsed their "straightforward naturalness" as opposed to those who layered each story with varied historical motifs. Nonetheless, he felt that while mastering the elementary stages of logical design, "thus far the results are only partial and tentative at best."

In the course of translating this new building type into an American art form, Sullivan replaced Viollet-le-Duc's rationalist strategy with an organic design process. Initially, he simply rephrased Viollet-le-Duc's rationalist idiom. But he also transferred architectural problems from the abstract order of logic into the dynamic flux of nature. Sullivan claimed that Viollet-le-Duc and, by extension, the Chicago School architects, made superficial analogies between architecture and nature, and that they based these analogies on surface resemblances. According to Sullivan, they did not interact with the forces of nature during the creative process of art. Thus, the problem that Sullivan set for himself was boldly stated:

How shall we impart to this sterile pile, this crude, harsh, brutal agglomeration, this stark, staring exclamation of eternal strife, the graciousness of those higher forms of sensibility and culture that rest on the lower and fiercer passions? How shall we proclaim from the dizzy height of this strange, weird, modern housetop the peaceful evangel of sentiment, of beauty, the cult of a higher life?[12]

Here he overtly diverged from Viollet-le-Duc's precepts. But by asking how to transform "crude" reactions to "brute" needs into "eloquent" expressions of "higher" aspirations, he responded to Emerson's philosophical inquiries of the natural origins of a new American art form.

In the last part of "The Tall Office Building," Sullivan suspended his rationalist responses to recount how the artistic solution to the tall office building issued from "the region of calm, philosophic observation," where the artist-architect can "seek a comprehensive, a final solution: let the problem indeed dissolve."[13] Most important, it was from this philosophical perspective—from an interior view of nature's processes rather than an external view of its forms—that he first stated in his credo:

It is the pervading law of all things organic, and inorganic, of all things physical and metaphysical, of all things human and all things superhuman, of all true manifestations of the head, of the heart, of the soul, that the life is recognizable in its expression, that form ever follows function. This is the law.[14]

In order to reclaim this credo as a natural law, Sullivan reviewed the concept of nature's self-generating life cycle as a form-giving and transformational process.

For Sullivan, "form follows function" engendered a critical standard as well as a principle of design. He accused revival-style copyists of causing the death of architecture by severing the life of a building from its material expression. This accusation echoed Viollet-le-Duc's criticism of modern French architecture. Sullivan also implied that the Chicago School rationalists postponed stylistic renewal because, like revivalist designers, they "merely [spoke] a foreign language with a noticeable

American accent." He wanted to realign American architecture with indigenous, rather than European, artistic origins.

We can now see why Sullivan turned to Emerson's transcendentalist program for a new American mode of artistic expression. He could not find in Viollet-le-Duc's system an organic language of architecture to connote what he considered primordial American conditions. Therefore, in the second and third parts of "The Tall Office Building," Sullivan made verbal references to Emerson's essay "The Poet" to explain how a true artist-architect responds to such indigenous conditions.

In "The Poet" Emerson argued that the poet sanctifies the nation's material gains with spiritual growth in nature.[15] Emerson identified the poet's acts of naming and saying with the double capacity of the genius for interpreting and recreating a universal, symbolic language of nature.[16] Emerson assigned to the poet the roles of "initiator...a beholder of ideas, and an utterer of the necessary and causal." Sullivan adapted just such a combination of symbol-reading and symbol-making to reshape the elements of architecture into a symbolic language of expression.[17] He also borrowed Emerson's strategy for penetrating surface-depth relationships. Emerson described the poet's creative process as a dynamic psychological interaction with nature, in which the poet's thoughts,

actions, and words become contiguous with "divine energy" or the "Divine Mind."[18] Emerson observed that the poet

stands one step nearer to things, and sees the flowing or metamorphosis; perceives that thought that is multiform; that within the form of every creature is a force impelling it to ascend to a higher form; and following with his eyes the life, uses the forms which express that life, and so his speech flows with the flowing of nature.[19]

Emerson subsequently explained that metaphor functions for and represents the transformational processes of metamorphosis. Analogously, the metaphoric process and the resulting poetic form show that "nature has a higher end in the production of individuals...namely, *ascension*, or the passage of the soul into higher forms."[20] For Emerson, and for Sullivan, the poet's transformational acts issue from and parallel metamorphosis.

Emerson's exegesis regarding the poet's mode of representing metamorphosis suggests that Sullivan intended "form follows function" to be synonymous with metamorphosis.[21] Likewise, in "The Tall Office Building," Sullivan indicated how he enacted the poet's revelatory function as a namer or sayer by redeeming the skyscraper as a God-given species; the true architect "must realize at once and with the grasp of inspiration that the problem of the tall office building is one of the most stupendous, one of the most magnificent opportunities that the Lord of Nature in His beneficence has ever offered to the proud spirit of man." Having sanctified the skyscraper as a new organic form, Sullivan proceeded to transform the tall office building into a symbol of metamor-

phosis. To this end, he devised metaphoric functions for both its inherent verticality and its applied ornament.

Sullivan reformulated the vertical proportions of the skyscraper as a response to Emerson's precept that the poet use organic forms to depict the "ascension...of the soul." Sullivan claimed that the chief characteristic of the tall office building was its loftiness. Thus, he asserted that the skyscraper "must be tall, every inch of it tall.... It must be every inch a proud and soaring thing, rising in sheer exultation that from bottom to top it is a unit without a single dissenting line."[22]

The Schiller Building amply illustrates how Sullivan used the skyscraper to embody Emerson's philosophical concerns.[23] In this building, Sullivan refined two formal features to make ascension the essence of his design. First, he made a central tower the dominant motif of the main street elevation. Second, he attenuated the proportions of the tower, and the piers by which it is defined, in relation to the building as a whole. In the first case, the seventeen-story tower seems to pierce boldly through the cornice of the lower nine-story rectangular block (fig. 2). Its continuous upward motion is further accentuated by the contrast of flat planar elevations against the convex oriel windows of the lower block. Additional vertical emphasis is gained from a street-level view. From here the tower obscures the actual I-shaped massing of the building that extends through the rear of the narrow lot. The I-shape, in turn, obscures the multifunctional nature of the interior,

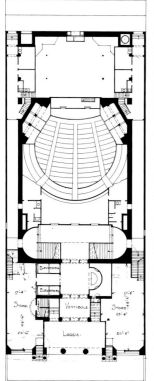

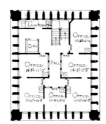

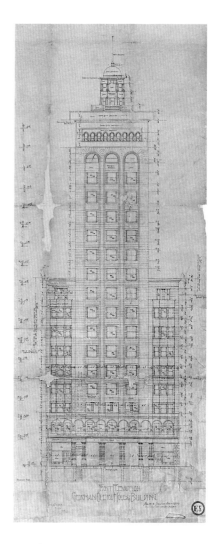

comprising a ground-floor theater, rooms for the German Club, and business offices (figs. 3-5). The immediate image of the Schiller Building as a single tower, however, depends upon Sullivan's much more subtle manipulation of detail, proportions, and of the composition of masses within the tower scheme.

Here, as in his other skyscraper buildings, Sullivan exaggerated the height of the office block by raising it from the horizontal dimensions of a two-story base. For the main elevation of the Schiller Building (fig. 6), Sullivan defined the ground story with two massive square piers that enclose staircases and, together with the side wall piers, frame two glazed storefronts and a central loggia entrance. On the second story, the narrower structural piers recede behind an ornamented balcony arcade. But on the third story, where the tower begins its unbroken ascent, and continuing to the sixteenth story, structural realism gives way to organic lyricism. Indeed, it is in the tower that the circuitous path of metamorphosis unfolds.

For the tower shaft Sullivan redefined the underlying support-and-span grid construction with slender uprights enframed by wide corner piers. In so doing, he suppressed not only the reality of the structural system but also the building's physical mass. That is, he made the frontal plane of each pier appear thinnest in relation to the three receding parallel planes, the last of which becomes flush with the background plane of the horizontal spandrels. This sequence of planar recessions continues unbroken as the piers gracefully wrap around half-circle arches.[24] Repeating this pattern on the other two sides, Sullivan thus

transformed the rigid geometry of steel-cage construction to reproduce "the silent flow of life." Viewing the tower from this aspect, "the circulatory system [which] completes itself and makes its grand turn, ascending and descending" resists a mechanistic identity to become a metaphor for the organic life cycle.[25]

Figs. 3-5
Adler and Sullivan, Plans of the first, thirteenth, and seventeenth floors of the Schiller Building, ink on linen. Gifts of Mr. LaVergne Becker, 1982.1593, 1605, 1607.

Fig. 6
Adler and Sullivan, Elevation of the Schiller Building (originally to be known as the German Opera House Building); hectograph print, 100 x 40.5. Gift of Balaban and Katz, 1962.

In creating the illusion of upward motion, Sullivan directed the viewer's gaze to the arcaded attic story (fig. 7), where he gave an even more sonorous voice to "the silent flow of life." The two ranges of relief spandrels, placed at the beginning and end of the piers' vertical ascent, quicken the eye's movement over the blank spandrel surfaces, focusing attention on the lacelike relief that envelopes the attic arcade and the boldly projecting cornice. Whether ornament is rendered as realistic plant imagery (as on the spandrels) or as abstract geometric patterns (as on the cornice and surrounding arcade), its overall distribution provides a scintillating surface effect that reduces the appearance of weight and mass.[26] This effect is particularly evident in the relation between the cornice and the tower shaft; here the cornice appears to hover above the tower, and as a result, it provides an ethereal horizontal terminus to the slender upright forms.

The combination of geometric abstraction and organic ornament shows how Sullivan transformed tectonic into metaphoric representation throughout the building. The cornices and attic stories of the subordinate theater/office blocks, the colonnettes and jambs of the tower windows, and the twenty-six-foot belvedere, are also adorned with interlacing curvilinear forms occasionally integrated with leaf motifs (figs. 8, 9). In each case, the play of light and shadow on relief surfaces dissolves flat planes and animates inert masses. With these means, Sullivan fully demonstrated that as a poet-architect he used "not words but building materials as a medium of

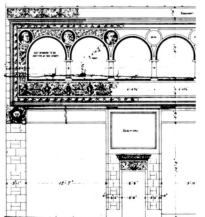

Fig. 7
Detail of the upper floors of the Schiller Building, showing cornice, cupola, and arcaded attic story.

Fig. 8
Detail of the exterior of the Schiller Building, taken at the time of its demolition in 1961.

Fig. 9
Adler and Sullivan, Detail of revised terracotta diagram; blueprint, December 24, 1891. Gift of Balaban and Katz and Gordon C. Orr, 1962.

Fig. 10
Detail of the exterior of the Schiller Building, taken at the time of its demolition in 1961.

with the transcendentalist poet's acts of reconciliation. In attempting the act of reconciliation, Sullivan further signified his adherence to Emerson's prospects for an indigenous art form and his divergence from Viollet-le-Duc's precepts for a nineteenth-century rationalist style. For Emerson, the poet as "Language-maker" not only names and speaks with word-symbols but retrieves lost poetic origins of words.[28] Emerson denounced "the dislocation and detachment" of words from their natural meanings, and he claimed that the poet is a "genius who repairs the decay of all things" and restores the beauty and symbolic unity of the world; he "reattaches things [and words] to nature and to the whole."[29]

Sullivan invoked such passages from Emerson's text in the conclusion to "The Tall Office Building." In doing so he prophesied that when the true architect reveals "the beauty, the exquisite spontaneity, with which life seeks and takes on its forms in an accord perfectly responsive to its needs," then "it may be proclaimed that we are on the high-road to a natural and satisfying art, an architecture that will soon become a fine art, in the true, the best sense of the word."[30] These Emersonian references suggest that Sullivan's skyscrapers should be read as poetic acts, for the skyscraper depicts the ways in which Sullivan reconnected a mechanistic, rationalist law with its natural origins. Moreover, the skyscraper made it possible for him to reconcile material needs and practical solutions with organic meaning and spiritual causes. Writing in 1896, Sullivan surveyed his actual achievements in light of his metaphysical insights. Still at the peak of his career, he was justifiably confident that he had transformed brute reality into artistic ideality and thereby had initiated a new American style.

expression."[27] As we have seen, steel-frame construction encased in brick and terracotta (see fig. 10) became his materials for depicting the fluid reciprocity between physical and spiritual facts. Thus in the Schiller Building, as in his other skyscraper designs, the fusion of structural forms and evanescent surface textures resonates with the poet's "speech which flows with the flowing of nature."

This metaphoric reading of the Schiller Building provides a basis for explaining how Sullivan's search for a new American style was consonant

1. *Lippincott's Magazine* 57 (March 1896), pp. 403-09; *Inland Architect and News Record* 27 (May 1896), pp. 453-58; reprinted in *Kindergarten Chats (1918) and Other Writings*, ed. Isabella Athey (New York. 1947), pp. 202-13; and more recently, in *Louis Sullivan: The Public Papers*, ed. Robert Twombly (Chicago, 1988), pp. 103-13. Hereinafter, "The Tall Office Building" and other essays by Sullivan will be cited from Athey's *Kindergarten Chats* anthology.

2. Sullivan, "Emotional Architecture as Compared with Intellectual: A Study in Objective and Subjective," a paper presented to the annual meeting of the American Institute of Architects, October 1894; *Inland Architect and News Record* 24 (Nov. 1894), pp. 32-34; *Kindergarten Chats* (note 1), p. 200. For a historical survey of rationalist and functionalist theories, see Edward Robert de Zurko, *Origins of Functionalist Theory* (New York, 1957).

3. Sullivan owned Benjamin Bucknall's two-volume English translation of Viollet-le-Duc's *Discourses on Architecture* (Boston, 1889; rpt. New York, 1959); see *Auction Catalogue of the Household Effects, Library, . . . of Louis H. Sullivan, November 29, 1909* (Chicago, 1909), a pamphlet in the Ryerson and Burnham Libraries of The Art Institute of Chicago. On Sullivan and Viollet-le-Duc, see Fiske Kimball, *American Architecture* (Indianapolis, 1928), p. 150; Carl W. Condit, *The Chicago School of Architecture: A History of Commercial and Public Building in the Chicago Area, 1875-1925* (Chicago, 1964), pp. 9, 36; Hugh Morrison, *Louis Sullivan: Prophet of Modern Architecture* (New York, 1935), pp. 265-68.

4. For discussions of Sullivan's transcendentalist philosophy, see Narciso G. Menocal, *Architecture as Nature: The Transcendentalist Idea of Louis Sullivan* (Madison, 1981); Sherman Paul, *Louis Sullivan: An Architect in American Thought* (Englewood Cliffs, N. J., 1962); and Lauren S. Weingarden, "Louis H. Sullivan and the Metaphysics of Architecture (1885-1901): Sources and Correspondences with Symbolist Art Theories" (Ph.D. diss., University of Chicago, 1981).

5. For a discussion of Viollet-le-Duc's anti-academic attitudes, see Richard Chafee, "The Teaching of Architecture at the Ecole des Beaux-Arts," in *The Architecture of the Ecole des Beaux-Arts*, ed. Arthur Drexler (New York, and Cambridge, Mass., 1977), pp. 99-104. On Viollet-le-Duc's codifications of rationalist theories, see John Summerson, "Viollet-le-Duc and the Rational Point of View," in *Heavenly Mansions and Other Essays on Architecture* (New York, 1966); Kenneth Frampton, *Modern Architecture: A Critical History* (1980; rev. ed., New York, 1985), pp. 12-41, 64-73.

6. Viollet-le-Duc, *Discourses* (note 3), p. 190.

7. Sullivan, "The Tall Office Building" (note 1), p. 202.

8. Ibid., pp. 203, 205.

9. Viollet-le-Duc, *Discourses* (note 3), pp. 303-04.

10. See, for example, Sullivan's "Style," a paper read at the Chicago Architectural Sketch Club, April 9, 1888; published in *Inland Architect and Building News* 11 (May 1888), pp. 59-60.

11. Sullivan, "Emotional Architecture as Compared with Intellectual" (note 2), p. 200.

12. Sullivan, "The Tall Office Building" (note 1), p. 202.

13. Ibid., p. 206.

14. Ibid., p. 208.

15. Quotations from Emerson's "The Poet" (*Essays; Second Series* [1844]) will be cited from *Essays and Lectures*, ed. Joel Porte (New York, 1983). Unless otherwise indicated, all citations of Emerson's writings will be from this edition.

16. Emerson, "The Poet" (note 15), p. 454; see the references to nature as a "picture language," comprised of "signs" and "symbols" of the "Divine Mind" or "Spirit," pp. 452-54, 456.

17. Prior to naming the principle "form follows function," Sullivan matched objects in nature with their "natural" names, functions, and forms; see Sullivan, "The Tall Office Building" (note 1), p. 207.

18. Emerson, "The Poet" (note 15), p. 450.

19. Ibid., p. 456.

20. Ibid., p. 458.

21. Sullivan further developed the metamorphic/metaphoric connotations of "form follows function" for two chapters entitled "Function and Form" in his *Kindergarten Chats* (note 1), pp. 42-48.

22. Sullivan, "The Tall Office Building" (note 1), p. 206.

23. For a detailed account of the Schiller Building's history and design, see Paul Sprague, "Adler and Sullivan's Schiller Building," *The Prairie School Review* 2 (Second Quarter 1965), pp. 5-20. Sprague attributes the overall distribution of ornament on the exterior elevations to Sullivan, but he attributes the "unimaginative" intersecting circle motifs and other flat geometric configurations to Frank Lloyd Wright, Sullivan's chief draftsman at the time of the Schiller Building project. The only motif on the exterior that Sprague assigns to Sullivan is the lower frieze on the second-floor balcony. Nonetheless, he attributes the whole interior of the theater to Sullivan. See also two contemporaneous descriptions of the Schiller: Barr Ferree, "Architecture," *Engineering Magazine* 4 (Nov. 1892), pp. 297-302; and "Letter from Chicago," *American Architect and Building News* 39 (Feb. 1893), p. 72.

24. This appearance of reduced physical mass can also be read as an expression of non-load-bearing walls made possible by steel-cage construction.

25. Sullivan also attributed symbolic functions to the pier and lintel as the primary forms with which to represent the life cycle; see his chapters on "The Elements of Architecture" in *Kindergarten Chats* (note 1), pp. 120-25. Here and in the seventeenth-story loggia of the Schiller, artistic license outweighs rhetorical stricture. Even though in "The Tall Office Building" Sullivan identified the "grand turn" with mechanical systems housed in the attic story, the tall arcade of the Schiller is a metaphor independent of any such schemes. Likewise, the expanse of ornament in the attic story does not denote a change in interior spatial function.

26. Sullivan explained the poetic function of his ornament in "Ornament in Architecture" (1892; see *Kindergarten Chats* [note 1], pp. 187-90) and the symbolic values of the objective-geometric and subjective-organic motifs of his ornament in *A System of Architectural Ornament According with a Philosophy of Man's Powers* (New York, 1924).

27. Sullivan, *Kindergarten Chats* (note 1), p. 140.

28. Emerson, "The Poet" (note 15), p. 456.

29. Ibid., pp. 455, 457.

30. Sullivan, "The Tall Office Building" (note 1), pp. 208, 213.

. . . .

It has long been acknowledged that Dankmar Adler (1844-1900) and Louis H. Sullivan (1856-1924) altered the course of American architecture through the engineering and design innovations that they made in commercial architecture in late-nineteenth-century Chicago. Together and alone, these two architects distinguished themselves in the fields of engineering theory and practice, and of architectural theory and what might be called the philosophy of architecture, as well as in their designs for residences, theaters, hotels, warehouses, and most importantly, the tall office building or "skyscraper."

In the late nineteenth century, many American architects across the nation responded to the challenge to develop a unique style of architecture that would express the values of a democratic republic that had just celebrated the centennial of its formation. But in their search for an American style, many simply borrowed from earlier styles and produced eclectic variations that are today identified as High Victorian Gothic, Queen Anne, and Colonial Revival.

Unlike his contemporaries, however, Louis Sullivan's vision of American architecture was largely independent of historical precedent. His philosophy of architecture and ornament transcended the battle of styles. It was instead based on a highly individualistic interpretation of architecture that saw the perfect building as one whose physical characteristics expressed factors unique to the building, such as its site, materials, function, and structure—the whole given form in the creative mind of the individual. Although rooted in eighteenth-century thought, this theory was popularized in writings familiar to Sullivan by such nineteenth-century architects as A. W. N. Pugin, John Ruskin, and Eugène Emmanuel Viollet-le-Duc.

When applied to America's unique contribution to architecture, the skyscraper, this philosophy led Sullivan to use continuous vertical piers, such as those on the Wainwright Building in St. Louis, to express the building's height. When Sullivan applied this philosophy to the design of architectural ornament, he developed an organic style, such as on the terracotta column and frieze from the Schiller Building (cat. nos. 52, 55), which derives its forms from nature and geometry. Sullivan also sought to express a building's interior volumes on the exterior, so that they would be parts of a unified design. The arcade of two-story arches running across the facade of the Chicago Stock Exchange, for example, represented the high cubic volume in the interior of the Trading Room (see Saliga, fig. 16). It is this all-encompassing philosophy of architectural design that Sullivan summed up in his famous dictum, "form follows function."

Like many other nineteenth-century architects, Sullivan not only expressed his philosophy in buildings, in ornament, and in beautifully detailed drawings, but he also wrote extensively about architecture and his individual view of it. From 1885 to 1924, Sullivan proved himself a prolific theoretical essayist. In seminal articles such as "Ornament in Architecture" (*Engineering Magazine*, 1892) and "The Tall Office Building Artistically Considered" (*Lippincott's Magazine*, 1896), Sullivan's philosophy reached American and European audiences and had great impact on both his contemporaries and generations of architects to follow.

Although he did not write about theoretical issues, Sullivan's partner, Dankmar Adler, also published numerous articles about architecture, engineering, and professional standards in the 1880s and 1890s. His articles, published in professional periodicals such as *Engineering Magazine*, the *Economist*, and *Inland Architect*, concentrated primarily on functional concerns and detailed the engineering innovations that he developed for his building designs. For example, in a two-part article for *Engineering Magazine* (August and September 1894) titled "Theatre Building for American Cities," Adler described how the functional requirements of acoustics and vision dictated the configuration of an auditorium, such as the Schiller Theater. Adler's other influential articles include "Light in Tall Office Buildings" (*Engineering Magazine*, November 1892) and "Foundations" (*Economist*, June 27, 1891).

By the time Adler and Sullivan became associated, Adler had a well-established career and Sullivan had absorbed a wide variety of influences from his apprenticeships and his formal architectural training at the Massachusetts Institute of Technology and the Ecole des Beaux-Arts. Their work together comprised three basic time periods: 1880-83, when Sullivan worked in Adler's office; 1883-1895, when Adler and Sullivan were formal partners and produced some of their most accomplished designs; and 1895 and after, when each architect worked alone.

I. *Sullivan Working for Adler, 1880-83*

Rothschild Building

From 1880 to 1883 Louis Sullivan worked for Dankmar Adler as a draftsman and designer. During these years Adler's firm was identified as "Dankmar Adler, Architect" and "D. Adler & Co." The salesroom and manufacturing building for the clothing firm of E. Rothschild and Brothers was designed in 1880 while Sullivan was serving as one of Adler's draftsmen and designers. Sullivan's contribution was formally acknowledged in a review of the completed building published in the *Chicago Evening Journal* (July 16, 1881), which credited the unique qualities of the building to Adler and "his talented assistant Mr. Sullivan." The hand of Louis Sullivan is indelibly marked in the composition and detail of the Rothschild facade, and the fragments of iron ornament in the Art Institute's collection represent the earliest extant examples of his executed architectural ornament.

The facade of the five-story building (fig. 1) was dominated by three carved Joliet limestone piers, spanned by generous window bays composed completely of cast iron from the second floor to the full height of the facade. The use of iron opened up the facade for maximum window area, a critical consideration for the operation of the salesrooms and the delicate needlework conducted within. The facade was given a graduated verticality as the stone piers and iron infill intensified in detail with each successive story, culminating in a rich parapet frieze, of which the Art Institute's cast-iron panel (cat. no. 39) was a part. Removed during the demolition of the building in 1972, the panel is an excellent example of the grammar of Sullivan's ornament of the period.

Cat. no. 39
Louis Sullivan for Dankmar Adler, Panel from the roofline of the Max M. Rothschild Building; painted cast iron, 172 x 95 x 13 cm. Gift of the Antiquarian Society through the Mr. and Mrs. Robert Hixon Glore Fund, 1972.319.

Fig. 1
Louis Sullivan for Dankmar Adler, Max M. Rothschild Building, 210 W. Madison Street, 1880-81 (demolished 1972); view of the upper floors.

As suggested earlier, his highly original personal style owed much to the organically derived philosophies of the decorative arts of the late nineteenth century. The piece has been repainted its original pearl grey color, which was applied to all iron elements on the facade to differentiate them from the buff limestone piers. Originally, each panel had a large, three-dimensional rosette at the top of the "stem," but these were removed when the building began to deteriorate and fragments of the screwed-on cast-iron ornament started to fall off. In the original installation, the large vertical cast-iron panel was topped by a cast-iron frieze (cat. no. 40), which featured four stylized fans or plant forms.

Historian Paul Sprague, who analyzed the development of Sullivan's ornaments in *The Drawings of Louis Henry Sullivan* (Princeton, 1979), has described the ornament from this early period of his works as "sharply delineated botanical abstractions [that] consisted of fan-shaped leaves and petals, spiral leaves with scalloped edges, broad leaves resembling scallop shells, and smooth-edged leaves." Sprague also noted that during the period 1879 to 1883 Sullivan separated his ornamental motifs from one another "by avoiding interpenetrating parts and by placing each motif against a smooth ground plane." Such characteristics are evident in the panel and frieze from the Rothschild and two commissions of the same period, the Rosenfeld and Jewelers' buildings.

Rosenfeld Building

The Rosenfeld Building (1881-82), which Sullivan also probably designed for Adler, was located at Washington and Halsted streets. The building was three stories high, with a section at the corner rising to five stories. An orange-red, unglazed terracotta panel from the building (cat. no. 41) features the same kind of plantlike spirals and stylized fan shapes typical of Sullivan's work from this period. Manufactured by the Northwestern Terra Cotta Company, the piece is one of Sullivan's earliest efforts in exploring the creative possibilities of architectural terracotta, a material that he experimented with throughout his career.

Jewelers' Building

The Jewelers' Building (fig. 2), constructed on Wabash Street in 1881-82, was one of several Loop loft buildings commissioned by prominent Chicago businessman Martin Ryerson. The five-story building had store space on the ground floor, and its loft interiors were constructed of iron columns and girders sheathed in fireproofing material developed by architect P. B. Wight. A sample of the fireproofing is in the Art Institute's collection. The most distinctive feature of the Jewelers' Building is the unique arrangement of its windows which open up the facade to an unprecedented degree. The facade was principally of masonry bearing-wall construction, yet it was opened up for maximum daylight by the introduction of a central window bay of cast-iron spandrels and mullions extending from the third floor to the

top-floor lintels. In addition, the north corner of the building turned at a forty-five-degree angle to the street, thereby admitting more light into the interior.

As the ground floor of the Jewelers' was remodeled over the years, most of its distinctive ornament was stripped off. A small, surviving cast-iron piece (cat. no. 42) is an organic spiral that branches out into spikey leaves and other smaller spirals. This piece was part of the supportive iron columns of the first-floor storefront. One small section of the original ground-floor facade remains intact on the building's north alley elevation (fig. 3). A solitary remaining pier gives some indication of how the iron spiral in the Art Institute's collection would have been integrated into the larger facade design.

Cat. no. 42
Louis Sullivan for Dankmar Adler, Scroll from the exterior of the Jewelers' Building; cast iron, 22.5 x 10 x 4 cm. Gift of Richard Nickel, 1956.410.

Fig. 2
Louis Sullivan for Dankmar Adler, Jewelers' Building, 15-19 S. Wabash Avenue, 1881-82; view of the upper floors.

Fig. 3
Detail of the Jewelers' Building, showing existing exterior ornament.

Fig. 4
Adler and Sullivan, Morris Selz House, 1717 S. Michigan Avenue, 1883 (demolished 1967).

Cat. no. 43
Adler and Sullivan, Newel post from the exterior of the Morris Selz House; cast iron, 126 x 6.5 x 51 cm. Gift by exchange from Southern Illinois University at Edwardsville, 1974.81.

II. *Adler and Sullivan Partnership, May 1, 1883-June 30, 1895*

In the early years of their partnership, Adler and Sullivan received commissions for far more residences than commercial structures. Residences, such as the Selz and Lindauer houses, were the mainstay of the young practice until the construction of the Auditorium Building, which has been described by Robert Twombly in his monograph *Louis Sullivan and His Life* (New York, 1986) as a "decisive turning point," after which the number of commissions for important warehouses, factories, stores, and office buildings soared dramatically.

Morris Selz House

The Selz House (1883; fig. 4) adjoined another residence designed by Sullivan and occupied by Morris Selz's business partner, Charles H. Schwab. The Selz residence was designed in a style appropriate for the upper-middle-class status of its client and its location in the then prestigious Prairie Avenue neighborhood on Chicago's South Side, where four years later the Glessner family would engage H. H. Richardson to design a new home for them. Twombly has observed that Adler and Sullivan's "social objective in residential work was to create emblems of dignity, material well-being, and permanence befitting the accomplishments and ambitions of the upper middle class." To that end, the Selz House harmonized with its picturesque Victorian neighbors and featured bay windows, dormers, mansards, and an abundance of exotic botanic ornament that was repeated in various forms on the exterior of the house. In keeping with the design motif, an exterior cast-iron newel post from the house (cat. no. 43) featured curling tendrils and Egyptoid petal-like shapes. As Paul Sprague has noted, in 1883 Sullivan's ornament became more complex: "During this period motifs were intertwined and overlapped, integrating the ornament in both two and three dimensions. To this end, the former individuality of each motif was sacrificed. A freer, more vivacious curvilinear rhythm began to manifest itself. New motifs such as elongated buds and sinuous tendrils also appeared."

Benjamin Lindauer House

Like the Selz House, the Benjamin Lindauer House (1885) was built for a wealthy client who was part of the large and very close upper-middle-class Jewish community residing between the 1800 and 3900 blocks of South Michigan, Wabash, and Prairie avenues, and nearby streets. Dankmar Adler himself was also a member of that upper-middle-class community, and he received many of his early commissions from nearby family members and friends.

Sullivan's treatment of ornament had changed by the time he received the commission to design the Lindauer House. Instead of covering the facade in ornament as he had done on the Selz House, Sullivan relied on rusticated stone for surface or trim and on the interplay of stone with brick. He began to experiment

with what Twombly has called the "self-decorating possibilities inherent in the contrasts and textures of plain materials." A terracotta block from a band of ornament around the chimney of the house (cat. no. 44) shows the beginnings of Sullivan's mature ornamental style. The heavy, chunky forms of the Selz House newel post begin to give way to ornament with more energy, as seen in the Lindauer block's sinuous vine that connects with a spiral and a large, curving fan shape.

Cat. no. 44
Adler and Sullivan, Corner piece from a chimney stringcourse of the Benjamin Lindauer House, 3312 S. Wabash Avenue, 1885 (demolished 1959); unglazed terracotta, 25.6 x 30.6 x 28 cm. Gift by exchange from Southern Illinois University at Edwardsville, 1974.79.

131

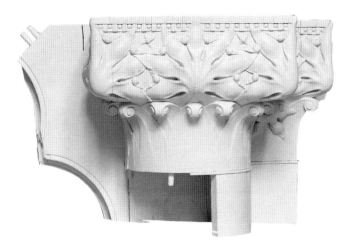

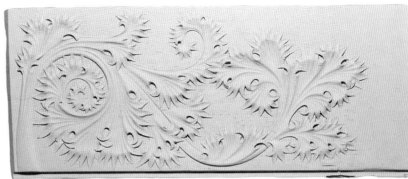

Cat. nos. 45, 46
**Adler and Sullivan,
Column capital and
portion of a frieze from
an elevator in the
Auditorium Building,
Congress Parkway
between Michigan
and Wabash avenues
1887-89;
carved oak;
capital: 50 x 30 x 24 cm;
frieze: 28 x 70 x 4.2 cm.
Gifts of Crombie Taylor,
1970.1197.1-2.**

Auditorium Building

After spending the early years of their partnership designing small commissions such as those described, Adler and Sullivan received their first big commission in 1886 from Ferdinand Peck and the Opera Festival to design the Auditorium Building. The firm was well prepared to handle the commission since, in addition to Adler's own Central Music Hall (1879), they had already designed several highly successful theaters including the Grand Opera House (1880), McVickers Theater (1883-85), and a theater in the Interstate Exposition Building (1885) that was renovated specifically to house the 1885 Chicago Opera Festival. Adler and Sullivan's Auditorium Building, a mixed-use building that combined a 400-room hotel, 136 offices, various stores, and a 4,200-seat theater, was clearly a design and engineering tour de force.

As one of the largest and most complex building projects of late-nineteenth-century Chicago, the Auditorium fully demonstrated Dankmar Adler's innovative engineering expertise. Among the myriad problems that he confronted were the design and construction of foundations that would negate any settlement between the solid masonry exterior walls of the ten-story main portion and the seventeen-story tower, and the complicated framing systems that would incorporate the building's many functions on a limited site. Adler's abilities also included a remarkable mastery of the principles of theater design, resulting in an auditorium of unsurpassed acoustics and sightlines, as well as advanced technical stage facilities and even an early form of air conditioning. The architectural solutions of the Auditorium Building were integrally worked out in collaboration with Louis Sullivan, whose own philosophically based abilities complemented those of his more pragmatic partner.

The exterior of the building, with solid granite blocks on the lower stories and a facing of Bedford limestone over brick on the upper ones, reflects the influence of H. H. Richardson's Marshall Field Wholesale Store (see p. 89). When completed, the building's office tower was the most prominent building on Chicago's skyline, and it housed an observatory and the United States Signal Service station at the top.

While the heavy forms of the exterior express the massive nature of the bearing masonry, the interiors reflect Sullivan's versatility in designing ornament in plaster, metal, wood, mosaics, and other materials. Sullivan integrated three-dimensional ornamentation with rich coloration and decorative stencils to create interplay of form, texture, light, and color. A carved

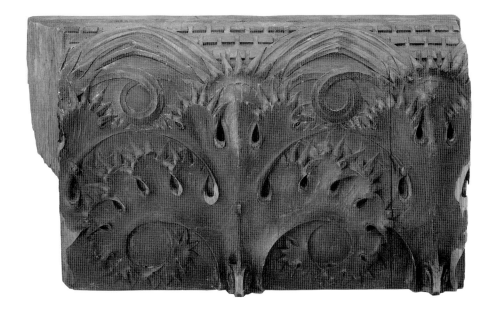

oak capital and a section of a frieze (cat. nos. 45, 46) show that by 1887 Sullivan's ornamental schemes had evolved from the stiff leaves and fan shapes of his earlier commissions to curving stems of lush, spiky leaves. Paul Sprague has described Sullivan's ornament from this period as more sophisticated and luxuriant: "Compositions [are] more relaxed and linear elements more flowing than in his ornament before 1885. Botanical motifs [are] freed from the previous restrictive schematization and [become] more natural although not entirely naturalistic." While the ornament was conceived and drawn by Sullivan, the preparation of the working drawings was left to his draftsmen, among whom was Frank Lloyd Wright, who entered the office in 1887.

Some of the Auditorium ornament, such as a carved oak capital featuring spirals of sharply pointed leaves (cat. no. 47), came to the Art Institute when the hotel bar on Congress Street was demolished to create a sidewalk arcade. Other smaller pieces have been donated as the building has deteriorated over the years. A small, gilt-plaster light setting (cat. no. 48) features four concentric swirls that converge around a central opening where a light bulb would be housed.

The Auditorium played an extremely important role in changing Chicago's image from an isolated prairie outpost to a center of culture in the United States, if not the world. Architect Thomas Tallmadge declared that "magnificence and culture shone forth unmistakably where once the world fancied it saw only mud and pig sticking." The Auditorium became the first home of the Chicago Opera Company and later, the birthplace of the Chicago Symphony Orchestra. Unfortunately, the construction of the Civic Opera House in 1929 and the onset of the Depression in the same year began a period of decline for the building.

During the 1920s and 1930s, several attempts were made to raze the building because the Auditorium Association that commissioned it charged that it was a financial failure and architecturally obsolete. What saved the building may have been the enormous cost of demolishing such a massive structure. Eventually, Roosevelt University purchased the Auditorium Building, and in 1967 the theater was reopened after a faithful restoration under the direction of Chicago architect Harry Weese. The Art Institute has a stained-glass panel from an interior skylight in the theater; the panel is on loan from the Auditorium Theater Council, the organization that oversaw the restoration of Adler and Sullivan's masterpiece.

Cat. no. 47
Adler and Sullivan, Section of the hotel bar from the Auditorium Building (bar demolished c. 1941); carved oak, 25.5 x 42.5 x 15 cm. Gift of John Randall, 1941.1259.

Cat. no. 48
Adler and Sullivan, Setting for a single light from the Auditorium Building; gilded plaster, 22.8 x 22.8 x 1 cm. Gift of Richard Nickel, 1954.1370.

Fig. 5
**Adler and Sullivan,
Wainwright Building,
709 Chestnut Street,
St. Louis, Missouri,
1890-91.**

Cat. no. 49
**Adler and Sullivan,
Doorknob and
escutcheon plate from
the Wainwright
Building;
fabricated by Yale and
Towne Lock Company;
cast iron, Bower-Barff
finish,
28.3 x 6.7 x 7 cm.
Gift of Harry J.
Scharres, 1973.738 a-b.**

Wainwright Building and
St. Nicholas Hotel

Following the success of the Auditorium Building, Adler and Sullivan
entered the most productive period
of their partnership. Among their
subsequent commissions were two in
St. Louis, the Wainwright Building
(1890-91) and the St. Nicholas Hotel
(1892-93). The ten-story Wainwright
(fig. 5), represented in the Art
Institute's collection by a doorknob
and escutcheon plate featuring the
initials and completion date of the
building (cat. no. 49), is considered
by historians to be Sullivan's first
true skyscraper. The exterior of the
building has been analogously compared to a classical column with its
base, shaft, and capital. By running
continuous vertical piers from the
second to the ninth floor, Sullivan,
for the first time, was able to suggest

the grid of the steel structure beneath the building's pressed-brick
and terracotta skin. In the late 1970s,
the Wainwright Building was renovated as a state office building as
part of a massive urban renewal
effort in downtown St. Louis.

The St. Nicholas Hotel (1892-93)
was Adler and Sullivan's last hotel
commission. The architects chose to
convey a residential feeling through
a gabled roof, prominent chimneys,
bay windows, arched openings, and
a long balcony face with terracotta
snowflake patterns (cat. no. 50).
According to historian Paul Sprague,
the hotel panels reflect another
change in Sullivan's approach to
ornament between 1892 and 1894.
Here geometric patterns have almost
entirely replaced the organic forms
that had dominated his earlier work.
Unlike the earlier ornament of the
Auditorium, where plantlike forms
were arranged on a flat background
in relief, the St. Nicholas design
had been carved into the surface of

the panel. After a fire in 1905, the
building was greatly altered and
remodeled into an office building,
known as the Victoria Building.
When it was finally demolished in
1973, fragments were distributed to
various public collections through
Southern Illinois University at
Edwardsville, which houses the Sullivan ornament collection compiled by
photographer and Sullivan historian
Richard Nickel.

Charnley House

Although the commission for the James Charnley House (1891) was one that came to the Adler and Sullivan office, it is widely believed that Frank Lloyd Wright, who was a designer in the firm at the time, was the chief designer of the house, since Sullivan routinely assigned residential designs to Wright. The two-story house is located on Astor Street, which was developing as an enclave of mansions for Chicago's wealthy, and rivaling the elegant and opulent mansions of Prairie Avenue on the South Side. The most striking feature of the house is a thirty-foot interior stairway rising in the center, with rooms arranged on either side. The exterior features a symmetrical facade of ashlar cut limestone and Roman brick with a central second-floor balcony projecting above the entrance. The Art Institute's fragments were originally part of that

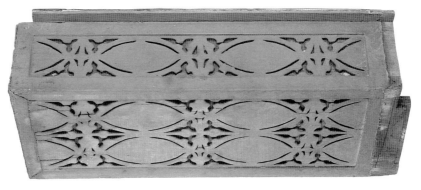

balcony—a front panel with two ellipses and a supporting bracket (cat. no. 51) with the same repeated elliptical pattern. The fragments, which are painted fret-sawn wood, are notable for their flat simplicity, a characteristic that Wright tried to incorporate throughout the house. The Art Institute's fragments were removed in 1984 when the house was being restored and these severely weather-damaged pieces were replaced by exact duplicates. In 1987-88 the house underwent another, more major restoration

when it was converted into the headquarters of the Skidmore, Owings and Merrill Foundation, an institution established in 1979 to support and advance studies in the fields of architecture and urban planning.

Cat. no. 50
Adler and Sullivan, Four-part spandrel panel from the St. Nicholas Hotel (later the Victoria Building), 8th and Locust streets, St. Louis, Missouri, 1892-93 (demolished 1973); terracotta, 137.1 x 147.3 x 11.4 cm. Gifts of Alice Rudolph and by exchange from Southern Illinois University at Edwardsville, 1973.556 a-b and 1974.82.

Cat. no. 51
Frank Lloyd Wright for Adler and Sullivan, Supporting bracket from the balcony of the James Charnley House, 1365 N. Astor Street, 1891; fret sawn wood, 16.5 x 33.6 x 78 cm. Gift of Lowell Wohlfeil, 1984.195.

Fig. 6 (cat. nos. 52, 54)
**Adler and Sullivan,
Column from an exterior
window soffit and an
entire panel from a bay
window on the ninth
floor of the Schiller
Building, 64 W.
Randolph, 1891-92
(demolished 1961);
terracotta column;
212.5 x 69.8 cm
diameter panel:
dimensions unavailable.
Gift of the Commission
on Chicago Architectural
Landmarks, 1962.937,
936.**

Fig. 7 (cat. no. 55)
**Adler and Sullivan,
Nine decorative
elements from the
thirteenth-floor window
frieze on the exterior of
the Schiller Building;
terracotta,
overall dimensions,
175.2 x 198 x 45.7 cm.
Gift of the Commission
on Chicago
Architectural
Landmarks, 1962.935.**

Cat. no. 53
**Adler and Sullivan,
Block of stringcourse
with repeated ribbon
design from the first-
floor loggia of the
Schiller Building;
terracotta,
91 x 49 x 20.5 cm.
Gift of the Commission
on Chicago Architectural
Landmarks, 1962.939.**

Schiller Building

Almost simultaneously with the St.
Louis projects, Adler and Sullivan
designed two of their most important commissions, the Schiller Building (1891-92) and the Chicago Stock
Exchange (1893-94). Originally
located in downtown Chicago, both
buildings were significant refinements of the principles for the
design of skyscrapers, first set forth
in the Wainwright Building. Like
the Wainwright, the Schiller and the
Stock Exchange reflected the mature
realization of Sullivan's philosophy
of American architecture, relying
on a new vocabulary of form and
ornament, rather than historical
precedent.

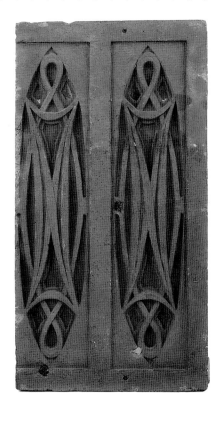

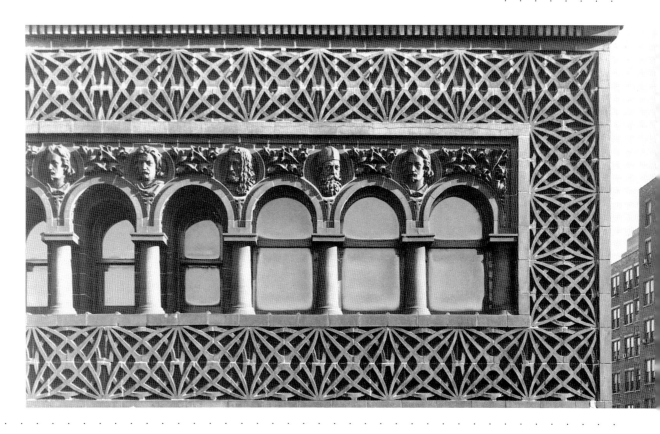

The Schiller (see Weingarden, fig. 1), considered Sullivan's second skyscraper, was modeled after the mixed-use concept of the Auditorium Building, and it proved to be the tallest building the firm ever constructed. Often identified by its later name, the Garrick Theater, the building combined a theater and an office tower in one structure. The I-shaped building consisted of a seventeen-story tower on Randolph Street, flanked on either side by a nine-story wing with oriel windows running from the third to eighth floors. The exterior of the building was sheathed in buff-colored ornamental terracotta that had been shaped into a variety of geometric patterns, skillfully intertwined with lush, leafy forms. An exterior column from the building (see fig. 6; cat. no. 52) illustrates how Sullivan combined geometric ornament on the shaft of a column with foliate ornament reserved for the capital. Other examples of the exterior ornament also in the museum's collection

vary from a simple, intertwining ribbon design for a stringcourse (cat. no. 53), to more complicated panels from window bays (see fig. 6; cat. no. 54), to a robust foliate section from the thirteenth-floor frieze (see fig. 7; cat. no. 55). The sculptor Richard Bock supplied Adler and Sullivan with terracotta busts of famous German poets, artists, and philosophers, two of which are in the Art Institute's collection (see fig. 8; cat. nos. 56, 57). Other busts have been installed in private homes in the Lincoln Park area and on the facade of Second City Theater on North Wells Street.

The 1,286-seat auditorium, clearly the major focus of the interior, filled most of the central portion of the building up to the sixth floor. The theater was one of Sullivan's most magnificent interior

spaces, its most striking feature being a series of eight huge vaults that formed the ceiling above the theater's main floor. The vaults were faced in plaster panels that featured a repeated star-pod pattern (cat. no. 58) in which central, starlike shapes are surrounded by borders of intertwining vine and leaf forms. Other ornamental plaster panels of interlocking circles (see cat. no. 59) and flat circles separated by undulating leaf forms formed friezes in several areas of the theater including the balcony face (see fig. 9; cat. no. 60). The original color scheme of the theater ornament called for salmon, green, gold, yellow, and red. In an article in *Prairie School Review* 2,2 (1965), Paul Sprague aptly described the dramatic effect created by the plaster ornament: "Everywhere the enclosing surfaces were enriched with a delicate plaster ornament that served to establish an atmosphere of festivity and . . . . to subdivide the plaster envelope of the main space,

Fig. 8 (cat. nos. 56, 57)
Richard Bock, sculptor for Adler and Sullivan, Portrait heads from the seventeenth-floor arcade of the Schiller Building; terracotta, each 63.5 x 66 x 36.2 cm. Gift of the Commission on Chicago Architectural Landmarks.

Adler and Sullivan

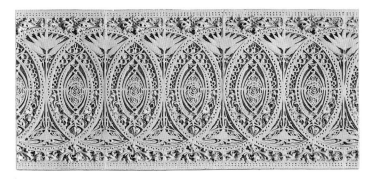

Cat. no. 58
Adler and Sullivan, Sections of a star-pod design from the proscenium vault of the Schiller Building Theater; painted plaster, 70 x 70 cm. Gift of the Commission on Chicago Architectural Landmarks, 1962.950.

Cat. no. 59
Adler and Sullivan, Section of a frieze from the banquet hall of the Schiller Building; painted plaster, 99 x 81 x 4 cm. Gift of the Commission on Chicago Architectural Landmarks, 1962.944.

Cat. no. 61
Adler and Sullivan, Mosaic stair landing from the Schiller Building; colored stone embedded in concrete, 252 x 503 cm. Gift of the Commission on Chicago Architectural Landmarks, 1962.942.

Fig. 9 (cat. no. 60)
Adler and Sullivan, Section of the balcony face from the Schiller Building Theater; painted plaster, 73.7 x 82.5 x 7.5 cm. Gift of the Commission on Chicago Architectural Landmarks, 1962.947.

to give scale to its broad surfaces, and to furnish the eye with a variety of incredibly intricate linear designs in low relief. And, by means of a masterful organization of these ornamental friezes, moldings, arch faces, soffits and individual panels, as well as by the internal stylistic consistency between them, an effective unity was achieved within the entire space" (p. 6). The ornamental motifs were also repeated throughout the building's interior, such as on the mosaics that were located on stair landings (cat. no. 61).

Despite the obvious importance of the Schiller Building in the history of Adler and Sullivan's work and in the history of American architecture, the building was demolished in 1961 to make way for a highrise parking lot. To lessen the blow of the demolition, the Commission on Chicago Architectural Landmarks distributed fragments from the building to major public institutions in the Chicago area; it was at this time that the Art Institute acquired its Schiller Building fragments.

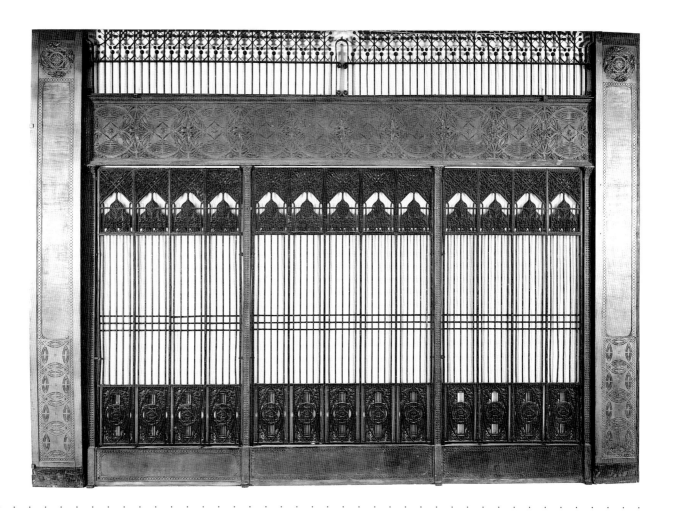

Chicago Stock Exchange

In the Chicago Stock Exchange (1893-94), the largest of their tall office buildings, Adler and Sullivan successfully integrated interior and exterior spaces, ornament, structure, and function. The thirteen-story sky-scraper contained banking facilities, a spectacular, two-story trading room for the Chicago Stock Exchange,

and 480 offices for brokers and businesses related to the Exchange. The buff-colored terracotta building had a three-story base that indicated the large trading room within behind an arcade of two-story arches. The nine-story shaft of the building marked Sullivan's first skyscraper use of the Chicago window, a large single pane of glass flanked on

either side by narrow, double-hung sash windows. The building terminated with a colonnaded, clearspan top floor and a heavily ornamented cornice.

The ornament that Sullivan designed for both the exterior and interior of the building was some of his most elegant and accomplished work. The elevator enclosure grille from the first floor (cat. no. 62), for example, combines wrought- and cast-iron grilles with copper-plated pilasters and lintels that feature leafy ornament incorporated into a geometric framework of elongated ovals and interlocking circles. Elevator enclosures on the upper floors were simpler strap-metal grilles that featured repeated oval shapes (cat. no. 64). In his monograph on Sullivan, Twombly observed that Sullivan associated the oval shape with "seed germs," the embryo of the life force

Cat. no. 62
Adler and Sullivan, Entire elevator bank from the ground floor of the Chicago Stock Exchange Building, 30 N. LaSalle Street, 1893-94 (demolished 1972); cast iron, wrought iron, and copper-plated cast iron, 303 x 325.5 x 5 cm. Restricted gift of the Graham Foundation for Advanced Studies in the Fine Arts, 1973.55 a-i.

Cat. no. 63
Adler and Sullivan, T-plate from an elevator enclosure grille from the Chicago Stock Exchange Building; bronze, 41 x 43.2 x 1 cm. Gift of Sudler and Co., 1960.913.

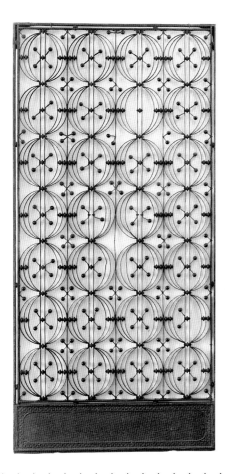  

Cat. no. 64
**Adler and Sullivan,
Two elevator enclosure
grilles from the Chicago
Stock Exchange
Building;
cast and wrought iron,
Bower-Barff finish,
205 x 104 x 2.5 cm.
Gift of Kenneth
Newberger,
1963.373 a-b.**

Fig. 10
**Adler and Sullivan,
Elevator grille with
T-plates from the
Chicago Stock
Exchange Building.**

discussed in "Inspiration," the prose poem he wrote in 1886. Originally, the moveable grille sections featured copper-plated T-plates (see fig. 10; cat. no. 63) that repeated variations on the motif of interlocking circles and ovals. Likewise, even the building's smallest features, such as kick-plates, doorknobs, and baluster panels (cat. nos. 65-67), were a microcosm of the geometric design pattern established for the major decorative elements. The ornament is based on Sullivan's philosophy that all ornament should be derived from nature and should express its underlying geometry.

Despite the obvious beauty of the building, it served its original function for only fourteen years. In 1908 the rent-free lease that had been offered to the Chicago Stock Exchange to entice them to move into the building had expired. Because the directors of the Exchange wanted to be closer to the

south end of LaSalle Street, they moved their operation to the Rookery. In the same year, Foreman Brothers' Bank took over and remodeled the Trading Room; they remained there until the bank failed following the 1929 stock market crash. The Trading Room was not occupied again until 1940 when Bell Savings and Loan located there. At a later period the U. S. O. used the room as a social center for military personnel. Although the building had been recognized as a landmark in 1960 by the Commission on Chicago Architectural Landmarks, in 1971 the building's owners decided to demolish the structure to make way for a much taller commercial building. The demolition threat sparked a bitter preservation battle, and when the attempt to save the entire building failed, the City of Chicago negotiated to preserve major artifacts from the building. The Art Institute was offered first choice of the artifacts and decided that, instead of acquiring numerous small fragments from the building,

they would undertake the reconstruction of one of the most important rooms in the history of American architecture, the Chicago Stock Exchange Trading Room. The Trading Room is justly renowned, and its fifteen wall, ceiling, and border stencils are unsurpassed in their richness and complexity. Among the fragments in the museum's collection is an original section of stencil on canvas (cat. no. 68; pl. 4) from the main truss of the ceiling. The reconstructed Trading Room (see Saliga, fig. 16) opened in the Art Institute's new East Wing in 1977. At the same time, the two-story Stock Exchange entrance arch (see Saliga, fig. 17) was re-erected in an adjacent Art Institute garden at Monroe Street and Columbus Drive.

Cat. no. 65
**Adler and Sullivan,
Kick plate from
the Chicago Stock
Exchange Building;
copper-plated bronze,
58.5 x 75 x 1 cm.
Gift of L. M. Ackley,
1973.338.**

Cat. no. 66
**Adler and Sullivan,
Doorknob and escutcheon
plate from the Chicago
Stock Exchange
Building; cast iron,
Bower-Barff finish,
24 x 8.5 x 6.5 cm.
Anonymous gift,
1972.808.**

Cat. no. 68
**Adler and Sullivan,
Section of a stencil
from the Trading Room
of the Chicago Stock
Exchange Building;
executed by Healy
and Millet;
oil on canvas mounted
on panel,
143.7 x 305.4 x 1 cm.
Gift of Mr. and Mrs.
Arthur Dubin, 1971.747.**

Cat. no. 67
**Adler and Sullivan,
Baluster panel from the
Chicago Stock Exchange
Building;
copper-plated cast iron,
65 x 27.6 x 2.5 cm.
Anonymous gift,
1972.805.**

Fig. 11
Adler and Sullivan, Guaranty Building (now the Prudential Building), Buffalo, New York, 1894-96; detail of the entrance facade.

Cat. no. 69
Adler and Sullivan, Doorknob and escutcheon plate from the Guaranty Building; fabricated by the Yale and Towne Lock Company; cast iron, Bower-Barff finish, 35.5 x 10.7 x 7 cm. Gift of Richard Nickel and Mr. H. Kealy, 1955.2689.

Guaranty Building

The Guaranty Building (1894-96; fig. 11) in Buffalo, New York, was the partnership's last skyscraper constructed. The building was commissioned by its owner and contractor, the Guaranty Construction Company of Chicago. Two years later, the building was refinanced and renamed the Prudential Building. Similar to the Wainwright Building, the twelve-story Guaranty has a U-shaped plan, a two-story base with large ground-floor windows, continuous vertical piers that emphasize the building's height, a row of ornamented porthole windows at the attic, and a flaring, overhanging cornice. What distinguishes the Guaranty from the Wainwright is that its entire red terracotta exterior is covered in leafy, foliate ornament combined with oval- and diamond-shaped motifs. No other Adler and

Sullivan exterior was as highly ornamented as that of the Guaranty. Like the Wainwright, Schiller, and Chicago Stock Exchange buildings, the interior of the Guaranty was composed of decorative elevator grilles, railings, mosaics, and skylights that offered variations on the exquisite exterior ornament. The Guaranty Building is represented in the Art Institute's collection by a door handle, a mail slot, and doorknobs and escutcheon plates (see cat. no. 69) that repeat the oval decorative motif and reveal the degree of attention that was paid to even the smallest of details in the building. The Guaranty recently underwent an eight-million-dollar restoration, completed in 1988.

III. *Louis H. Sullivan, Architect, 1895-1924*

In 1895 Adler and Sullivan terminated their partnership. Most historians agree that the economic depression of 1893 caused a severe decline in the number of commissions the firm received and finally forced the partners to separate. Adler was employed as an engineer for an elevator company for six months and later designed some small commissions with his sons, including Isaiah Temple on Chicago's South Side (drawings for which are in the Art Institute's collection). Adler died five years after the partnership ended; Sullivan lived for another three decades. In 1895 Sullivan entered the last important phase of his career, in which he received smaller commissions but produced some of his most notable designs.

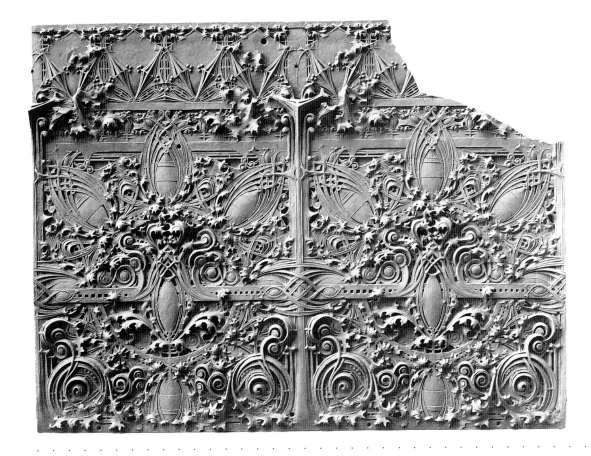

Gage Building

The Gage Building (1898-99; fig. 12) was one of three, small, steel-framed loft buildings designed by Holabird and Roche and constructed on Michigan Avenue for millinery firms. The two adjoining structures at 24 and 30 S. Michigan Avenue were entirely the work of Holabird and Roche, while the facade of the Gage at 18 S. Michigan was designed by Louis Sullivan. According to an 1899 issue of *Brickbuilder*, the Gage Brothers had requested Sullivan's participation and had offered to pay higher rent to cover the additional expense of hiring him because they thought his facade design would lend distinction to their business. (In fact, the Spring 1902 issue of the company magazine, *The Gage*, announced that the firm had become the country's largest millinery importer.)

The Gage Building was originally eight stories high and was covered in buff-colored terracotta and green/red painted cast-iron panels at ground level. Following the precedent set in Adler and Sullivan's other skyscrapers, the Gage Building's three bays of windows are separated by vertical piers that run continuously from the second floor to the roofline and terminate in a burst of splendid foliate ornament. The ground-floor ornament (see cat. no. 70; pl. 1), which framed the building's doorway and shop windows, was some of Sullivan's most luxuriant and elegant work. As the panel demonstrates, Sullivan used three geometric shapes to organize the symmetrical, repeated design: a large underlying grid, circles that intersect with the grid, and elongated oval shapes that radiate from the circles. These underlying geometric forms are interlaced with curving spikey leaves, sinuous spiraling vines, and clusters of berries.

The windows of the Gage Building are arranged in groups of four and five pivot or casement windows that are small compared to the huge Chicago windows that Holabird and Roche incorporated into the facades of adjacent buildings to the south. In designing the facade, Sullivan embraced new technology in his use of Luxfer prisms above the clearpane windows to direct as much light as possible into the interior of the millinery business that occupied the building.

In 1902, the Gage Brothers commissioned Holabird and Roche to add four stories to the building's top. Holabird's addition continued the ornament of the lower floors, and the cornice and roofline bursts of foliate ornament were reinstalled atop the new floors. The building remained essentially unchanged until it was "modernized" in the 1950s and the cast-iron ornament from the first floor was stripped off. When he saw the panels being discarded, architect Arthur Dubin managed to save several that were eventually donated to the Art Institute. Other sections of the foliate cast-iron ornament were later donated by architect L. Lattin Smith.

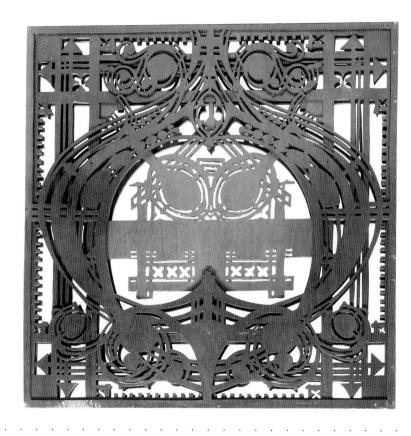

Schlesinger and Mayer Store

The Schlesinger and Mayer Store (1898-99, 1903-04), Sullivan's last large commercial commission, is a steel-frame structure covered in glazed white terracotta. The building was known by the Schlesinger and Mayer name for just a short time, because in 1904 Carson Pirie Scott and Company purchased the store and renamed it. The twelve-story building is arranged horizontally, with a two-story base wrapped in rich, green/red, painted cast-iron ornament that frame large display windows. The cast-iron ornament is similar to that originally installed on the base of the Gage Building and consists of leaves, berries, vines, geometric forms, and Sullivan's own initials that intertwine to produce lavish ornamental patterns. The store's upper ten floors have large Chicago windows. In deference to the original store on the site, Sullivan, with his assistant George Grant Elmslie, designed the northwest corner of the building facing State and Madison streets, once "the world's busiest corner," as a curved pavilion stretching from the ground floor to the cornice.

The interior of the building is organized like a simple warehouse, with large open spaces interrupted only by supporting columns. Nonetheless, Sullivan and Elmslie designed exquisite interior spaces in the store, including a women's lounge and writing room that was enclosed by a mahogany screen composed of numerous individual panels (fig. 13; cat. no. 71). These panels, which are essentially laminates of five layers of fret-sawn wood, are somewhat uncharacteristic of the style of ornament found elsewhere in the store, as, for example, on the medallions that adorned the store's cage elevators (fig. 14), or on the baluster panels (cat. no. 73) located in the stairways throughout the building (fig. 15). The elevator medallion (cat. no. 72; pl. 5) is composed of a central cross from which four flat shield shapes radiate. As Paul Sprague has described, during the period 1895 to 1902, Sullivan "continued to employ the sinuous geometry of his previous period but now he used it as a background against which the more fluent shield-shaped and organic motifs were seen." A similar elongated shield shape has been stretched the length of the baluster panels. Like the medallion and the baluster, the mahogany screen has a rectilinear geometric background, but its focal point is an onion shape. The depth of the screen is created by the layering of the five carved panels, not by foliate forms carved in relief, as in the other ornament.

The balusters from the Schlesinger and Mayer Store were donated to the Art Institute following a fire in the store in 1967; other fragments became available when the cage elevators were replaced with modern enclosed cabs and when the women's writing room was dismantled. Despite these interior changes, the store's paneled interior rotunda was restored by the Office of John Vinci in 1980.

Cat. no. 72
Louis H. Sullivan, Circular medallion from an elevator enclosure grille from the Schlesinger and Mayer Store; copper-plated cast iron, diameter 56 cm. Restricted gift of the Graham Foundation for Advanced Studies in the Fine Arts, 1971.450.

Cat. no. 73
Louis H. Sullivan, Baluster from the Schlesinger and Mayer Store; cast iron, 89 x 25 x 5 cm. Gift of Carson Pirie Scott and Company, 1968.794.

Figs. 14, 15
Louis H. Sullivan, Elevator enclosure grilles and stairway balusters from the Schlesinger and Mayer Store; *from* **Ornamental Iron and Bronze** *(Chicago:* **Winslow Brothers Company, 1901).**

Cyrus Hall McCormick House

After Sullivan completed the first phase of the Schlesinger and Mayer Store in 1900, he undertook a number of smaller commissions such as an interior remodeling for the McCormick House. Designed by the Chicago firm of Cudell and Blumenthal, this elaborate, French Renaissance, forty-five-room mansion was described by Thomas Tallmadge as second in fame only to Potter Palmer's on Lake Shore Drive. Although Cyrus Hall McCormick lived in the house for only five years before his death in 1884, the house remained in the McCormick family until after World War II. Sullivan's interior remodeling was probably done to accommodate the family's youngest son Stanley and his bride Katherine Dexter. The McCormick family had been Sullivan's client three years earlier with the Gage Building.

The only fragment that survives from Sullivan's remodeling is a bronze-plated radiator screen (cat. no. 74). Like the screen from the Schlesinger and Mayer Store, the open, lacy radiator screen is composed of a repeated onion shape that has three slightly different centers — a shield, two interlocking vines, and a square with a central snowflake pattern. The perimeter of the screen is composed of repeated trefoils that are interrupted at regular points by the vines that spill out of the center. The radiator screen was donated to the Art Institute before the house was demolished in 1954 to make way for a new administration building for the Sanitary District of Metropolitan Chicago.

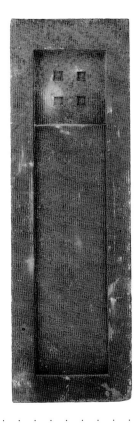

Felsenthal Store

The Felsenthal Store (1906) and the National Farmers Bank (1906-08) in Owatonna, Minnesota, are typical of the small commissions that Sullivan received during the final part of his career. Eleven years after he and Adler had dissolved their partnership, Eli B. Felsenthal, who was the Adler family's lawyer and who lived in a row house adjacent to Adler's own residence on Ellis Avenue, hired Sullivan to design a small commercial building incorporating shops, rental offices, a private apartment, and loft space (fig. 16). The rental stores occupied the entire first floor, while the upper floors were divided among the diverse interior functions of the building's program. Each section was given a distinctive expression on the facade, yet all portions were skillfully integrated into a unified composition. The Felsenthal Store marked the transition in Sullivan's practice from tall commercial buildings to low-rise structures.

Like much of Sullivan's work after the turn of the century, the facades of the Felsenthal Store were composed of large expanses of rough-faced tapestry brick punctuated by panels of ornament. Sullivan's design formula was repeated by numerous other architects who purchased stock Sullivanesque ornament from companies such as Midland Terra Cotta and used it to break up the surfaces of their otherwise plain buildings (see fig. 18). One of the panels from the Felsenthal Store (cat. no. 76), which was originally installed above the second floor, is a large square block whose symmetrical design is composed of four adjoining shield shapes that float over elongated ovals and intertwine with clusters of leaves and berries. The perimeter of the panel has two borders, one a sinuous vine, the other of alternating ovals and rectangular bars. The Art Institute also has in its collection sections of the decorative cornice, a large ornamental block featuring the letter "F," and a carved stone pier (cat. no. 75) that was located between two second-story windows. The rectilinear geometry of the pier is reminiscent of Prairie School designs of the period. Despite the importance of this late Sullivan building, it was demolished in 1982.

Cat. no. 75
Louis H. Sullivan,
Pier originally located
between two second-floor
windows of the Eli B.
Felsenthal Store;
limestone,
94.5 x 30 x 30 cm.
Gift of the Commission
on Chicago Historical
and Architectural
Landmarks, 1984.188.

Cat. no. 76
Louis H. Sullivan,
Block from the second
story of the Eli B.
Felsenthal Store;
terracotta,
84.5 x 84.5 x 20 cm.
Gift of the Commission
on Chicago Historical
and Architectural
Landmarks, 1984.190.

Fig. 16
Louis H. Sullivan,
Eli B. Felsenthal Store,
701-09 E. 47th Street,
1906 (demolished 1982).

Fig. 17
**Louis H. Sullivan,
National Farmers Bank
(now Norwest Bank),
101 N. Cedar Street,
Owatonna, Minnesota,
1906-08;
interior view.**

Cat. no. 77
**Louis H. Sullivan,
Teller's wicket from the
National Farmers Bank;
copper-plated cast iron,
104 x 58 x 1 cm.
Gift of the Winslow
Brothers Company,
1908.73.**

National Farmers Bank

The National Farmers Bank (1906-08) of Owatonna, Minnesota, was the first, and is considered by many the best, of the eight small midwestern banks that Sullivan designed late in his career. Its design is significant because while other architects of the period generally used a classical style for bank buildings, Sullivan rejected the use of such overtly historical references and, instead, developed a design that is unique both in plan and in decoration. The Owatonna bank has a cubic banking space separated from private office space, a distinction that expressed Sullivan's philosophy of "form follows function." The two main facades of the bank feature single great arches that are filled with enormous, colored-glass windows. The interior of the banking hall presents an extraordinarily rich blend of colors and exquisite foliate ornament. The bank has been likened to a jewel box, a comparison drawn from its cubic shape and its azure, emerald, gold, and rust color scheme, which Sullivan described as a "color symphony."

The elaborate interior details of the bank (fig. 17) were designed by Sullivan with assistance from his long-time chief designer, George Grant Elmslie. The teller's wicket in the Art Institute's collection (cat. no. 77; pl. 6) displays many of the forms that characterize Sullivan's late ornament. An elongated onion shape forms the opening that framed the face of the bank teller. The opening is an arabesque of intertwining seed pods, undulating leaves, and clusters of berries. At its top, two large and two small shield shapes interlock with an oval topped by a small, unopened seed pod. The onion-shaped opening is surrounded at top and bottom by equally exquisite foliage, vines, and long sagging branches. Sullivan's ornament was never more luxuriant than in his bank in Owatonna. The teller's wicket was donated to the Art Institute at the time of its fabrication by the Winslow Brothers firm, the Chicago cast-iron fabricators who worked closely with Sullivan to execute the richly ornamented metalwork for many of his buildings, including the Chicago Stock Exchange, the Gage Building, and the Schlesinger and Mayer Store.

As the business of the National Farmers Bank increased and banking functions changed, the interior of the Owatonna bank was reorganized in the 1940s. All of the interior brick walls and the teller counters and wickets were removed and replaced by open counters. The bank has undergone several subsequent remodelings and is still open for business under the name of Norwest Bank.

The success of this extraordinarily beautiful bank, which was widely published in architectural journals and financial publications in the early years of this century, led to several other bank commissions for Sullivan in small midwestern towns. As all of Sullivan's subsequent work consisted of small commissions, this bank signified the end of his skyscraper period. Regardless of the size of his later projects, however, Sullivan vigorously maintained his philosophy that American architecture and ornament should take its inspiration from the geometry underlying natural forms, not from historical European styles. Sullivan's argument was strong, and his philosophy is still a subject of debate today.

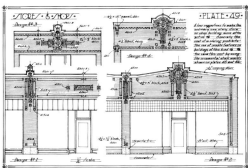

The Jordan Building (1916-17) was the first major commercial building to be developed by a black man in the "Black Metropolis" on the city's South Side. The three-story building combined five stores and eight five-room apartments in a brick and terracotta structure. The building's developer, Joseph J. Jordan, was a musician and composer who used the profits from music publishing to finance this and several other real estate ventures in Chicago.

The exterior terracotta on the Jordan Building is of particular interest because it is principally stock "Sullivanesque" ornament that was sold by the Northwestern Terra Cotta Company in the 1900s. Like the Midland Terra Cotta Company, which also produced stock Sullivanesque ornament (fig. 18), Northwestern routinely sold white terracotta blocks that were somewhat crudely modeled after Sullivan's

highly refined designs, such as that for the Felsenthal Store (cat. no. 76). The terracotta from the Jordan Building is among the earliest commercializations of Sullivan's ornament, which reached its peak of popularity in the early 1920s in small commercial structures across the United States. The lintel from the Jordan Building (cat. no. 78; fig. 19) is composed of three blocks with shield shapes, curving vines, leafy branches, and rows of berries. The shield motif that Sullivan incorporated into some of his later work, such as the Schlesinger and Mayer Store and the Felsenthal Store, is reinterpreted in the central panel of this lintel. It is clear that these simplified stock designs are awkward imitations of the elegant and intricate foliate ornament that Sullivan produced late in his career.

Because the Jordan Building was such an important structure in the history of the Black Metropolis, it was listed on the National Register of Historic Places in 1986. In 1987, however, the building partially

collapsed after vandals had been removing and selling bricks from the building. Damage to the building was considered irreparable, and the structure was demolished the same year. The Art Institute acquired its fragments at that time.

Fig. 18
Midland Terra Cotta Company, Ornamental stock molds for stores and shops; from a promotional brochure, c. 1922-25.

Cat. no. 78
John Nevin Coleman, Ornament from the facade of the Jordan Building; glazed terracotta, 42 x 95 x 13 cm. Gift of the Commission on Chicago and Historical and Architectural Landmarks, 1987.3.

Fig. 19
John Nevin Coleman, Jordan Building, 3539-49 S. State Street, 1916-17 (demolished 1986).

. . . .

by Donald Hoffmann

*I*t is curious that Aristotle describes Hippodamos, who invented the art of city planning, as "a strange man, whose fondness for distinction led him into a general eccentricity of life," a man who wore "flowing hair and expensive ornaments" and who "besides aspiring to be an adept in the knowledge of nature, was the first person not a statesman who made inquiries about the best form of government."[1] For these words come very close to fitting Frank Lloyd Wright. Not by chance did Wright so often present his work through drawings in bird's-eye perspective; the lofty overview, or sometimes the swooping view from below, could best express the command his vision assumed, how he took charge of everything in sight, making sure that a chair belonged to the room, a room to the building, a building to its site and to the nation and the ideals for which the nation stood. In most of Wright's designs — whether they are of vast dreamy projects or of buildings in fact constructed, of the panes in a

window or the parts of a chair, a table, or a lamp — we find not just the sense of new human settings, but of new human settlements (fig. 1). It is a mistake to think of Wright as a mere regionalist. He addressed the primary question of how we on earth ought to be living.

Wright took architecture to be an elementary act of spirit, the assertion of man's right to imagine, then build, his own environment. He came to maturity in an era when industry for the first time in history existed apart from art.[2] The real problem did not lie in simply the separation of architecture from engineering. Wright faced the Goliath of a wanton assault upon nature, the separation of daily life from what should have been a healthy, natural environment for the growth of democracy. As Nietzsche observed, only an overweening pride could have so ruthlessly violated nature with the help of machines and a heedlessly inventive technology while God continued to be regarded "as some alleged spider of purpose and morality behind the great captious web of causality."[3] Any true work of art thus represented an act of rebellion. Through the creation of a new unity, it necessarily became environmental.[4] When he published his first important essay in 1908, "In the Cause of Architecture," Wright spoke of the modern opportunity to make of a building a complete work of art. He told of his own effort toward achieving that unity "which is the soul of the individual work of art."[5] He took his stand against the established industrial order not as an enemy of the

machine, like so many who lapsed into nostalgia for the handicrafts of the Middle Ages, but in opposition to its gross misuse. He was only forty years old, but already he reviewed his life's work; and already he could claim a fairly long list of buildings and projects unequalled in clarity and power of imagination by the work of any other architect in American history. The essential question about Wright has always been the same: how did he come so far?

Wright's character, as is common, was formed by certain predispositions and experiences reinforced through recurrence or recollection. He was born in 1867 in rural Wisconsin, and he was most impressed in his growing years not by his brief sessions in school but by the long hard months he spent on the farms of several uncles, near Spring Green. Despite his lack of formal training, he was determined to be an architect. He began from a tradition of independence deep within his Welsh ancestors and family, composed mostly of farmers, teachers, and preachers. Wright was a born protestant — as Emerson had said of poor Thoreau, only a few years before — and in later years he liked to think of the Larkin Building of 1903-06 (fig. 2), his first great realized commission that was beyond residential scale, as "the first emphatic protestant in architecture."[6] It appears that he arrived in Chicago, a place of sprawling industrial squalor, before his twentieth birthday; and when he was only about twenty-two he became chief draftsman in the office of Adler and Sullivan, and thus first assistant to Louis H. Sullivan. The years of Wright's extraordinary development occurred in the 1890s. In the first few years of the twentieth century, architecture began to come to him as second nature.[7]

Sullivan's architecture bears little essential resemblance to Wright's, and because of the influence of George Elmslie, once an assistant to Wright and later more directly to Sullivan, it is apparent that Sullivan in his declining years took at least as much from Wright as, in earlier years, Wright took from him. So it is important to ask why Wright nonetheless continued to venerate Sullivan, to speak of him as his "beloved master." Above all, Sullivan took nature to heart: he found nature to be inexhaustibly poetic, strong, chaste, vital, fertile, serene, unerring in instinct, and eloquent of organization. Nature, he said, nurtured all great ideas. Nature furnished the final criteria for judging architectural form. Nature endowed man with his creative faculties, and although man had misused them because of false education, he might still discover nature's ways and proceed to express democracy, what Whitman called "the purport and aim of all the past," as an unfolding of the sovereign individual.[8] Wright absorbed all these ideas as if they were his own. With the encouragement of Sullivan's high seriousness about nature, he could recall his days on the farm in a new light, as if they had been filled with epiphanies of aesthetic wonder. Wright, too, began to speak for the outdoor spirit; and to consider how architecture might grow at home in nature as it somehow became like natural form. Moreover, in his attention to Sullivan's brilliant flourishes of architectural ornament (excusing the excessive naturalism and the relative indifference to the material in which it was executed), Wright glimpsed the great ideal that he was to make his own: to carry through the entire fabric of a building the same sense of a vital organized being.[9] At this same time, Wright had settled into suburban Oak Park, on the edge of the prairie.

Fig. 1
Frank Lloyd Wright, Project for the Harold McCormick House, Lake Forest, Illinois, 1907-08; from Frank Lloyd Wright, Ausgeführte Bauten und Entwürfe (Berlin: Ernst Wasmuth Verlag, 1910), pl. 58.

Fig. 2
Frank Lloyd Wright, Larkin Building, Buffalo, New York, 1903-04 (demolished 1950); from Frank Lloyd Wright, Ausgeführte Bauten (Berlin: Ernst Wasmuth Verlag, 1911), p. 131.

Fig. 3
**Frank Lloyd Wright,
Avery Coonley House,
300 Scottswood Road,
Riverside, Illinois,
1908; interior view.**

He began to realize that because of the rise of mechanized agriculture and the crush of the industrial city his years in Wisconsin had coincided with the loss of the most salient feature of the land — the great prairie, in all its profusion of wildflowers and marvelous tall grasses.[10] An architecture as surely constituted as natural form could make restitution (fig. 3).

Of course the cry for a new architecture had been heard for decades, with very little effect; but the dawn of a new century, in America as in Great Britain and on the Continent, built much greater pressure for a brave start. Chicago was a particularly good place for Wright to be; the city had surprisingly few pretensions and no architectural traditions to speak of. Even the vast stage-set of the Court of Honor for the World's Columbian Exposition of 1893 had

argued that it was possible to build from the whole cloth a unified and harmonious environment. The scale of this spectacle, and its swift execution, must have meant much to Wright — and more than did the three small Japanese pavilions of the Ho-o-den at the north end of the Wooded Island. Chicago was a city proud of being able to get things done.

In this new work Wright was nurtured too by his belief in the kindergarten idea. His first five children were born in the 1890s, and their home kindergarten training, a concern shared by both his mother and his wife, brought back memories of his own playtime with the Froebel "gifts," those tiny design and construction elements intended to teach a child the basic shapes, their combinations, and a sense of proportions. Kindergarten went back to the root of things. The writer and publisher Elbert Hubbard had also admired Froebel: "We are all children in the

Kindergarten of God." Louis Sullivan, who titled his architectural discourses *Kindergarten Chats*, asked, "Why do we flower so wondrously in childhood, and then, as the years pass, turn dull and inglorious?" Why, indeed. Sullivan proposed an architectural kindergarten, "a garden of the heart wherein the simple, obvious truths, the truths that any child might consent to, are brought fresh to the faculties."[11]

This sense of the immanence in elementary shapes of countless form-patterns awaiting playful and spontaneous invention perhaps came to Wright with more force from another source, the common buildings on the prairie. Barns, sheds, cribs, silos, and windmills were all strong in geometric shape, and they spoke more directly of the simple conduct of life upon the land. Humble landmarks though they were, they took their place with more vigor and grace than any of the buildings typical of the city. So it was significant that some of Wright's carriage houses and stables were among the most advanced of his earliest designs.[12] He could have hardly overlooked the immense roofs of prairie barns and how they expressed the essence of shelter. These would have offered to his own architecture some very rich suggestions.

Through the strength drawn from such experiences and observations, Wright was able to work his way past the several architectural modes of his day, while learning from each of them certain skills and devices. His relation to the Art and Crafts movement proved more important, for it helped him see that design could be pervasive, and it confirmed his resolve to take control of virtually every visual detail (fig. 4).

In this ostensibly reformist movement, Wright nevertheless found
a thinly veiled sentimentality and
often a mincing preciousness. As
early as 1898 he lampooned Arts and
Crafts devotees with the plaster casts
of spindly secretary birds that he
placed by the entranceway of his Oak
Park studio. He proposed in place
of an immaculate craft, a clean and
virile beauty contemporary with the
age of the machine; later, in mocking
those who had pounded their fin-
gers "making useless things," he
turned the very words of William
Morris against the futile efforts of
his followers.[13] Wright found better
instruction in the thinking of Thor-
stein Veblen, another native of Wisconsin and one who spent his best
years at the University of Chicago. In
pondering the middle-class rage for
household adornment, Veblen was
not convinced of either a concern
for morals or an expression of joy in
good workmanship. He discerned
instead the vicarious leisure of a
housewife conspicuously wasteful of
time and substance. Veblen also
observed the decadent aspect of
superfluous articles made by hand,
mostly in "pecuniary emulation,"
when machines could easily make
more perfect and more serviceable
objects that might be faulted only for
being common. Household furnishings in this late stage of capitalism
represented a rather subtle attempt
to transform the original Protestant
spirit, and what Max Weber called
"the strict avoidance of all spontaneous enjoyment of life," into a
disguised opportunity for an increasing display of leisure and honorific
consumption.[14] Wright began to see
that if he could first banish the bric-
a-brac and then design all the furnishings necessary in terms of either
function or grace, he might turn all
the parts of a building into architectural elements of an aesthetically

complete living or working environment. Freestanding objects fashioned or collected essentially for
invidious display would become
irrelevant and unwelcome; and if a
particular building in a particular
place could be conceived as an
organism, the separation from it of
any part would be an act of vandal-
ism, a perversion of architectural
detail.

No wonder that Wright cleaned
house in so many ways. He took
inspiration again from the prairie, its
simplicity and repose. At first his
sense of pattern remained too literal
in its imitation of natural forms, and
in that respect was like Sullivan's; but
he soon discovered a new world of
geometries latent within the ordinary tools and techniques of the
drafting-board, where already he felt
so much at home. This was a different order and the source of his

unending romance in the invention
of abstract form. With his understanding of a true basis for architecture, Wright moved toward a level
of imagination and discipline that
continually aspired to nature as
metaphor, not mere representation.
Thus his new order: new through
his sense of form-pattern, and his
intuitions of space and landscape,
and the natural beauty of materials
used in building; ordered, because
of his will to make the grammar
of each building perfect in its way,
through the self-sacrifice of interior
discipline.[15]

It was peculiar, then, of Wright's
poetic buildings on the prairie that
the reiterated horizontals responded
so well to the land and yet resulted
from the simplest and most natural
patterns that can be drawn with the
primary tool of the drafting-board:
a series of parallel lines from the T-
square. Those long lines and planes
served, as well, to express the expan-
sive spirit of democratic life on the
American continent, and also the
clean swift speed that Wright took to

Fig. 4
**Frank Lloyd Wright,
Darwin D. Martin
House, 125 Jewett
Parkway, Buffalo, New
York, 1904-06; interior
view, from Wright,
Ausgeführte Bauten
(1911), p. 53.**

Fig. 5
Frank Lloyd Wright, William R. Heath House, 76 Soldiers Place, Buffalo, New York, 1905-06; interior view, from Wright, Ausgeführte Bauten (1911), p. 81.

Fig. 6
Frank Lloyd Wright, Unity Temple, Lake Street at Kenilworth Avenue, Oak Park, Illinois, 1905-06; interior view, from Wright, Ausgeführte Bauten (1911), p. 16.

Fig. 7
Frank Lloyd Wright, Ward Willits House, 1445 Sheridan Road, Highland Park, Illinois, 1902-03.

be the sign of modernity. In this vision of the coincidence of landscape and purpose with symbolic expression lay Wright's characteristic strength. His affection for the prairie also accounted for the fact that, within a single building, he created complementary qualities of space. His building plans do not deconstruct the traditional idea of a room, nor do they blur rooms. Instead, he liberates space through free perspectives and choices in movement, all the while maintaining the measured rhythm of a slow pulse sympathetic to the flow and ebb of a day, or a season, or a life (fig. 5). Sallies outward to sunlight and the open air give way, by turn, to moments of withdrawal. Complex passages and changes of level create unpredictable vistas that come to rest eventually in the warmth of inglenook and hearth. Such basic phases of space and mood can be fairly seen as condensations and metaphors of the prairie, which

was rarely a uniformly flat plane, and more typically a gently shifting field penetrated by winding creeks or rivers, and deep ravines. For the open land so assiduously tilled for crops found relief in shadowed and covert places, where prairie children lit fires and searched for caves.[16]

In this richly imaginative development of space, the ground-plan did not serve so much as the generator of a building, but as the projection and clarification on paper of Wright's interior vision. He could advance all aspects of the design together, so that plan, elevations, and perspectives conversed with one another to sustain a unity of scale and character. Details came later and with much care, yet with no great anxiety; they were implicit in the form traits of the plan, a work of art in itself. The small spoke to the large, the large to the small; and the whole reverberated with echoes. Wright often gave his plans the look of having been dictated by a module or a definite grid system, but close

study of his best work never indicates that it resulted from any mere routine.[17] His loving attention to qualities of light and nuances of relation between indoor and outdoor space might find parallels in the traditional architecture of Japan, but his admiration for the Orient came about from an honest kinship of sensibilities and attitudes toward nature. Wright in fact was dismayed to learn that his intuitive grasp of the vitality of space had already been set forth clearly in words ascribed to the ancient Lao Tzu:

He claimed that only in vacuum lay the truly essential. The reality of a room, for instance, was to be found in the vacant space enclosed by the roof and walls, not in the roof and walls themselves. The usefulness of a water pitcher dwelt in the emptiness where the water might be put, not in the form of the pitcher or the material of which it is made.

This revelation he found in *The Book of Tea*, published originally in Boston, in 1906; the date may indicate why in later years Wright looked back to the Unity Temple, from precisely that time, as his breakthrough building, his first self-conscious assertion of interior space (fig. 6).[18]

During this first decade of the twentieth century, Wright's work embodied a coordinated group of principles that proved capable of serving him until his death, so many years later, in 1959. In those early and golden years, his forms grew more virile, pure, abstract, uncompromised; his lines and planes became "clean as the flight of an arrow" and, in homage to the horizon, predominantly parallel to the ground; the materials were induced to revel in their natural character and to exploit their best strengths;

his colors suggested those of earth, bark, and leaves ("cheerful and profound," as Nietzsche asked of music, "like an afternoon in October"); he admitted daylight in cunning ways, often fragrant with the surprise of the outdoors, and filtered the artificial light with wood screens, rice paper, frosted glass or colored panes and patterned cames, as though through leafy branches.[19]

Two other aspects of this work can serve particularly well in demonstrating its radical nature. Wright had perceived windows and doors as ugly violations of a building's mass and volume, as punctures through the walls—"You rows of houses! you window-pierced facades," wrote Whitman—and as insistent symbols of the estrangement of human life from the free world of nature.[20] By arranging windows into long horizontal screens, or continuous planes of transparency, he changed them into constituent panels of the building fabric; and by associating them with the broad shadows of overhanging roofs, as well as with outreaching terraces and long boxes for plantings, he dematerialized any sudden boundaries between outdoors and in, so that one felt embraced by a building even before entering it. To the same effect, he withdrew structural support from the corners. Instead, he folded wall planes into pylons that stood as massive terminals but stopped short of the sheltering roof, thereby expressing the roof as heroically cantilevered and hovering (fig. 7). He opened just those parts of a building one expected to be closed. Doors represented more isolated and necessarily vertical interruptions to the broad disposition of a building, so he began to conceal them in darker places, deep within the domain of a building, where they would appear as private and almost secret ways, like wooded trails, to those obscure successions of space inside.

Second, in the details intended to maintain an intimacy of scale and nicety of proportion in the building, Wright found the most fascinating phase of his work, "the true poetry of conception."[21] He considered ornament the final flowering from the constitution and form-character of the structure, the part pregnant with the whole just as the whole had given birth to the part. Ideally, every bit of casework or furniture, every fabric design, fixture, or pattern in the panes and cames of a window or glass door could find its parent in the ground-plan or the principal elevations. This meant that he had to conceive the plan as a seed-germ for ornament, a vital motif able to engender melodic elaborations and lyrical variations.

So fresh and powerful were the buildings Wright designed after

. . . .

Notes

1900 that he was bound to attract an eager following. Countless imitations of his architecture can be discovered in cities and suburbs throughout the Middle West. To think of Wright as the most distinguished member of a "Prairie School" is thus to mistake cause for effect, and to ignore the rare phenomenon of a profound imagination. True, he benefited from his assistants, most of whom were faithful even when he failed to meet the payroll; and some of them went on to do reasonably good work of their own, but it was not of much originality. Wright's optimism was remarkably resilient, and so was his affection for the young; but he soon doubted the validity of a new school of the Middle West. The very notion of a school or a style was repugnant to his philosophy of change, growth, and the sovereign individual — favored by nature and thus full of praise for nature as the great bene-factor — who creates out of an intui-tive sympathy for the inward abstract rhythms of natural form. "Why turn superficially to *a* style," he asked, "instead of being deeply concerned with style?"[22]

Wright's imagination came from far within. The work of his followers proved too largely derivative, medi-ocre, and insipid. "One repays a teacher badly if one always remains nothing but a pupil," said Nietzsche. If there was indeed a Prairie School and anything tragic about it, the sorrow should come not from the fact that all was over so soon, but that it could never have amounted to much anyway.[23] The architecture of Frank Lloyd Wright did not ask to be quantified or codified. Art, unlike science, does not advance by incre-ments and through schools and the tedious efforts of lesser minds. That part of the world which performs consistently at the highest aesthetic level without regard for the life or death of an individual is not art, but nature.

1.   Aristotle, *Politics*, II, chap. 8, in *The Basic Works of Aristotle*, ed. Richard McKeon (New York, 1941), p. 1161. Hippodamos in the fifth century B.C. further developed the gridiron plan.

2.   See Ananda K. Coomaraswamy, "Is Art a Superstition or a Way of Life?" (1937), in *Christian and Oriental Philosphy of Art* (New York, 1956), pp. 61-85.

3.   Nietzsche, *On the Genealogy of Morals* (1887), in *Basic Writings of Nietzsche*, ed. Walter Kaufmann (New York, 1968), p. 549. Nietzsche, whom Wright admired, attacked the industrial city as a place where all great feelings decayed and where great thoughts "are boiled alive and cooked till they are small." See his popular *Thus Spoke Zarathustra* (1883-92), trans. Walter Kaufmann (New York, 1966), p. 176.

4.   See "Rebellion and Art" in Albert Camus, *The Rebel* (1951), trans. Anthony Bower (New York, 1956), pp. 253-58.

5.   Wright, "In the Cause of Architecture," *Architectural Record* 23 (March 1908), pp. 162, 164. Wright addressed what John Dewey, in *Art as Experience* (New York, 1934), p. 10, nicely called the problem of "recovering the continuity of esthetic experience with normal processes of living."

6.   Wright, *An Autobiography* (New York, 1943), p. 150. In a later book, *A Testament* (New York, 1957), p. 225, he calls it "the original affirmative negation (the great protestant)." The Larkin Building was sited amid industrial structures of no pretension to architecture.

7.   The true imagination proves itself "very powerful in creating another nature, as it were, out of the material that actual nature gives it," Kant writes in the *Critique of Judgment* (1790), trans. J. H. Bernard (New York, 1951), p. 157. Adler and Sullivan's office plan was published in *Engineering and Building*

Record 22 (June 7, 1890), p. 5. It shows that Wright's room was next to Sullivan's and was in fact larger than Adler's. Wright proudly republished the plan in *Genius and the Mobocracy* (New York, 1949), p. 47.

8.   Walt Whitman, "I was Looking a Long While," in *Leaves of Grass* (New York, 1891-92), p. 305. The best exposition of Sullivan's ideas can be found in his own words, especially in *Kindergarten Chats (1918) and Other Writings*, ed. Isabella Athey (New York, 1947).

9.   Wright tried to tell what he had learned from Sullivan in *Genius and the Mobocracy* (note 7). The title expresses his attraction to the thinking of Nietzsche.

10.   For a classic and poetic account of the vanishing prairie, see Hamlin Garland, *Boy Life on the Prairie* (New York, 1899), published just as Wright was about to reach the maturity of his imagination. But perhaps the most beautiful of all tributes to the prairie came from a man who never saw it, Arthur Schopenhauer: it can be found in his major work, *The World as Will and Representation* (1819; rpt. New York, 1969), vol. 1, pp. 203-04. Schopenhauer describes the boundless and silent prairie as a species of the sublime and a summons to solitude, and in that sense a measure of one's intellectual worth.

11.   Felix Shay, *Elbert Hubbard of East Aurora* (New York, 1926), p. 429; Sullivan, *Kindergarten Chats* (note 8), pp. 74, 100. Wright in 1895 added to his small house in Oak Park a vaulted playroom; the Coonley playhouse in Riverside, Ill., and the "Little Dipper" kindergarten project for Aline Barnsdall, in Los Angeles, were also among his significant works. In later years Wright tended to exaggerate the importance of the Froebel gifts, doubtless in tribute to his mother, who seems to have been the first to inflate their influence: "To this fortunate early training as a beginning she ascribes his instinctive grasp of the niceties of line, form and color," Robert C. Spencer, Jr., noted carefully in "The Work of Frank Lloyd Wright," *Architectural Review* 7 (June 1900), p. 69.

12. See those for W. H. Winslow and H. M. Cooper, in Spencer (note 11) pp. 62, 64. "When power becomes gracious and descends into the visible—such descent I call beauty," wrote Nietzsche in *Thus Spoke Zarathustra* (note 3), p. 118. Elsewhere, he defined architecture as a kind of eloquence of power in forms. There is a nice irony to the fact that an architecture so largely inspired by nature and the rural vernacular became so much more sophisticated than the supposedly urbane buildings of the city.

13. Wright, "In the Cause of Architecture: The Third Dimension," in *The Life-Work of the American Architect Frank Lloyd Wright* (1925; rpt. New York, 1965), p. 49; and William Morris, "Art and Socialism" (1884), in *A Modern Book of Esthetics*, ed. Melvin M. Rader (New York, 1935), p. 429.

14. Weber, *The Protestant Ethic and the Spirit of Capitalism* (1904-05), trans. Talcott Parsons (London, 1930), p. 53; and Veblen, *The Theory of the Leisure Class* (1899; rpt. New York, 1931), pp. 81-82, 162-64. Veblen viewed the kindergarten idea as a worthy cause of the more intelligent housewives who found themselves "ill at ease under the pecuniary code of reputable life" (p. 389).

15. "Only that will which obeys law is free; for it obeys itself—it is independent and so free," Hegel writes in *The Philosophy of History* (1830-31; rpt. New York, 1956), p. 39. See Wright, "In the Cause of Architecture" (note 5), p. 163; *An Autobiography* (note 6), p. 163; and *Genius and the Mobocracy* (note 7), pp. 6, 8, 20. Wright's abstraction far surpassed George Maher's plant-motif theories as well as Jens Jensen's landscape compositions in indigenous plants. "I am an abstractionist seeking the pattern behind the realism—the interior structure instead of the comparatively superficial exterior effects you delight in," he wrote Jensen. "In other words I am a builder." See his *Letters to Architects*, ed. Bruce Brooks Pfeiffer (Fresno, Calif., 1984), p. 104.

16. Wilhelm Miller, in *The Prairie Spirit in Landscape Gardening* (Urbana, Ill., 1915), pp. 12-15, identified eight other types of Illinois scenery serving as foils to the prairie.

17. Hegel found artistic production to be not a formal activity according with a series of definitions, but instead "constrained to work out of its own wealth." See *Philosophies of Art and Beauty*, ed. Albert Hofstadter and Richard Kuhns (Chicago, 1964), p. 396.

18. Surely this understanding of architectural space did not derive from a belated and direct encounter in the Southwest with an Indian pot or basket. Okakura Kakuzo's rendering of the idea in *The Book of Tea* (Boston, 1906; rpt. Rutland, Vt., 1956), p. 45, is much more vivid than the original text of the *Tao Te Ching*, which reads: "Clay is fashioned into vessels; but it is on their empty hollowness, that their use depends. The door and windows are cut out (from the walls) to form an apartment; but it is on the empty space (within), that its use depends." See *The Sacred Books of the East*, ed. Max Müller (London, 1891), vol. 39, p. 55. See also Wright's comments in *The Master Architect: Conversations with Frank Lloyd Wright*, ed. Patrick J. Meehan (New York, 1984), pp. 77-79; as well in several of his other works, including *An Organic Architecture* (1939; rpt. Cambridge, Mass., 1977), pp.2-4; *Architectural Forum* 68 (Jan. 1938), p. 35; and *A Testament* (note 6), p. 224. The plans for Unity Temple were accepted in April 1906 and ground was broken in May.

19. Wright, *Modern Architecture* (Princeton, 1931), p. 35; and Nietzsche, *Ecce Homo* (1908), in *Basic Writings of Nietzsche* (note 3), p. 707. Wright's architectural propositions appear most succinctly in the Princeton lectures and in his first "In the Cause of Architecture" (note 5), pp. 156-57.

20. Whitman, "Song of the Open Road," in *Leaves of Grass* (note 8), p. 118.

21. Wright, "In the Cause of Architecture" (note 5), p. 161.

22. Wright, *Architectural Forum* (note 18), p. 100. Also see *Letters to Architects* (note 15), p. 71, in which he writes of the projected Taliesin Fellowship as "a little experimental station" where the creative instinct "might be wooed and won, if only to a small extent." He adds, "I know it cannot be taught." For a discerning discussion of genius in relation to schools, see Kant's *Critique of Judgment* (note 7), pp. 161-63.

23. Nietzsche, *Thus Spoke Zarathustra* (note 3), p. 78. Miller notes at the end of *The Prairie Spirit* (note 16) that Wright has refused "to give or recognize any name" for the work he was the first to develop. Wright's letter to Miller appears in *Letters to Architects* (note 15), pp. 50-52: he says he has never used the phrase "Prairie Style of Architecture," asserts that Sullivan never thought about the prairie as an influence and thus could not figure "in any form other than grotesque as the founder of a 'Prairie School of Architecture,'" and attacks the academic habit of predicating schools instead of recognizing artistic creation as the work of an individual. Even in his first published version of "In the Cause of Architecture" (note 5), p. 164, Wright wrote of the danger of having followers, and deplored those who served in his studio "only long enough to acquire a smattering of form" and then left "to sell a superficial proficiency elsewhere."

· ·

Cat. no. 79
Arthur Heun,
Window from the
Sedgwick Brinsmaid
House, Des Moines,
Iowa, c. 1897-1902
(demolished 1971);
fabricated by Giannini
and Hilgart;
clear glass in lead
cames,
122 x 71 cm.
Department of
Architecture Purchase
Fund, 1985.593.

The Sedgwick Brinsmaid House, built sometime between 1897 and 1902, is thought to be the earliest Prairie School building constructed in Iowa. Designed by Arthur Heun, an architect not usually associated with the Prairie School, the house is one of the earliest examples of the dissemination of the Prairie style throughout the Midwest. Heun (1866-1946), who received his architectural training in the Grand Rapids office of his uncle Volusin Bude, came to Chicago in 1887. He began as a draftsman in the office of Francis Whitehouse, a specialist in residential architecture. When Whitehouse retired in 1893, Heun assumed the practice and distinguished himself in the field of residential architecture, designing in a variety of revival styles. Among his most notable commissions were the Renaissance Revival style Melody Farm, built for J. Ogden Armour in Lake Forest, and the residence of William McCormick Blair on Astor Street.

One of Heun's lesser-known and uncharacteristic commissions was the Sedgwick Brinsmaid House in Des Moines. This two-story house was reminiscent of Prairie designs with its open plan; earth-tone color scheme of brown, and shades of white and green; horizontal orientation and banding; long, overhanging eaves; and groupings of leaded-glass windows. Some of the furniture in the house was designed by George Mann Niedecken, a well-known designer and manufacturer who often worked with Frank Lloyd Wright and his protégés on custom interior designs. A window from the Brinsmaid House, now in the Art Institute's collection (cat. no. 79), however, is less typical. It features a central pane of clear glass that is surrounded by a symmetrical geometric design made up of smaller sections of clear glass. Heun did not incorporate any colored or iridescent glass into the window, both of which were common features of Prairie School windows.

In his monographic article on the Brinsmaid House (*Journal of the Society of Architectural Historians* 29 [1970], pp. 56-59), Wesley Shank speculated about Brinsmaid's reasons for wanting a Prairie School house, considering that Prairie style influence had not yet spread to Iowa. Brinsmaid was a prominent importer of china, glass, and silver in Des Moines in the early twentieth century. Given the fact that he had to travel extensively to conduct his business, it is likely that he was both aware of and sympathetic to the new architectural developments taking place in Chicago with Wright and his disciples. Shank further speculated that if Brinsmaid's firm were to stand for good taste and fine design, it is likely that he felt his own home must demonstrate that fact and show residents of Des Moines the latest trends in the world of design. A Prairie School house would, certainly, accomplish these ends. What remains unclear is why Brinsmaid gave the commission to Heun, who generally built in revival styles, rather than to Wright or another architect who would have been well-versed in the Prairie School idiom.

The Brinsmaid House was demolished in 1971, and the Art Institute's window was purchased at auction in 1985.

George W. Maher's family came to Chicago from New Albany, Indiana, in the hopes of sharing some of the prosperity following the 1871 Fire. Family prosperity, however, never materialized, and at the age of thirteen Maher (1864-1926) entered an architectural apprenticeship in the office of two German immigrant architects, Augustus Bauer and Henry W. Hill. Shortly thereafter, Maher worked in the office of Joseph Lyman Silsbee, head of one of the largest and most successful firms designing residences in the 1880s. It was in Silsbee's office that Maher received a solid architectural training and was exposed to a philosophy of design that greatly influenced his own residential work.

In 1888, at the age of 24, Maher left Silsbee's office to open his own practice. A later partnership with Charles Corwin was short-lived. Maher's work at the time consisted primarily of residences, many for Chicago's emerging business tycoons, who wanted houses that would represent their new-found status: these include the John Farson House in Oak Park, the James Patten House in Evanston, and the Harry Rubens House in Glencoe. Maher's residential designs often featured symmetrical facades that were imbued with classical influences, but were devoid of specific classical ornament. Instead, their horizontal lines and clear, leaded-glass windows reveal the influence of the Prairie School. The resulting designs are, nonetheless, uniquely attributable to Maher. In addition, Maher developed a theory of design, called the "motif-rhythm theory." Using this theory, Maher would choose a plant or a geometric shape to be used throughout a building to unify diverse elements such as capitals, leaded-glass windows, and newel posts.

Maher employed the motif-rhythm theory in the Mosser House (1902), in which a thistle is repeated throughout the interior and on exterior capitals as well. The Art Institute owns a plaster exterior capital from the Mosser House, which was replaced when the house was renovated in 1987. A poppy window (cat. no. 80) attributed to Maher is believed to be the principal motif from an as yet unidentified residence. The rectilinear panes of clear glass in the window reveal the influence of the Prairie School, while the central, realistic poppy design is a typical realization of Maher's theory, which was widely published in the major American and European periodicals of the day.

Maher's career peaked in the early years of the twentieth century when he began to receive important public commissions. Two of the most important were for the Patten Gymnasium and the Swift Science Building, both constructed at Northwestern University in Evanston between 1908 and 1910. J. William Rudd has called the Patten Gymnasium "undoubtedly the most successful public design Maher developed. The use of the motif-rhythm theory in this design found support in the form chosen and the structural system employed. Consequently, a unity between conception and expression was achieved which was unequaled in most of Maher's designs" (*Prairie School Review* 1 [1964], p. 9). Maher later did a great deal of work for the J. R. Watkins Medical Company of Winona, Minnesota, including a commission for the company's Administration Building (1914), and the Winona Savings Bank (1915). With the onset of the First World War, Maher's commissions naturally dwindled. Following the war, his son Philip joined him in partnership, and Maher was free to pursue planning work in the Chicago suburbs of Glencoe, Kenilworth, and Hinsdale.

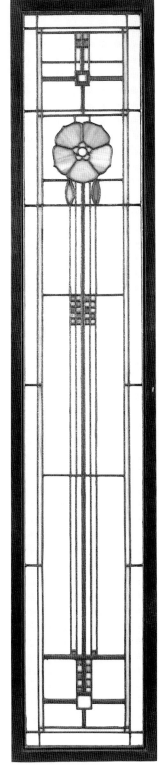

Cat. no. 80
**George W. Maher,
Window depicting
a poppy from an
unidentified residence,
c.1900/1915;
clear and opaque
colored glass
in lead cames,
168.2 x 33.4 cm.
Gift of Mrs. Eugene A.
Davidson, 1973.344.**

Peter J. Weber

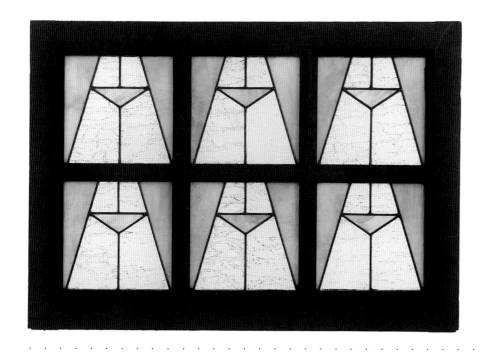

Peter J. Weber (1864-1923) continued the tradition set in the mid-nineteenth century of German architects immigrating to Chicago to practice their profession. Weber studied architecture through the atelier system, working from 1886 until 1889 in the Berlin office of Kayser and von Grossheim. In 1889 the firm sent Weber to South America to supervise construction of a resort hotel, but when that project fell through, Weber came to the U.S., arriving in Chicago in 1891. He spent a brief time with Adler and Sullivan, but almost immediately he began working with Charles B. Atwood, the Chief of Design for the World's Columbian Exposition. Weber worked on the development of the Palace of Fine Arts and a number of other structures including the Chocolat Menier Pavilion and the Van Houten Chocolate Building. He soon joined the office of D. H. Burnham and Company, assisting in the design of such buildings as

Ellicott Square in Buffalo, and in Chicago, the Great Northern Hotel (1890-91), the Fisher Building (1895-96), and the Illinois Trust and Savings Bank (1896). In 1900 Weber established his own firm and designed a number of important commissions including the Casino and Theater at Ravinia Park (1904), an addition to the Fisher Building (1907), the Seattle Public Library (1909), and an apartment building at 3400 N. Sheridan Road (1910). Finally, Weber was responsible for a plan to renovate and rehabilitate the old Fine Arts Building from the World's Fair into the Museum of Science and Industry.

Two of Weber's most notable designs were the Casino and Theater at Ravinia in Highland Park, Illinois. Ravinia Park began as an amusement park built by the Chicago and Milwaukee Electric Railroad. It was planned as a year-round pleasure resort and was intended to increase ridership on the railroad. The thirty-six-acre park opened in 1904 and included such amusements as an

electric arm swing, a skating rink, a toboggan slide, and an electric fountain. Classical music was also featured at the Pavilion. When the railroad went out of business, the Ravinia Park Company was formed to continue operation of the park, but with opera, rather than amusement, as its primary focus. Ravinia Park was very successful from 1911 until the Depression. The park was closed for a short time in the early 1930s, but it reopened in 1936, serving its current function as the summer home of the Chicago Symphony Orchestra.

The Casino and Theater that Weber designed for the original park combined elements of Spanish Colonial architecture with Arts and Crafts sensibilities. Both buildings featured curved brackets supporting large timber roof beams, white stucco walls, and leaded art-glass windows. The two-story, white stucco Casino featured two three-story towers flanking its entrance. Its windows (see cat. no. 81) were composed of panes of opaque blue glass combined with a rare crazed clear glass. The windows were located on inner transoms and in the stairways.

In 1984 Ravinia announced plans to remove a 1956 addition to the Casino and to restore the original building for use as a recital hall and reception area. When it was discovered that the acoustics in the building were not suitable for such an adaptive reuse, the Casino was demolished in 1986 so that a more appropriate building could be constructed on its site. The window from the building was donated to the Art Institute at that time. The Ravinia Theater that Weber designed is still standing.

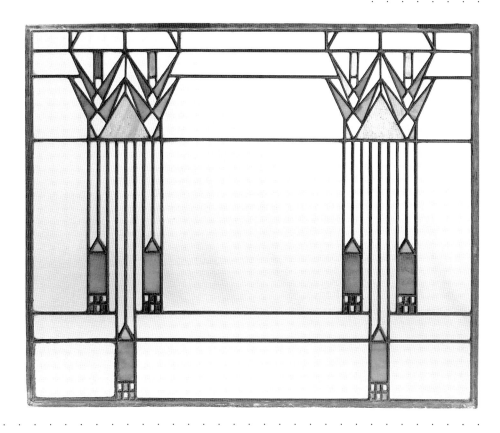

Marion Mahony Griffin, a prominent draftsman and designer in the office of Frank Lloyd Wright, was one of the nation's first women to distinguish herself in the field of architecture. Born in Chicago, Marion Mahony (1871-1962) was the first of two women to graduate with a bachelor's degree in architecture from the Massachusetts Institute of Technology, and she was the first female architect to be licensed in Illinois. She worked for a year in the office of her cousin Dwight Perkins, before entering Wright's office, where she worked on and off from 1895 until 1909. From about 1900 to 1909, Mahony was Wright's chief assistant. Although it is difficult to determine precisely her contribution to Wright's designs and projects, many scholars credit Wright with the initial design plan and Mahony with the secondary decorative schemes, such as furniture, glass, lighting fixtures, and mosaics. Mahony is also renowned for producing some of the finest renderings of Wright's projects; her striking perspectives frequently reveal the influence of traditional Japanese renderings.

During the fourteen years that Mahony was in Wright's office, she also worked with other architects and accepted independent commissions. Among her own most notable designs were the All Soul's Church (1902) in Evanston; the Gerald Mahony House (1907) in Elkhart, Indiana; the David Amberg House (1909) in Grand Rapids; and the E. P. Irving, Robert Mueller, and Adolph Mueller houses in Decatur, Illinois, from the early teens. Around 1906 Gerald Mahony, Marion's brother, commissioned her to renovate his traditional midwestern farmhouse into a Prairie style home. Ironically, Gerald's wife knew the Wrights when both families lived in Madison, Wisconsin, and Frank Lloyd Wright's younger sister was her close friend. Few details about the Mahony com-

mission are known, but a window from the house (cat. no. 82; pl. 7), clearly in the Prairie style, has large panes of clear glass punctuated by two vertical designs composed of chevrons, thin bands, triangles, and rectangles of amber, iridescent, and gold glass. Although smaller and much simpler in design, the window for the Mahony House is similar to that of Wright's Darwin D. Martin House of 1904-06 (see cat. no. 90).

After Wright left for Europe in 1909, Marion Mahony worked with Herman Von Holst, the Prairie School architect who agreed to take Wright's remaining commissions if Mahony would come into the firm as a designer. At the same time, she prepared drawings for fellow architect Walter Burley Griffin, who had left the Wright office in 1905 and whom she married in 1911, the same year Griffin entered the competition to plan Canberra, the new capital city of Australia. Griffin's plans enhanced the actual topography of the site, one of the principal factors in his winning the commission. Mahony's drawings for the plan,

which were also a persuasive factor, were exhibited in all the major cities of Europe after the commission was awarded. In 1913 Marion Mahony and Walter Burley Griffin finished their respective work in Chicago and left for Australia to supervise the construction of Canberra. They spent twenty-five years in Australia, before moving to Lucknow, India. There Griffin designed several buildings, including a library, and he was building a palace for a rajah when he suffered an accidental death in February 1937. In 1940 Mahony returned to the U.S. During her remaining years, she designed several town plans for utopian communities, and wrote a twelve-volume autobiography titled *The Magic of America*. The house she designed for Gerald Mahony was demolished in 1965 to make way for a factory. Portions of the house were auctioned off before demolition, but the window in the Art Institute's collection was held by the Warner Demolition Company until it was sold to a private gallery in 1984.

Cat. no. 82
Marion Mahony Griffin, Window from the Gerald Mahony House, Elkhart, Indiana, 1907 (demolished c. 1965); clear, opaque, and iridescent glass in lead cames, 61 x 76 cm. Restricted gift of David C. Hilliard and the Department of Architecture Purchase Fund, 1984.193.

Alfonso Iannelli

Cat. no. 83
Alfonso Iannelli,
Study model for
the head of a sprite for
Midway Gardens;
plaster,
33 x 24 x 25 cm.
Restricted gift of the
Thomas J. and Mary E.
Eyerman Foundation,
1984.1293.

Cat. no. 84
Alfonso Iannelli,
Study model for
the head of a sprite for
Midway Gardens;
plaster,
54 x 24 x 29 cm.
Fractional gift of Mr.
and Mrs. Seymour H.
Persky, 1984.1254.

In his seminal book about Frank Lloyd Wright, *In the Nature of Materials* (New York, 1942), the renowned architectural historian Henry-Russell Hitchcock called Midway Gardens Wright's "last great Chicago work." Hitchcock observed that at Midway Gardens Wright sought to create "a fresh open fantasia in which sculpture and painting, not as independent entities but closely related to the essential architectural conception, should play an important part" (p. 63). Midway Gardens on the city's South Side was a tightly knit collaborative effort between Wright and the artist Alfonso Iannelli.

Alfonso Iannelli (1888-1965) was a native Italian whose family immigrated to the United States when he was ten years old. Iannelli received training in the fine arts at the Art Student's League of New York, and he began to combine the fine and applied arts early in his career when

he worked on the sculpture for the Cathedral of St. John the Divine in New York and produced artwork for popular magazines such as *Harper's Weekly*, *Collier's*, and *Ladies' Home Journal*. Iannelli traveled across the United States from New York to Los Angeles trying to find artistic expression suited to the needs of America, rather than turning to Europe for inspiration as many of his contemporaries did. In his search for an "American" art and in his rejection of the widely held belief in the supremacy of European culture, Iannelli's philosophy unwittingly paralleled a late-nineteenth-century movement in architecture that was at the core of the work of Louis Sullivan and his contemporaries and that was perpetuated by a succeeding generation of architects including Frank Lloyd Wright. In Los Angeles, Iannelli became acquainted with Wright's two sons, the Prairie School architects Lloyd Wright and John Lloyd Wright, and with another Prairie School disciple, Barry Byrne.

It was through John Lloyd Wright that Iannelli met the elder Wright and received the commission to design sculpture for Midway Gardens.

Wright's Midway Gardens, an elaborate entertainment complex based on the European concept of the casino, consisted of indoor and outdoor spaces for the purposes of eating, drinking, ballroom dancing, listening to symphonic music, and viewing ballet (see fig. 8). The complex enclosed nearly an entire city block and was constructed of brick and concrete blocks of various geometric patterns that were cast at the site (see cat. no. 98). As plans for the building were completed in 1913, Wright commissioned sculptors and painters to execute his artistic conceptions for the building. Wright attempted to unify the various artforms through a decorative motif of basic geometric shapes. He commissioned Alfonso Iannelli to design the

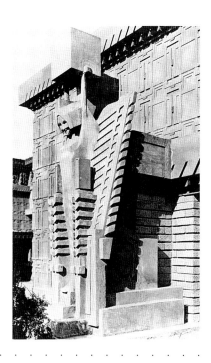

many sprites (disembodied spirits) that were located in the summer garden and main dining room. According to Wright's specifications, the sprites were modeled in flat planes, not in rounded naturalistic forms as was the common practice of the day. These figures, which are integrated with cubes, spheres, triangles, and octagons, were the joint effort of the sculptor and architect. According to David Hanks in *The Decorative Designs of Frank Lloyd Wright* (New York, 1979), "Iannelli made scale drawings and models before they were then finally approved by Wright for execution by Iannelli" (p. 122). The Art Institute holds two such plaster studio models (cat. nos. 83, 84; pl. 10), which were later cast in concrete for actual installation in the building. As a result of this close collaborative effort, the sprite sculptures functioned as part of the very fabric of the building complex, rather than as decorative additions (fig. 1; cat. no. 85).

The outbreak of the First World War, the introduction of Prohibition in 1919, and the onset of the Depression all contributed to the eventual demise of Midway Gardens. The complex was demolished in 1929, only fifteen years after its construction. Of the fragments of that building that survive, the Iannelli sprites are the most characteristic of the spirit of the design that made the building one of Wright's, and Iannelli's, most important works.

Despite the success of their collaborative effort, Midway Gardens was the last project for which Wright used a professional sculptor. Wright offered Iannelli the commission for the interior decoration of the Imperial Hotel in Tokyo, but Iannelli refused it. So distraught was he at never receiving credit for the sculpture of Midway Gardens, that Iannelli chose not to collaborate with Wright again. Ultimately he regretted that decision. The success of Midway Gardens, however, prompted him to move to Chicago, where he opened a studio and continued to collaborate with a great many architects including Purcell and Elmslie, Barry Byrne, Bruce Goff, and R. Harold Zook. Among the many architectural projects in which Iannelli collaborated, several were interior designs of sculpture for theaters—such as Zook's Pickwick Theater (1929) in Park Ridge, Illinois—and for churches — such as Barry Byrne's St. Thomas the Apostle Church (1923-24) in Chicago. In 1928 Iannelli was invited to head a new Department of Design at The Art Institute of Chicago which was to be sponsored by the Association of

Arts and Industries, a group of Chicago industrialists who understood the need for a school that could train young designers. Iannelli himself did design a number of industrial objects that were actually put into production, including a hair dryer and a toaster for Sunbeam. Unfortunately, the progressive program did not take shape, and it was in 1937, when László Moholy-Nagy brought the New Bauhaus to Chicago, that a new design school was established by the Association.

Cat. no. 85
***Alfonso Iannelli,
Figure for an
unidentified fountain,
c. 1925;
cast concrete,
113 x 20.4 x 28 cm.
Gift of Mr. Donald R.
Sunshine, 1975.688.***

Fig. 1
***Frank Lloyd Wright,
Midway Gardens,
60th Street and Cottage
Grove Avenue, 1913-14
(demolished 1929);
detail of the exterior,
showing a sprite
designed by Alfonso
Iannelli.***

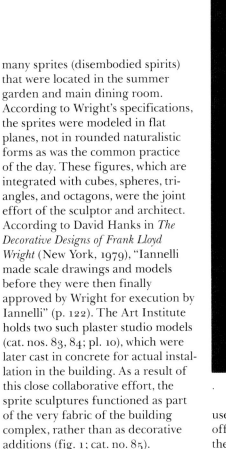

Frank Lloyd Wright, one of America's most famous architects, had a distinguished and prolific seventy-year career that has given him legendary status among twentieth-century architects. His impact on world architecture was tremendous, and he, more than any other late-nineteenth- or twentieth-century architect, defined and then exported a unique form of American architecture to Europe and the Orient.

Born in Wisconsin, Wright (1867-1959) was influenced at an early age by the agrarian character of nineteenth-century Wisconsin and the pervasive nineteenth-century respect for nature as expressed in the writings of Emerson, Whitman, and Jefferson. His fascination with and respect for nature eventually was given form in his theory of "organic architecture," the belief that every small detail of a building should reflect the design of the whole, as it does in nature. His theory is based on the architectural philosophy of his mentor, Louis H. Sullivan, for whom he worked from 1888 to 1893. Sullivan, who initiated a lifelong quest for a form of architecture that would express the democratic values of America, believed that architectural ornament should be organic, deriving its form from nature, and that it should be integrated with the structure of a building, reflecting the building's structure and function. While in Adler and Sullivan's office, Wright worked on several buildings that came to be appreciated as milestones in modern American architecture, among them the Auditorium Building (see pp. 132-33). Wright established his own practice in 1893 following a falling out with Sullivan over Wright's independent commissions. These commissions, starting as early as 1889, were primarily for small, eclectic residential designs, such as his own house in Oak Park.

By 1900 Wright had become a mature and successful designer, producing public buildings and large private homes. His remarkable body of work is identified with the Prairie School of architecture of which he was clearly the figurehead. Among his most respected designs of this period are the Dana House (1903) in Springfield, Illinois; the Martin House (1904) and the Larkin Company Administration Building (1903-04), both in Buffalo, New York; the Coonley Estate (1908) in Riverside, Illinois; and Unity Temple (1905-06) in Oak Park.

At the peak of his success, Wright's life suddenly became filled with controversy. In 1909 he left his family in Oak Park and sojourned in Europe with one of his clients, Mamah Borthwick Cheney. While he was in Europe, two portfolios of his work, *Ausgeführte Bauten und Entwürfe* (1910), were published by Ernst Wasmuth in Berlin. These publications — one a portfolio of 100 drawings; the other, a book of photographs illustrating his work — catapulted the architect to fame in Europe and secured for him a position as a leader in the modern movement. Upon his return in 1911, Wright separated from his first wife and embarked on the creation of a new home, studio, and place of retreat in Wisconsin. In 1914 at Taliesin, as Wright called it, Mamah Cheney and her children were killed and the estate burned to the ground. The controversies surrounding Wright drove his conservative clientele away, and he entered a twenty-year period of decline, although he did design two commissions of great importance during this period — Midway Gardens (1913-14) in Chicago and the Imperial Hotel (1915-22) in Tokyo. In addition, Wright also designed residences in California, including the Barnsdall House (1917-20) in Los Angeles and the Millard House (1923) in Pasadena.

In the 1930s Wright began to re-emerge with a series of remarkable buildings including Fallingwater (1936-39) near Mill Run, Pennsylvania; the S.C. Johnson and Son Administration Building (1936-46) in Racine, Wisconsin; and the first of his Usonian houses, the Jacobs House (1936-37) in Madison, Wisconsin. Wright continued to practice actively until his death in 1959. His legacy includes a school of architecture, Taliesin, which continues today, and nearly 1,000 designs for buildings, of which approximately 400 were built.

The Wright fragments in the Art Institute's collection date roughly from four periods. First, early in his independent career, Wright's designs

and his style of ornament were largely influenced by his mentor, Louis Sullivan. Fragments of these early projects represented in the Art Institute's collection are from the Charnley House (1891), the Roloson Houses (1894), the Francis Apartments (1895), and the Heller House (1897). Second, objects from Wright's renowned Prairie School period, roughly 1900 to 1909, represent the Darwin D. Martin (1904-06), Tomek (1907), Evans (1908), and Coonley (1908) houses. The period of personal turmoil in Wright's life is reflected in a third group of fragments from the Coonley Playhouse (1912), the Little House (1912-14), Midway Gardens (1913-14), and the Bach House (1915). Finally, later in his career, Wright was concerned with prefabrication and affordable housing, as represented by a fragment in the collection from the Weltzheimer House (1948-50).

Roloson Houses and Francis Apartments

Shortly after Wright left the firm of Adler and Sullivan to establish his own practice, he received the commission to design four party-wall houses for Robert W. Roloson. Roloson was the son-in-law of Edward C. Waller, one of Wright's most important early clients. (Waller's son would later commission Wright to design Midway Gardens.) The Roloson Houses are a combination of English Tudor design and the kind of geometric detailing Wright learned from Sullivan. Although Wright was still tremendously influenced by Sullivan, the design of these houses is more akin to the work of John Wellborn Root. The four-story residences of brick with limestone trim originally featured a paved front terrace surrounded by a terracotta balustrade that separated the terraces from each other and the street. The individual buff-colored balusters (cat. no. 86) feature a central sphere whose lower third is covered by foliate ornament reminiscent of Sulli-

van's work. The beading at the top and bottom of the globe shows the influence of Sullivan's "berry motif."

Like the Roloson Houses, the Francis Apartments (1895; fig. 2) reveal both Sullivan's influence and Wright's genius for planning and design. Historians have credited the Francis Apartments with establishing a new level for apartment-house design in the Midwest, inspiring numerous later imitations. The exterior design of the four-story brick building reflected Wright's concerns for ample interior light and ventilation. The plain, buff-colored Roman brick on the exterior was embellished with bands of decorative terracotta at the cornice and street level. The street-level terracotta consisted of overlapping circles surrounded by leafy Sullivanesque ornament. The building's entrance gate, now in the Art Institute's collec-

Cat. no. 86
Frank Lloyd Wright, Baluster from the Robert W. Roloson Houses, 3213-19 Calumet Avenue, 1894; terracotta, 43.2 x 19.7 x 19.7 cm. Gift of The Antiquarian Society through the Twentieth-Century Decorative Arts Fund, 1972.287.

Fig. 2
Frank Lloyd Wright, Francis Apartments, 4304 S. Forrestville Avenue, 1895 (demolished 1971).

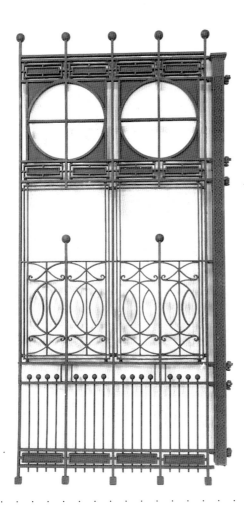

Frank Lloyd Wright

. . . .

Cat. no. 87

**Frank Lloyd Wright,
Entry gate from the
Francis Apartments;
painted cast and
wrought iron,
253 x 119.4 x 5 cm.
Gift of the Graham
Foundation for
Advanced Studies in the
Fine Arts, 1971.449.**

Cat. no. 88

**Frank Lloyd Wright,
Circular ventilator
grille from the Francis
Apartments;
cast iron,
diameter 97.8 cm.
Gift of the Antiquarian
Society through the Mr.
and Mrs. Robert Hixon
Glore Fund, 1971.787.**

tion (cat. no. 87), repeated the circle motif, but it had none of the leafy ornament of the terracotta. The fact that Wright's own early signature — a cross within a circle within a square — appears in the upper portion of the gate suggests that Wright himself, not one of his draftsmen, designed the gate. Since Wright often designed his buildings in a monochromatic scheme, the gate was repainted in 1987 the same buff color as the terracotta that would have been adjacent to it. A circular ventilator grille from the interior of the building, also in the museum's collection (cat. no. 88), reveals a combination of the repeated circular motif and a central star shape. Like the gate, the ventilator grille shows no leafy ornament, but the intricacy of its geometric pattern, nonetheless, reveals the influence of Sullivan. In both the Francis Apartments and the Francisco Terrace Apartments of the same year, Wright not only showed what he had inherited from Sullivan, but also indicated his own ideas on geometric simplicity.

Heller House

The Heller House (fig. 3) of 1897 is considered one of the finest of Wright's transitional buildings, revealing the influence of Sullivan and prefiguring Wright's Prairie houses. The Heller House was adapted to a double city lot in Hyde Park, which began to develop in the 1880s as an area of substantial upper-class residences set amidst large gardens. Hyde Park flourished in the late nineteenth century with the construction of the University of Chicago in 1892 and the staging of the World's Columbian Exposition the following year. Wright's three-story house was constructed of the same materials that he had used in his earlier projects — grey and buff Roman brick, Bedford limestone, plaster, and fret-sawn wood. The unusual third floor of the house features a grouping of windows set within arcades that rest on colonnettes topped by elaborate ornamented capitals. In between the

arcades is a plaster frieze of figures sculpted by Richard Bock, a sculptor with whom Wright often worked. The second floor also features a colonnade of recessed pilasters with ornate Sullivanesque capitals. The Art Institute received one of these plaster capitals as a gift when the original, weather-damaged capitals were replaced by exact duplicates.

The Art Institute also has two sections of exterior frieze made of fret-sawn wood (see cat. no. 89). The simple, repeated geometric pattern, which pierces the wood completely, is reminiscent of the fret-sawn ornament that Wright helped contribute to Sullivan's Charnley House (see cat. no. 51). The Heller House bears other similarities to the Charnley with its one-room-deep plan and new relationships of interior volumes that are reflected in the exterior massing. The wide overhanging eaves on the second and third floors of the Heller House and the groupings of clear and colored leaded-glass windows give a horizontal

166

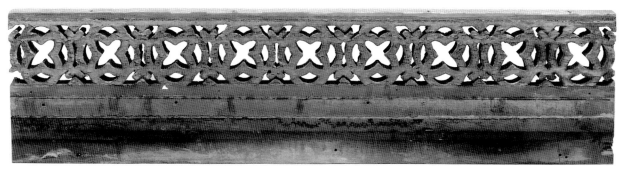

emphasis to the structure, making it a precursor of the new geometric aesthetic that Wright more fully realized in his Prairie houses.

By 1900 Wright's work had reached a highly sophisticated level of achievement; he had also codified his philosophy of residential design into what he called an "organic architecture," and an early manifestation of which is known familiarly as the Prairie style. The Prairie School was a uniquely midwestern architectural style, used primarily for residential structures, that flourished between 1900 and the First World War. The Prairie School had two principal premises: one, that a building should function as an organic whole, with all details and spaces related to one another; and the other, that the interior should relate to the landscape outside by bringing that environment indoors.

Prairie School houses were often designed with a great deal of attention paid to interior furnishings (see

the radiator grille from the Evans House, for example, cat. no. 93), and art objects were designed expressly for the buildings in which they were used. Also, to communicate the interdependence of the outdoors and indoors, Prairie School architects designed exquisite art-glass windows (see the Tree of Life window, cat. no. 90) with stylized geometric designs. It was Louis Sullivan who championed the development of an American architecture devoid of historical references, and it was his most famous protégé, Frank Lloyd Wright, who synthesized this philosophy of organic architecture and ornament to develop the only unique form of modern American architecture. Following this philosophy, the Prairie architects rejected the incorporation of historic details and styles into their work. Their architecture was, instead, based on the reduction of forms to their basic

geometric essentials: cubes, rectangles, squares, triangles, circles, and straight lines. When applied to ornament, their designs took the form of stylized floral abstractions and complicated geometric patterns.

Wright became the leader of the group of midwestern architects of the Prairie School which included, among others, Marion Mahony Griffin (see entry), William Drummond, George W. Maher (see entry), William Gray Purcell, George Grant Elmslie, and Francis Barry Byrne. Prairie School houses are generally low, rectangular masses featuring horizontal planes and rambling, open interior spaces revolving around a central hearth. In many of the houses, such as the Martin (1904-06), Tomek (1907), Evans (1908), and Coonley (1908), the windows are arranged in horizontal bands and open the interior to the outdoors. The Prairie style window was a dramatic break with its predecessors, the colorful and picturesque Victorian windows that obscured one's view of the outdoors.

Cat. no. 89
Frank Lloyd Wright, Frieze from the exterior eaves trim of the Isidor J. Heller House, 1897 (removed 1984); fret-sawn wood, 23.8 x 98 x 2 cm. Gift of Victor and Danielle Barcilon, 1984.1242.

Fig. 3
Frank Lloyd Wright, Isidor J. Heller House, 5132 S. Woodlawn Avenue, 1897.

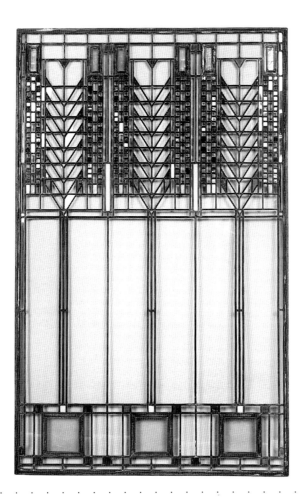

Darwin D. Martin House

The Darwin D. Martin House (see Hoffmann, fig. 4), one of Wright's mature Prairie style houses, was built for an associate of the Larkin Company, a mail-order and wholesale company dealing in household goods. The house was built with two other buildings on the site, a garage and conservatory, and the Barton House for Martin's sister and brother-in-law. The Martin House was finely executed in all details because Wright had few financial restrictions and was free to create the most extravagant fittings and furniture he wished. As a result, Wright concerned himself with the production of all elements of the house, including small interior details such as fixtures, rugs, lamps, windows, and even a grand piano.

The massive, two-story Martin House featured all of the characteristics associated with the Prairie style—long overhanging eaves, horizontal emphasis, exquisite geometric art-glass windows, and an organic flow among interior rooms and between indoors and outdoors. The plan of the house featured immense interior spaces defined by groups of freestanding piers. In addition, its use of casement windows and both exterior and interior brickwork was the most striking example of Wright's dissolution of the barriers between the interior and exterior of a house to date. Given the extraordinary success of the Martin House, the commission for a new administration building for Martin's company, the Larkin Building (1903-04; see Hoffman, fig. 2), followed almost immediately.

Although the Robie House (1908) in Chicago's Hyde Park is considered Wright's most fully integrated Prairie house, the Martin House windows are regarded as his most important Prairie windows and are second only to those from the Coonley Playhouse (cat. no. 95) in rarity and importance.

Best known among the Martin House windows are the Tree of Life windows, which are composed of minute pieces of clear, opaque, and iridescent glass that were cut by extremely skilled craftsmen at the Linden Glass Company in Chicago. The window in the Art Institute's collection (cat. no. 90) features stylized tree branches at the top, a vertical trunk in the center, and a square, rootlike form at the bottom. The windows were originally installed in the upstairs rooms and the reception area. The Tree of Life window was purchased from a gallery in 1972.

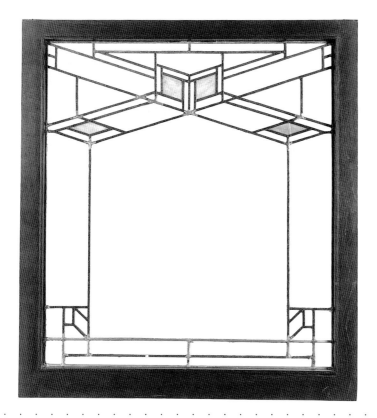

Tomek and Evans Houses

Wright also designed windows that were based on abstract rather than natural forms. Two such windows in the Art Institute's collection are from houses that are typical of the mature Prairie style idiom — the Tomek (fig. 4) and Evans houses. Windows from both feature symmetrical designs with large panes of clear glass punctuated by small rectangular and diamond-shaped panes of colored and iridescent glass. The Tomek House (1907), with its long narrow plan, has a raised living floor with

the entrance below and a semicircular terrace at one end. Its configuration gives it a shiplike appearance with a chimney emerging from its center. The Tomek House was largely restored between 1974 and 1982 and, remarkably, over the years not one of its windows was removed. In the Art Institute's collection is one of a pair of original spare windows (see cat. no. 91) whose proportions are slightly different from those actually installed in the house.

The Evans House (1908), built in the Beverly neighborhood on Chicago's southwest side, is more of a

typical Prairie style pinwheel plan with a porch, porte cochère, and servants' wings that radiate from the living room with its central fireplace. Again, rows of windows were installed in both the first and second floors. The Art Institute has in its holdings a window (cat. no. 92) donated in 1971 by the owners of the house, who were interested in having it preserved in a museum. The same donors also gave a radiator cover (cat. no. 93) from the house. Wright considered radiators an offensive intrusion and attempted to camouflage them under simple, rectilinear covers such as this one with vertical slats on the sides and horizontal spindles on top. In other attempts to deal with unsightly radiators, Wright installed heating elements into large supporting piers, and eventually he developed his own system of radiant heating with hot water pipes installed beneath concrete floors.

Cat. no. 92
Frank Lloyd Wright,
Window from
the R. W. Evans House,
9914 S. Longwood Drive,
1908;
clear and opaque green
glass in zinc cames,
105.2 x 94.8 cm.
Gift of Mr. and Mrs.
F. M. Fahrenwald,
1971.749.

Cat. no. 93
Frank Lloyd Wright,
Radiator cover from the
R. W. Evans House;
oak,
74.8 x 166 x 33.8 cm.
Gift of Mr. and Mrs.
F. M. Fahrenwald,
1970.431.

Fig. 4
Frank Lloyd Wright,
F. F. Tomek House,
150 Nuttall, Riverside,
Illinois, 1904-05.

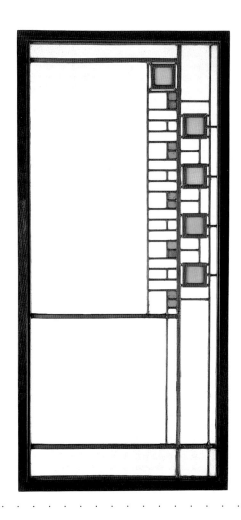

Fig. 5
**Frank Lloyd Wright,
Avery Coonley House,
300 Scottswood Road,
Riverside, Illinois, 1908.**

Cat. no. 94
**Frank Lloyd Wright,
Window from the
Avery Coonley House;
clear and green/yellow
iridescent glass in
zinc cames,
116 x 55 cm.
Gift of Mr. and Mrs.
James W. Howlett,
1973.351.**

Coonley House and Coonley Playhouse

Wright himself felt that the Avery Coonley House (1908; fig. 5) in Riverside, Illinois, was the most successful of his Prairie designs. Like the Martins and like Susan Lawrence Dana, whose house Wright had designed in 1903, the Coonleys gave Wright complete freedom to create a design that would meet their needs. The house has a U-shaped plan with principal rooms on the second floor. The only room located on the ground floor is a large playroom, but the most spectacular room is the great living room, which has a huge hipped ceiling and wood-framed skylights. The large house displays all the hallmarks of Wright's Prairie School designs.

The Coonley House is one of the most elaborate of Wright's decorative schemes, with custom-designed furnishings, rugs, linens, and drapes throughout. The windows in the house are asymmetrical variations on a flat, geometric theme. One type of window in the house (cat. no. 94) has yellow, green, and white squares set into a rectilinear field of clear glass. Its design represents Wright's philosophy as expressed in his essay "In the Cause of Architecture" (*Architectural Record* 23, 3 [1908]): "The windows usually are provided with characteristic straight line patterns absolutely in the flat and usually severe. The nature of the glass is taken into account in these designs as is also the metal bar used in their construction, and most of them are treated as metal 'grilles' with glass inserted forming a simple rhythmic arrangement of straight lines and squares made as cunning as possible so long as the result is quiet" (p. 7). The window was donated in 1973 by people who lived on the Coonley estate and wanted to ensure its preservation.

Four years after the Coonley House was completed, the family commissioned Wright to design a building to house a progressive school begun by Mrs. Coonley for her daughter Elizabeth. Known as the Coonley Playhouse, the small building bears little resemblance to the large house. The Playhouse, symmetrical in design with a flat slab roof, is reminiscent of Wright's early Prairie houses and projects such as the Yahara Boat Club (1902), and it leads immediately to the vastly greater complexity of Midway Gardens (1913-14). The windows from the Playhouse also differ greatly from those of the main house. They are complex asymmetrical designs of

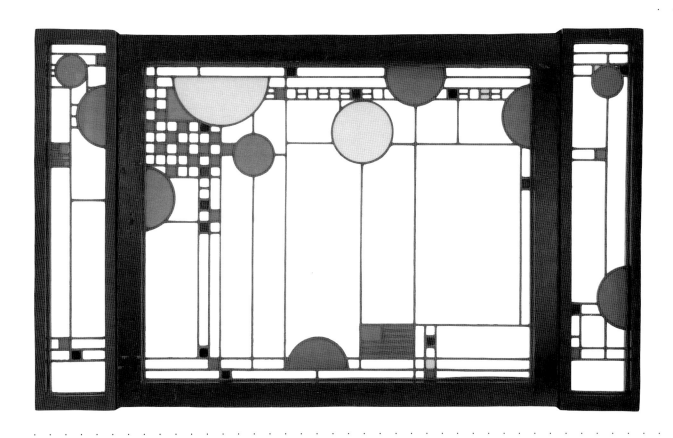

blue, red, and green circles, small clustered black and white rectangles, and American flags, as can be seen in a triptych (cat. no. 95; pl. 9) now in the Art Institute. The Playhouse was extensively documented in photographs, which reveal that the Art Institute's triptych was originally installed in a niche above a radiator (fig. 6). The great majority of the windows, however, were installed at the clerestory level on either side of the main room.

According to Elizabeth Coonley Faulkner, the windows in the Playhouse were inspired by Wright's observations of a parade with its colorful balloons, flags, and confetti. The circular motif, first introduced in these windows, became a major design element in later murals for Midway Gardens and the decorative designs for the Imperial Hotel in Tokyo. Wright was so enamored with

the energetic beauty of these windows that he displayed them in exhibitions such as the 1914 Chicago Architectural Club show at the Art Institute. The designs for the windows were contemporary with the first totally abstract European paintings and have affinities with the work of Wassily Kandinsky and Piet Mondrian. Nearly all of the approximately fifty windows in the Playhouse were removed as the estate changed hands over the years. In 1985, however, a number of Playhouse windows appeared for sale, and the Art Institute acquired the triptych. To this day, the Playhouse windows still rank at the top of Wright's most important decorative achievements.

Fig. 6
Frank Lloyd Wright,
Avery Coonley
Playhouse;
interior view showing
triptych window as
originally installed in
a radiator niche.

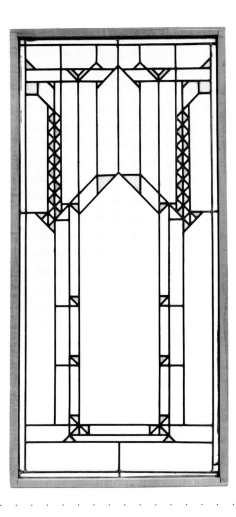

Little House

The Francis W. Little House (1912-14), in rural Wayzata, Minnesota, was built as a country house on Lake Minnetonka for a prosperous and cultured family. Five years earlier Wright had designed for the Littles a rather formal, symmetrical Prairie style house in Peoria, Illinois. The Wayzata house went beyond the Prairie idiom and, as Edgar Kaufmann, Jr., described it in *Frank Lloyd Wright at The Metropolitan Museum of Art* (New York, 1982), "The country house was more extended and casual, with wide views over the lake on one side and tree-strewn knolls on the other." The living room of the

house was, at the time, one of the largest and most magnificent that Wright had designed, rivaling that of the Coonley House. The Little House took four years to design and two years to build. Tension resulted between client and architect, especially since the Littles expected, but did not receive, a typical Prairie house like they had in Peoria. Many of Mr. Little's objections were directed at the clear and green art-glass windows that Wright proposed. He and the Littles finally agreed on a nearly colorless window design (cat. no. 96) with small panes of white and frosted rectangles that were occasionally highlighted by tiny red squares — a feature that had become Wright's signature. Although the window in the Art Institute's collection has a symmetrical design, the living room, for example, featured windows that were complete only when a series of them

were grouped together. In the early 1970s, the decision was made to demolish the Little House to build another structure immediately adjacent to it. The Metropolitan Museum of Art acquired the interiors of the house in 1971 and 1972, and in the early 1980s installed the living room in their American Wing. The Art Institute received its Little House windows from the Metropolitan Museum in 1986.

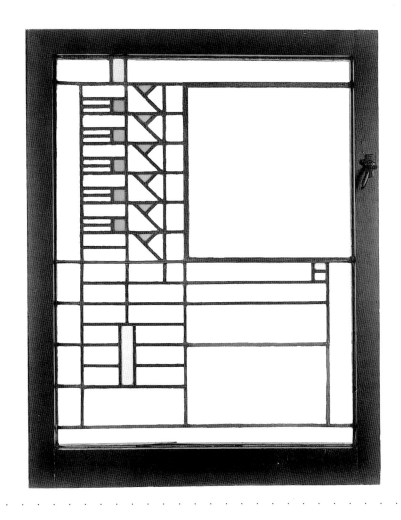

Bach House

The Prairie house was the perfect suburban house type with airy terraces and sprawling proportions necessitating large building lots. When applying the Prairie style to a house on a small city lot, such as the Bach House (1915), Wright arranged the house vertically and turned it inward for more privacy (fig. 7). · Although very different in style, the Bach House harks back to the Heller House, which Wright also designed vertically to accommodate city lots. The Bach House was one of Wright's last small urban commissions and one of the few commissions that he built in the city of Chicago. The "semi-cubist" design of the facade is defined by strong parallel lines, right angles, and dark contrasting trim, all of which reflect the underlying structure. Although this post-Prairie style house is extremely compact, its open floor plan makes good use of

the space, here organized around a central fireplace and staircase. The windows from the house (see cat. no. 97; pl. 8) feature brightly colored triangular and square panes of glass set into a field of clear glass. This same, brightly colored glass was used in the Coonley Playhouse windows. The Art Institute's window was originally one half of a pair of windows whose designs would have been the exact reverse of one another, leaving a large field of clear glass in the center. The Art Institute's window was donated in 1965 by the owner of the house, who said that the windows had been replaced with clear glass.

Cat. no. 97
Frank Lloyd Wright,
Window from the
Emil Bach House;
clear and opaque white,
green, and orange glass
in copper cames,
99.1 x 77.6 cm.
Gift of Mr. James F.
Blinder, 1965.126.

Fig. 7
Frank Lloyd Wright,
Emil Bach House,
7415 N. Sheridan Road,
1915.

. . . .

Fig. 8
Frank Lloyd Wright,
Midway Gardens,
60th Street and Cottage
Grove Avenue, 1913-14
(demolished 1929).

Cat. no. 98
Frank Lloyd Wright,
Block from Midway
Gardens;
cast concrete,
45 x 52 x 7 cm.
Gift of Mr. and Mrs.
Hal Chalmers and
Mr. Rexford Battenberg,
1972.811.

Midway Gardens

At the same time that Wright was designing the Bach House, he was also working on one of his largest and most spectacular projects, Midway Gardens (fig. 8). Based on the European casino, the building was a year-round entertainment and restaurant complex built at the western end of what had been the Midway Plaisance of the 1893 World's Columbian Exposition. Unfortunately, Midway Gardens was never successful. The importance of Midway Gardens is fully described in the section of this catalogue on Alfonso Iannelli (see pp. 162-63), who designed the sculpture for the complex (see cat. nos. 83-85). In addition to several pieces of

Iannelli sculpture for Midway Gardens, the Art Institute also has an actual fragment from the building, a cast concrete block with a geometric design (cat. no. 98). This motif, which later became what Wright called a textile block, was used in many of his projects, particularly the houses he designed in California in the 1920s. The block was discovered around 1948 amid the dirt and rubble of the demolished building.

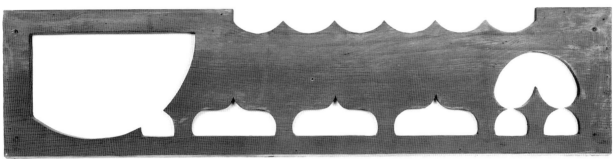

Weltzheimer House

A fine example of Wright's later work in the Art Institute's collection is from the Weltzheimer House in Oberlin, Ohio (fig. 9). The Weltzheimer House (1948-50) is one of the true Usonian designs constructed after the Second World War. Wright's Usonian ideal called for low-cost housing that was constructed of simple, directly stated materials which are related to nature through color, texture, and structure. The L-shaped plan and two-by-four-foot design module relate the Weltzheimer House to Wright's prewar Usonian structures, such as the Jacobs House (1936-37) in Madison, Wisconsin. In the Weltzheimer House, Wright incorporated radiant heating in the concrete slab floor, and he designed much of the furniture as built-ins, so that the interior space would be unencumbered. The perforated redwood clerestory panels on the exterior of the house (cat. no. 99) were originally installed below the roofline. The roofline panels played an important role in defining the character of the house's exterior. As Kenneth Severens described in a 1976 article in *The Art Institute of Chicago Museum Studies*, the panels "emphasize the modular design and the structure of the redwood walls. Furthermore, they visually dematerialize somewhat the juncture between the wall and the flat roof by giving the impression that the cantilevered horizontals extend outward with only minimal vertical support" (pp. 114-15). The clerestory boards were removed in 1965, when the owner wanted more light to filter into the interior of the house and replaced them with panes of glass.

Fig. 9
Frank Lloyd Wright, Charles E. Weltzheimer House, Oberlin, Ohio, 1948-50.

Cat. no. 99
**Frank Lloyd Wright, Perforated panel from the clerestory of the Charles E. Weltzheimer House;
redwood,
28.5 x 122 x 2.3 cm.
Gift of Mr. and Mrs. Duilio Giannitrapani, 1970.1203.**

P. B. Wight,
*Lunette depicting winter and fireplace tiles
from the E. W. Blatchford House, 375 N.
LaSalle Street (now 1111 N. LaSalle Street),
c. 1875-77 (demolished 1929); lunette:
carved by James Legge; white sandstone, 74 x
117 x 15 cm; fireplace tiles: glazed terracotta,
each 12.7 x 12.7 x 4 cm. Gifts of Thomas
Blatchford, 1982.1278 and 1983.650a-b,
d-g.*

P. B. Wight,
*Section of fireproofing casing from an iron
column in the Jewelers' Building, designed by
Adler and Sullivan, 19 S. Wabash Avenue,
1881; terracotta and cement, 38 x 33 x 13.5
cm. Gift of Timothy Samuelson, Study
Collection.*

Treat and Foltz,
*Three blocks from the facade of a building for
E. G. Raymond, 526 S. State Street, 1884
(demolished 1985); terracotta, dimensions
vary. Gifts of Timothy Samuelson,
1985.119c-e.*

Burnham and Root,
*Blocks from the James C. Lombard House,
1805 Jefferson Street, Kansas City, Missouri,
1887-88 (now demolished); terracotta,
dimensions vary. By exchange from Carson
Pirie Scott and Company, 1987.342.3 and
Study Collection.*

Jenney and Mundie,
*Blocks with central shell shape from the
facade of The Fair store, Adams Street
between State and Dearborn streets, 1890-91
(addition 1896-97; demolished 1986); terracotta, each 53.5 x 47 x 14 cm. Gifts of the
Dearborn Land Company, 1985.804a-c.*

Harry B. Wheelock,
*Four-part spandrel panel from the Stop and
Shop Warehouse (formerly the Western
Methodist Book Exchange), 12-14 W.
Washington Street, c. 1899 (demolished
1990); terracotta, each panel 46 x 42 x 11.5
cm. Gift of Mike Donley and Pete Miller.*

Holabird and Roche,
*Door hinge and a doorknob and escutcheon
plate from the Marquette Building, 140 S.
Dearborn Street, 1894-95; fabricated by the
Yale and Towne Lock Company; nickel silver,
17.5 x 13 x 2 and 21 x 6 x 15.5 cm. Gifts of
Seymour H. Persky, Study Collection.*

Holabird and Roche,
*Doorknob and escutcheon plate from the
LaSalle Hotel, northwest corner of LaSalle
and Madison streets, 1908-09 (now demol-
ished); brass and iron, 27.5 x 7.5 x 18 cm.
Gift of Seymour H. Persky, Study Collection.*

Barnett, Haynes and Barnett,
*Three porthole windows from the top floor of
the Illinois Athletic Club, 112 S. Michigan
Avenue, 1908 (remodeled 1989); colored
leaded glass in a brass frame, each 68.6 cm
diameter. Gifts of Charles Vavrus,
1989.228.1-3.*

D. H. Burnham and Co.,
*Blocks from the Railway Exchange Building
(now the Santa Fe Building), 224 S. Michigan Avenue, 1903-04 (restored 1983); white
glazed terracotta, dimensions vary. Gifts of
the Santa Fe Southern Pacific Corporation,
1984.805c-h.*

D. H. Burnham and Co.,
*Blocks featuring a stylized acanthus leaf
pattern from the lobby of the Conway Building (now the Chicago Title and Trust Building), 111 W. Washington Street, 1912-14
(remodeled 1983-84); white glazed terracotta, 22 x 87 x 9 cm. Gifts of Jack Train
Associates and Pepper Construction,
1983.909-10.*

Holabird and Root,
*Directory frame from the Michigan Square
Building, 540 N. Michigan Avenue, 1929-
31 (demolished 1973); steel, 135.5 x 121.5 x
4.3 cm. Gift of Joel Goldberg, 1974.446.*

Graham, Anderson, Probst and White,
*Reproduction finial from the Wrigley Build-
ing, 400-10 N. Michigan Avenue, 1919-21
(addition 1924; remodeled 1984); composite
material, 99 x 47 x 47 cm. Gift of the William Wrigley Jr. Company, 1984.196.*

Howells and Hood,
*Full-scale plaster mock-up of Gothic orna-
ment on the facade of the Chicago Tribune
Tower, 435 N. Michigan Ave., c. 1922;
plaster of paris, approx. 166 x 107 x 81 cm.
Gift of Tribune Properties, Inc.*

Attributed to **Jarvis Hunt,**
*Section of railing and a Renaissance-style
mantel from 900 N. Michigan Avenue, 1926
(demolished 1984); wrought iron and marble,
dimensions vary. Gifts of Urban Investment
and Development Co., Study Collection and
1984.728.*

Edward Eichenbaum,
*Blocks from the Granada Theater, Sheridan
Road at Devon Avenue, 1926 (demolished
1989-90); white glazed terracotta, dimen-
sions vary. Gifts of Joe Masterson and G. M.
Wrecking Company.*

Adler and Sullivan,
*Stained-glass panel from an interior skylight
of the Auditorium Building Theater, Con-
gress Parkway between Michigan Avenue and
Wabash Street, 1887-89; colored glass set in
a handcrafted lead frame, 91 x 149 x 9 cm.
On extended loan from the Auditorium
Theatre Council, 1974.81.*

Adler and Sullivan,
*Two doorhandles from the Auditorium Build-
ing; brass, 37 x 12.5 x 7 cm. Gifts of Dr. and
Mrs. Edwin J. DeCosta, 1984.1244-45.*

Adler and Sullivan,
*Angel from the third-story stringcourse of the
Victor Falkenau House, 3420-24 S. Wabash
Avenue, 1888-89; terracotta, 80 x 90 x 46
cm. Gift of John Vinci in honor of Howard
Dearstyne and Carlos Hudson.*

**Frank Lloyd Wright for Adler and
Sullivan,**
*Panel from the balcony of the Charnley
House, 1365 N. Astor Street, 1892; fret-sawn
wood, 78.7 x 233.7 x 1.2 cm. Gift of Lowell
Wohlfeil, 1984.194.*

Adler and Sullivan,
*Sections of plaster ornament from the ban-
quet hall frieze, proscenium vault, and balcony face from the Schiller Building, 64
W. Randolph Street, 1891-92 (demolished
1961); painted plaster, dimensions vary.
Gifts of the Commission on Chicago Architectural Landmarks, 1962.945-46, 1962.951-
53, 1982.948-49.*

Adler and Sullivan,
*Blocks of stringcourse with repeated ribbon
design from the first-floor loggia of the
Schiller Building; terracotta, each 91 x 49 x
20.5 cm. Gift of the Commission on Chicago
Architectural Landmarks, 1962.940-41.*

Adler and Sullivan,
*Elevator enclosure grilles from the Chicago
Stock Exchange Building, 30 N. LaSalle
Street, 1893-94 (demolished 1972); wrought
iron, dimensions vary. Gifts of Mr. Kenneth
Newberger, 1963.373a-e.*

Adler and Sullivan,
*Mail slot from Chicago Stock Exchange
Building; cast iron, Bower-Barff finish, 6 x
21.5 x 2 cm. Gift of L.M. Ackley, 1973.339.*

Adler and Sullivan,
*Push plate and window pull from Chicago
Stock Exchange Building; cast iron, dimen-
sions vary. Anonymous gifts, 1972.806-07.*

Adler and Sullivan,
*Four doorknobs and escutcheon plates from
the Chicago Stock Exchange Building;
fabricated by Yale and Towne Lock Co.; cast
iron, dimensions vary. Anonymous gifts,
1972.809-10, 1965.1228a-b, 1965.1229a-b.*

Louis H. Sullivan,
*Mail slot and door handle from the Guaranty
Building (now the Prudential Building),
Buffalo, New York, 1894-95; fabricated by
the Yale and Towne Lock Company; cast iron,
dimensions vary. Gifts of Mr. and Mrs.
Arthur A. Carrara, 1978.62-63.*

Louis H. Sullivan,
*Cornice entablature and foliate ornament
from the facade of the Gage Building, 18 S.
Michigan Avenue, 1898-99 (addition 1902);
fabricated by the Winslow Brothers Company;
cast iron, dimensions vary. Gifts of Mr.
and Mrs. L. Lattin Smith, 1982.1657 and
1976.686.*

Louis H. Sullivan,
*Spandrel fascia panel from the facade of
Gage Building; fabricated by the Winslow
Brothers Company; cast iron, 91.5 x 85 x 7.5
cm. Gift of Dubin, Dubin and Black, Archi-
tects, in memory of Henry and Anne Dubin.*

Louis H. Sullivan,
*Balusters from the Schlesinger and Mayer
Store (now Carson Pirie Scott and Company), southeast corner of State and Madison
streets, 1899, 1903-04 (removed 1968); cast
iron, 89 x 25 x 5 cm and 99 x 25 x 5 cm.
Gifts of Carson Pirie Scott and Company,
1968.948-59 and 1968.1032-43.*

Louis H. Sullivan,
*Sections of cornice and a foliate block featur-
ing the letter "F" from the facade of the Eli B.
Felsenthal Store, 701-09 E. 47th Street,
1906 (demolished 1982); terracotta,
dimensions vary. Gifts of the Commission on
Chicago Historical and Architectural Landmarks, 1984.187a-c and 1984.189a-e.*

George W. Maher,
*Capital from the Mosser House, 750 W.
Hutchinson Street, 1902 (renovated 1987);
plaster, 51 x 55 x 55 cm. Gift of Dr. and Mrs.
Marc Karlan, 1987.350.*

Frank Lloyd Wright,
*Exterior column capital from the second-floor
arcade of the Isidor J. Heller House, 5132 S.
Woodlawn Avenue, 1897; plaster, approximately 40 x 49 x 49 cm. Anonymous gift,
1983.1022.*

Frank Lloyd Wright,
*Section of cornice from the Francisco Terrace
Apartment, 253-57 Francisco Avenue, 1895
(now demolished); terracotta, 39 x 51 x 23 cm.
Gift of William and Ruth Knack, Study
Collection.*

Frank Lloyd Wright,
*Windows from the R. W. Evans House, 9914
S. Longwood Drive, c. 1908; clear and
opaque green glass in zinc cames, each 119 x
107 cm. Gifts of Mr. and Mrs. F. M. Fahrenwald, 1971.750-51.*

Frank Lloyd Wright,
*Three windows from the billiard room of the
Francis W. Little House, Wayzata, Minne-
sota, 1912-14 (demolished 1972); clear and
opaque white and red glass in copper cames,
116.8 x 57 x 5 cm and 137.8 x 176 x 62.2 cm.
Gifts by exchange from The Metropolitan
Museum of Art and Three Oaks Wrecking
Co., 1986.1706-07, 1709.*

George Grant Elmslie,
*Lamppost from the Amy Hamilton Hunter
House, 1441 Braeburn Road, Flossmoor,
Illinois, c. 1916; cast iron, sheet metal, and
leaded glass panels, dimensions unavailable.
Gift of Mrs. Emile F. Faure, 1973.549.*

Index of Architects and Designers